BOLLINGEN SERIES XXXII

PAIR OF ROYAL FIGURES. Bronze, h. 12 in. *Ife, Nigeria*

African
Folktales & Sculpture

BOLLINGEN SERIES XXXII

PANTHEON BOOKS

Copyright *1952* by Bollingen Foundation Inc., *New York, N. Y.*
New material copyright © *1964* by Bollingen Foundation
Published by Bollingen Foundation and
Distributed by Pantheon Books, a Division
of Random House, Inc.

First Edition
FIRST PRINTING, NOVEMBER 1952
SECOND PRINTING, NOVEMBER 1953

Second Edition, revised, with additions
FIRST PRINTING, SEPTEMBER 1964
SECOND PRINTING, OCTOBER 1966

THIS VOLUME IS THE THIRTY-SECOND
IN A SERIES OF BOOKS
SPONSORED AND PUBLISHED BY
BOLLINGEN FOUNDATION

Library of Congress Catalog Card No.: 64-23669

Manufactured in the United States of America
by Kingsport Press, Inc., Kingsport, Tenn.

DESIGNED BY ANDOR BRAUN

Folktales selected and edited by Paul Radin
with the collaboration of Elinore Marvel

Introduction to the tales by Paul Radin

Sculpture selected with an introduction
by James Johnson Sweeney

Foreword to the Second Edition

Since the publication of the original edition of this book in 1952, most of native Africa has become politically independent (see p. xiv). For the second edition, accordingly, the preface, captions, catalogue of plates, map, and index have been revised to take historical changes into account; and population figures have been revised in accordance with the United Nations *Population and Vital Statistics Report* for Jan. 1, 1964. In order to illustrate works of sculpture that have become known during the last decade, James Johnson Sweeney has added twenty-two new photographs and a postscript of comment. The text of the folk-tales and the introductions by Paul Radin (1883–1959) and James Johnson Sweeney have otherwise not been altered.

For assistance in the preparation of the new material for the second edition, grateful acknowledgment is made to Dr. Robert Goldwater, director of the Museum of Primitive Art, New York; to Mrs. Tamara Northern and Miss Elizabeth Little, of the Museum staff; and to Mr. John J. Klejman and Mr. Arnold Newman, both of New York.

For the second printing (1966), the following name changes should be considered to apply: Botswana for Bechuanaland; Kinshasa for Leopoldville; Lesotho for Basutoland; Republic of South Africa for Union of South Africa; Rhodesia for Southern Rhodesia; Tanzania for Tanganyika and Zanzibar; Zambia for Northern Rhodesia.

Preface

IN THIS volume, "native Africa" is understood in the sense defined by the great Africanist C. G. Seligman:[1] Africa south of an imaginary line running from the Senegal River, on the Atlantic coast, east through Timbuktu and Khartoum, then south and east to the Ethiopian border roughly at latitude 12° N., and then along that border to the Juba River and the Indian Ocean (see map, facing p. xii). North of this line are, in general, Caucasian Hamites and Semites; south of it Negroes, people of dark skin and woolly hair. But throughout native Africa (perhaps 140,000,000 people) there is admixture, greater or less, of Hamitic stock and culture. The true Negro—that is, the type that has remained almost free of Hamitic strains—is found in a relatively restricted area: roughly, the Guinea coast and its hinterlands, from the mouth of the Senegal River eastward to the mouth of the Cross River, in eastern Nigeria. All the rest of native Africa consists of (1) people of varying Negro-Hamite mixture—the Nilotes, the "half-Hamites," the many millions of Bantu-speaking tribes—and of (2) non-Negro peoples: Bushmen, Hottentots (both of the southern extremity), and the Pygmies (in small, scattered groups in the densest rain forest, near the equator; particularly interesting and particularly little known; but not dealt with in this book). We are of course not concerned with the comparatively few (perhaps less than 3,000,000) Europeans, Arabs, and Orientals who have settled among the native Africans.

The two parts of this book, folktales and sculpture, coincide and interrelate only in part. The great sculpture area of native Africa encompasses practically all of the west Africa of the true Negro and most of the Bantu-speaking region centering in the Congo. For reasons not entirely understood, almost no plastic art of much interest has come from the Nilotic, the eastern and southern Bantu, and the Bushman-Hottentot areas. But for the folktale this does not hold. Rich stores of the folktale are encountered everywhere. This volume contains only a selection. It does not touch at all some native African art of admitted value, such as the rock-paintings of the Bushmen, music, and much of the domestic craft-arts, inasmuch as it is the outgrowth of folkloristic and plastic interests. The following

---

1. *Races of Africa* (London, 1930), p. 53. This work has been drawn on for much of the material contained in this preface.

rather impressionistic notes on, among other things, the ethnography of native Africa are not meant for the anthropologist, the student of primitive art, or their like, but for the general reader who may not possess very much organized information about this subject.

The true Negroes share some cultural features. They practise intensive agriculture; they own domesticated dogs, goats, pigs, and chickens, but not cattle. They work in iron, bronze, wood, and ivory. Until lately, cannibalism and human sacrifice were surely not unknown. The people waged war with bows, swords, and wicker shields, but not clubs or slings. Their achievement in plastic art not only is the highest known among aboriginal peoples, but compares more than favourably with that of the major European and Asiatic civilizations. It reached a zenith in southern Nigeria, among the peoples of Ife and Benin.[2] Music plays a role almost as great; it is exemplified by their well-known drums and amazing drum-language, and their harp, really a peculiar kind of guitar. They also perform on the musical bow, seemingly a primitive fiddle. West African social-political organization consists typically of the clan, upon which have been superimposed monarchy and stratified classes. Pre-eminent are the secret societies, often arranged in graded series, with elaborate rituals of initiation. In their observances, masks and carved wooden figures often are part of the trappings. There are societies for both men and women, youths and the mature. Some are occasionally antisocial in function, and terrorism is not uncommon (viz., the Leopard Society). But most are mutual-benefit clubs, whose membership confers social distinction and adds to prestige.[3]

The culture of the tribes of west Africa centres along the Guinea coast, notably in the highly organized states of Ashanti, Dahomey, Yoruba, and Benin. These extend inland and in a sense are embedded in the western Sudan. In the vast parkland stretching westward to the Atlantic we find a melange of the pagan, Christian, and Moslem. To the west are the Mandingo, a people whose ancestors, in the thirteenth and fourteenth centuries, ruled the most powerful Sudanese state of which there is authentic record. The Mende of Sierra Leone and the Bambara of Mali are related to them. The Bambara have occupational guilds and a clan structure in which the "joking relationship" figures: colleagues in the alliance can publicly exchange insults without giving offense. Serpents, rats, donkeys, goats, and other animals are sacred as the mounts of divine ancestors. The Bambara wear startling animal masks, such as their towering "Tji-Wara" headdress, in their agricultural feast-dances. North of them, in a rocky plateau at the bend of the Niger River, live the Dogon, or Habe. Their villages sometimes are built on steep rock cliffs and are reached only by rope ladders. Surrounded by Moslems, the Dogon have yet kept free of Islamic influence, and until recently were prolific carvers of masks and figures. Some other tribes of west Africa, having been converted to Islam, have

2. Aspects of African Negro art, such as this one, are treated in more detail in an essay preceding the plates and in the notes that are interspersed among the catalogue of plates.

3. See glossary, s.v. "Egbo."

abandoned representational art and destroyed the specimens on their hands. The Baga, of Guinea, are such iconoclasts, though some pieces of their pre-Moslem art have survived. Along the central Guinea coast the secret societies especially thrive, among the tribes of the two ex-slave territories, Sierra Leone and Liberia, and those of the Ivory Coast. Here live the Mende and the Dan, and here is the powerful Poro Society, which Ptolemy may have known of in the second century. In Mendeland, little steatite (soapstone) figures are sometimes dug up; they are called *nomori*, "rice people," they are concerned with the success of the rice crop, nothing is known of their origin, and they are probably not ancient. The Baule, of upper Ivory Coast, migrated in the eighteenth century from Ashantiland, country of their kinsmen, and settled among the Senufo, a Sudanese people, with whom they have mingled cultures. They like to embellish useful objects, such as spoons, gong mallets, bobbins, and combs, with decorative carving. They honour artists in a remarkable way.

The Ashanti are the most prominent people of Ghana. The Ashanti king rules over a hierarchy of provincial chiefs, who in turn hold sway over subchiefs and village headmen. The king is not absolute; his government is an aristocracy rather than a personal despotism. Still, at one time, theoretically at least, he had power to take life whenever he chose. The Ashanti are famed for their Golden Stool, which seems to have come into being during the reign of their fourth known king, Osai Tutu (1700–1730). According to legend, a man named Anotchi appeared among the Ashanti and announced that he had been sent by the sky-god to make them a powerful nation. Osai Tutu summoned a great convocation to his capital, Kumasi, where Anotchi proceeded to draw down from the sky a wooden stool overlaid with gold. This, he told the assemblage, contained the soul of the Ashanti, their health, bravery, and welfare. Today every Ashanti chief has a stool that is the repository of his soul and that, when he dies, will be placed in the stool-house along with those of his ancestors. The religion of the Ashanti, like that of all the Guinea coast tribes, is highly developed and intricate. An earth goddess is acknowledged, and a supreme god in the firmament, called Nyankonpon or Nyame, from whom stems a bureaucracy of lesser gods, the Abosom, graded in a descending scale. The really operative part of Ashanti religion is the cult of the dead—or, precisely, of dead kings. It formerly was celebrated in a rather violent ceremony, the Odwira, impressive to Europeans for the quantities of spirits drunk and of human blood spilt. The Ashanti design and cast little bronze weights, by the *cire-perdue* method, for the weighing of gold dust. These may represent human figures, beasts, birds, fish, insects, fruit, weapons, useful objects, or even abstractions. They have vitality and wit, qualities that also distinguish much of Ashanti folklore, such as the cycle of Kwaku Ananse, or Spider, tales. (Ananse has survived in American Negro folklore as "Aunt Nancy," a metamorphosis of both species and sex.) The kinsmen of the Ashanti—the Baule, the Bron, the Lobi—also cast weights and ornaments of bronze. The Krachi, most of whom live in Ghana, have much in common, too, with the Ashanti.

The ancient kingdom of Dahomey surrounds its royal city of Abomey. The

Dahomans were formerly celebrated for, *inter alia*, their corps of female soldiers, whom they called "our mothers." Well into the nineteenth century, women numbering up to 2,500 composed the king's bodyguard, being armed with blunder-busses, muskets, and knives like eighteen-inch razors. They were sworn to celibacy (but the king could take any of them to wife). While some observers reported the ferocious courage of these ladies and their penchant for taking human heads or jawbones as battle trophies, another (Sir Richard Burton) noted that "they were mostly remarkable for a stupendous steatopygy, and for a development of adipose tissue which suggested anything but ancient virginity." [4] In Dahomey, upon the king's death, not only were the palace furnishings destroyed, but hundreds of his women and of soldiers, Amazons, eunuchs, and poets killed themselves in order to join their lord in the spirit world. Arts were a royal monopoly in Dahomey, at least brass-casting, clay-modeling, the appliquéing of cloth, and the carving of calabashes. Wood-carving alone was everyone's right. Besides working in brass, the Dahomans wrought cleverly out of the iron got from ships wrecked off the Slave Coast. They share some deities with the Yoruba.

In southern Nigeria, the Yoruba worship a numerous pantheon of gods and consecrate to them many carved figures and ritual objects. The goddess Odudua is honoured by statues of a nursing mother; Shango, god of thunder and lightning, is represented as an armed horseman. There is a special god for twins, whom the Yoruba hold sacred. If a twin dies, the parents commission the carving of a pair of small figures, one of which is hidden away, while the other, replacing the dead child, is bathed, dressed, and offered food at the same time as the surviving twin. In the north, around Nok, terracotta heads were excavated a few years ago which belong to a culture of *circa* the first millennium B.C. In southeast Nigeria and western Cameroon we find such peoples as the Efik-Ibibio and the Ekoi, all with less complicated social and ceremonial structures, but otherwise typically west African in culture. In this neighbourhood we are near the Bantu line, and some tribes are identified as semi-Bantu.

In northern Nigeria and its environs live the Hausa, who are mostly Moslems. The Hausa confederation of kingdoms attained great political power in the Middle Ages and held it until the Fulani, also Islamic in religion, came as conquerors in the nineteenth century. But today the Hausa, over five million of them, dominate the country; they are considered to be good farmers, stock-breeders, traders, and artisans.

Hamitic influence has been marked physically and culturally in two parts of east Africa. One is the area comprising most of Kenya and northern Uganda, near the boundary of the new nation of Sudan, and northern Tanganyika. The tribes living here are primarily the Masai, Nandi, and Suk, often categorized by the ethnologists as "half-Hamites." In their culture the dominant economic factor is cattle, the dominant social factor the arrangement of all males (who go, or went, naked) in a well-developed system of age-grades. Each cow is known by name; special words, not simply special grammatical forms, refer to cattle and to milk;

4. Cited in Seligman, *op. cit.*, p. 76.

milk itself is sacred, and precautions are taken to prevent its mixing with meat in one's stomach.

To the northwest, on the banks of the Nile in Sudan and south into Uganda, are peoples similarly Hamiticized physically and culturally. These the ethnologists categorize as Nilotes. Representative tribes are the Shilluk, the Lango, the Dinka, and the Nuer. Cattle, too, dominate their culture. A Dinka young man is, at puberty, given a bull by his father; he virtually "identifies" with it psychologically, assuming the bull's name and spending hours singing to and playing with it. Hippopotamus flesh is important provender of the Dinka and the Nuer. The Shilluk and the Dinka are celebrated for the special position of their kings or rainmakers. The Shilluk monarch is our best example of what Sir James Frazer, in *The Golden Bough*, called the "Divine King." He is believed to incarnate the spirit of the Shilluk culture hero, and formerly was slain directly he betrayed signs of ill health or of declining vigour as regarded his large group of wives; for the hero-spirit had to reside in a healthy body. The Dinka rainmaker himself commanded and supervised his own living burial, when he deemed himself too old to perform his duties competently.

Two thirds of native Africa speak Bantu languages. Bantu is, indeed, a linguistic term, applied to peoples of marked diversity. The Hamitic strain which sets them all apart from the true Negro is most marked in the area of the great lakes, is still strong in the east and south, and becomes minimal in the north and west. Ethnologists have been able to draw, with what they consider tolerable accuracy, a line representing the Bantu boundary. On the basis of geographical distribution, the only really feasible basis, the Bantu fall into three main groups, eastern, southern, and western.

The eastern Bantu include the tribes, almost nations, on the shores of the great lakes. Prominent among them are the Baganda, who, along with the Batikara, are the only Bantu folk who have developed cultures at all comparable to those of west Africa. But art is not highly developed. The Baganda government is a monarchy superimposed (as in west Africa) on a clan organization. The first king and empire founder was a legendary personage named Kintu, who brought from the north one each of cow, goat, chicken, banana root, and sweet potato. His retinue were white-skinned; this probably is legendary disguise of an historical fact, an invasion by Hamitic peoples. Yet the Baganda must have offered strenuous resistance to the invader, to judge from the persistence among them of many old true-Negro cultural traits. They build handsome dwellings, with lofty high-pitched thatched roofs, supported by slender columns of palm, and verandahs decorated with elephant-grass canework. A neighbour tribe, the Banyankole, keeps a sacred herd whose milk may be drunk, with due ceremony, by no one but the king. Another, the Banyoro, upon the death of their king, used to bury him in a grave lined with the living bodies of his wives and retainers, whose arms and legs had been broken to prevent their escaping.

Near by are the populous Akamba; their kinsmen, the Akikuyu; and, on the slopes of Mount Kilimanjaro, Africa's highest peak, the Chaga. All are cattle-herders. The Akamba are divided into totemic clans, with age-grades and rank-classes, position within which determines the part of the goat a man may eat. Any-one may join a grade upon paying the proper fee. The Akamba bleed their cattle, catching the blood in a calabash and drinking it on the spot or, later, as soup. The Akikuyu, good farmers, observe a rite known as the symbolical second birth, undergone by all at the age of ten; it apparently consists of a dramatization of the experience of birth. The Chaga do not have villages; each man has his own home-stead in the midst of his own banana grove, stables his cattle in his hut, and feeds them grass cut and carried up from the valley (owing to the scarcity of grazing on Kilimanjaro). The Makonde, of southeastern Tanganyika, are the only people of the eastern and southern Bantu who carve human figures and masks. The artistic activity of the other tribes is confined almost altogether to decoratively carved headrests, bowls, and shields. Also in the extreme east, around Zanzibar, are the Swahili, all of them converts to Islam. But they have kept their language (which, diluted with Arabic, Portuguese, Galla, and Somali, has become the *lingua franca* of east Africa) and many of their minor customs and beliefs. The Baila and the Bena Mukuni, of Northern Rhodesia, represent a westerly-migrating branch of the eastern Bantu, and serve as a connecting link with the western Bantu.

The southern Bantu outnumber all other groups of native inhabitants of south Africa. In the Union of South Africa they number over 11,500,000, in contrast to barely 3,300,000 persons of European origin. These people, among all native Afri-cans, have probably had the most poignant experience of the white man. They are divided into multifarious tribal units; while in mode of life, social organization, and religion the southern Bantu have broad resemblances, in details of history, lan-guage, and culture there are many important differences. The Zulu and the Xosa (sometimes called the Kafir, locally) are the dominant element among the eastern group of the southern Bantu. Their speech contains clicks, probably borrowed from the Bushmen. Ancestor worship is the chief basis of Bantu religious life. The Zulu also have the concept of a non-universal deity, a creator god, called Unkulunkulu. The Thonga and the Baronga, related peoples, also belong to the southern group. A central group is represented by the Bavenda, of the Transvaal; a northern by the Mashona, of Southern Rhodesia and Mozambique; and a western by the Herero, of South West Africa, and the Mbundu, of Angola. The southern Bantu usually live in small settlements, or kraals, each inhabited by the members of a single family. Their livestock are herded at night into a fenced cattle-fold. Milk, usually sour, is an important staple. Some of the tribes maintain sacred fires and sacred fig-trees. The tribal life is deteriorating more rapidly in the Union of South Africa than anywhere else on the continent.

The western Bantu are spread over an enormous area, constituting what has al-ways been called the "heart of Africa." It spans Cameroon, Gabon, the two Congo republics (formerly French and Belgian), and parts of Northern Rhodesia and Mozambique. Most of it goes to form, along with west Africa, the great sculpture area of the Negro. There is a baffling intermingling of tribes and diffusion of cul-

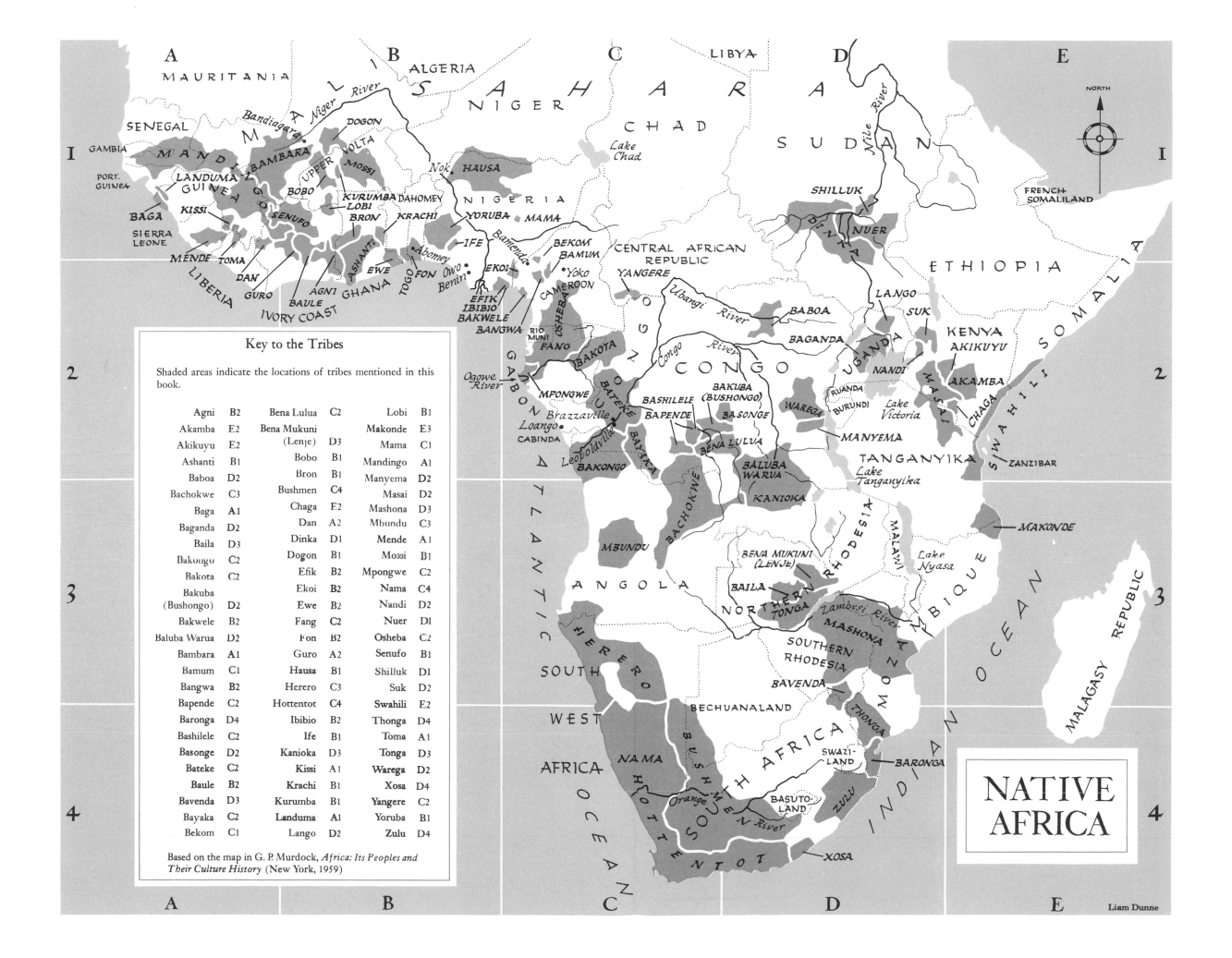

Key to the Tribes

Shaded areas indicate the locations of tribes mentioned in this book.

Agni	B2	Bena Lulua	C2	Lobi	B1
Akamba	E2	Bena Mukuni		Makonde	E3
Akikuyu	E2	(Lenje)	D3	Mama	C1
Ashanti	B1	Bobo	B1	Mandingo	A1
Baboa	D2	Bron	B1	Manyema	D2
Bachokwe	C3	Bushmen	C4	Masai	D2
Baga	A1	Chaga	E2	Mashona	D3
Baganda	D2	Dan	A2	Mbundu	C3
Baila	D3	Dinka	D1	Mende	A1
Bakongo	C2	Dogon	B1	Mossi	B1
Bakota	C2	Efik	B2	Mpongwe	C2
Bakuba		Ekoi	B2	Nama	C4
(Bushongo)	D2	Ewe	B2	Nandi	D2
Bakwele	B2	Fang	C2	Nuer	D1
Baluba Warua	D2	Fon	B2	Osheba	C2
Bambara	A1	Guro	A2	Senufo	B1
Bamum	C1	Hausa	B1	Shilluk	D1
Bangwa	B2	Herero	C3	Suk	D2
Bapende	C2	Hottentot	C4	Swahili	E2
Baronga	D4	Ibibio	B2	Thonga	D4
Bashilele	C2	Ife	B1	Toma	A1
Basonge	D2	Kanioka	D3	Tonga	D3
Bateke	C2	Kissi	A1	Warega	D2
Baule	B2	Krachi	B1	Xosa	D4
Bavenda	D3	Kurumba	B1	Yangere	C2
Bayaka	C2	Landuma	A1	Yoruba	B1
Bekom	C1	Lango	D2	Zulu	D4

Based on the map in G. P. Murdock, *Africa: Its Peoples and Their Culture History* (New York, 1959)

NATIVE AFRICA

Liam Dunne

tural elements, and on the fringes the Bantu type merges with other Negro types: for example, in Cameroon, where Bantu and true Negro elements meet. Here are found the Bekom, the Bangwa, and the Bamum, who all manufacture sculpture, both figures and masks. A strong ancestor cult prevails. In Gabon, there are the roving tribes grouped under the name Fang; the Bakota, who have no masks but have carved figures; and the Ogowe River people, who have no carved figures but have masks. (Variants of Fang: Pangwe, M'Pangwe, Fanwe, Pahouin, Paanway, etc.; a neighbouring but distinct tribe is named Mpongwe.) The Fang, who range over the Spanish colony of Rio Muni, as well as Gabon and Cameroon, attained considerable notoriety, some years ago, as cannibals; it was said that they had no slaves, no prisoners of war, and no cemeteries. The Bakota keep their ancestors' bones and skulls in boxes or bags, over which they mount characteristic mortuary figures made of copper-covered wood. The Ogowe River masks are noted for their Oriental quality.

A southerly outpost of the western Bantu is the Bachokwe tribe, of Angola and lower Congo (Leopoldville). (Another name with marked variants: Vatchivokoe, Batshioko, and Kioko, among others.) Around the mouth of the Congo River are the Bakongo, Kakongo, or Fjort. In this area the powerful Congo empire once held sway. It was evangelized by Portuguese friars in the fifteenth century, was vehemently Christian for two centuries, and then reverted to the native faiths. In the last century missionaries who returned found that saints' images were being worshipped as pagan gods. Hereabouts also the Lunda empire rose and fell.

Among the congeries of tribes of the Congo basin notable for their art production are the Warega, the Basonge Mino, the Bena Lulua, the Kanioka, the Manyema, the Bashilele, the Warua, and the Bakuba. The last named (also called Bushongo, after their throwing-knife, the *shongo*) have a line of kings that can be traced from the sixteenth century. The reputedly ninety-third king, or *nyimi*, Shamba Bolongongo, was a genuine culture hero. For years he wandered abroad, like the Buddha, seeking and apparently gaining wisdom. Upon assuming the throne, he reorganized government, taught the weaving of cloth, banned the *shongo*, sponsored the importation of tobacco, honoured craftsmen and artists, and instituted the custom of carving a wooden image of the *nyimi*, a custom which was maintained up to recent times. These statues are considered to represent one of the peaks of Negro art. The Baluba, to the south, are noted for making crouching figures that support a stool. The Bayaka, descendants of the Jaga, who invaded the Congo region at about the time the first Portuguese arrived on the coast, manufacture the most terrifying masks in Africa.[5]

The peoples of the far south of the continent, the Bushmen and the Hottentots, stand apart from Negro Africa; they have marked peculiarities of physical type and culture. Both are yellow or yellowish brown in colour; the Hottentots are slightly taller, are more prognathous, and are steatopygous. The Bushmen formerly

5. For a note on another people possibly allied to the
   Bantu, see glossary s.v. "Hill Damara."

dwelt over practically all of south Africa; their relics, rock-paintings, skeletal remains, and place-names are widespread. Today they are restricted almost altogether to the central and northern Kalahari Desert and the northern part of South West Africa. They form three tribes, each speaking a different language, though all have the celebrated clicks, one of which resembles the sound with which we urge on a horse. They are nomads, hunters and food-collectors, in fact the only ones left in Africa. Yet they executed polychrome paintings and engravings on the walls of caves and rock shelters which are of very high artistic merit. Many are of comparatively recent date, though the gift has now disappeared from the Bushmen. The paintings depict cattle-raids, dances, religious scenes, and such. The only form of Bushman art today is the ornamentation of ostrich-egg shells, which hold water. The Bushmen represent the oldest of native African peoples, excepting possibly the Pygmies. Between their stronger Hottentot and Bantu neighbours and the white man, their culture is rapidly dying out.

The culture of the Hottentots, represented today mainly by their southwestern division, the Nama, differs markedly from that of the Bushmen. They are a pastoral people, herding long-horned cattle and flocks of fat-tailed sheep. They smelt iron and they have clans; in general, their culture is superior to that of the Bushmen, yet they do not make rock-paintings and never did. They are apparently a mixture of Bushmen with early invading Hamites. They, too, are a passing people. Indeed, the once large Hottentot groups near the Cape of Good Hope have been transmuted, by admixture of European and Oriental strains, into the present-day "Cape Coloured."

Barely in the last decade, the greater part of native Africa has achieved political independence. Of the former French territories, most have retained their old names: Senegal, Guinea, Ivory Coast, Upper Volta, Dahomey, Niger, Chad, and Gabon. Ubangi-Shari is now the Central African Republic. French Sudan revived for itself the name of the famous medieval empire of Mali (or Melle), which, in the thirteenth century, was the most powerful Sudanese state of which there is authentic record. Middle Congo, on the northwest bank of the Congo River, has become the Republic of the Congo; the name of its capital, Brazzaville, is usually affixed to distinguish it from its namesake over the river, former Belgian Congo, whose capital is Leopoldville. Cameroon and Togo were the French-administered parts of the trust territories of Cameroons and Togoland; the British part of the former joined the new Commonwealth of Nigeria, and of the latter, the Republic of Ghana. Ghana itself, the former British colony of Gold Coast, revived the name of another great Negro empire of the Middle Ages, located actually somewhat northwesterly, in almost the same region as Mali. The most easterly extreme of the Sudanic belt extending four thousand miles across sub-Saharan Africa is former Anglo-Egyptian Sudan, now the mainly Arab state of Sudan. The former British protectorates of Sierra Leone, Uganda, and Kenya and the former trust territory of Tanganyika likewise are independent. Nyasaland and the Rhodesias, still under British hegemony, are in a transitional phase.

Neighboring to or within the Union of South Africa are the British protectorates of Bechuanaland, Swaziland, and Basutoland. The mandated territory of South West Africa is under the control of the Union. The former Belgian-administered trust territory of Ruanda-Urundi has become the Republic of Rwanda and the Kingdom of Burundi. Portuguese Guinea, Angola, and Mozambique remain at present under Portuguese control, and Fernando Po and Rio Muni under Spanish.

If the reader bears in mind the vast complex of cultures that makes up native Africa, he will understand why the folktales of many tribes have been omitted or given minimum representation. The number of examples from the Ashanti may seem disproportionate; this is owing to the richness of the material from this region and its unusual excellence and authenticity.

As sources of the folktales, publications in English have chiefly been relied upon. This does not imply that the many folktale collections in other languages are inferior in quality or importance; indeed, a number of the tales here presented, although published in English, were collected by Swiss, French, German, or Swedish scholars. But most types of folk-literature wanted for this book were to be found in English.

As far as possible, this collection was limited to folktales recorded in the original or by individuals who knew the native language well. Some of the translations have been revised for smoothness of diction, sometimes rather extensively, as in the case of tales from the Bushmen, certain of the Bantu tribes, and the Ashanti, which had been perhaps too literally translated. The basic content, however, was not changed, though some titles have been shortened or altered. The object was to present native African folk-literature in its full range and variety, both as to subject-matter and literary form, in so far as it can be done with eighty-one tales out of more than seven thousand in print.

If the sophisticated folktale and novelette has been overstressed at the expense of the folktale proper, or *Märchen*, it has been deliberate. The intention was to correct the erroneous impression, still widely current, that native African folk-literature is mainly animal tales and to bring home the fact that it is possibly the most sophisticated and realistic of all aboriginal literatures.

The narratives are in four groups. Group I, "The Universe and Its Beginnings," is self-explanatory. In Group II, "The Animal and His World," we have man's conception of the world as seen through animal eyes—a world much like man's, but where man is absent or incidental. In Group III, "The Realm of Man," we see man, with his loves and his hatreds, his cleverness and his stupidity, pitted against his fellow man, against the physical and the social environment, depicted objectively yet pitilessly. Man can be absent from the animal's world, but the animal can never be absent from man's. Group IV, "Man and His Fate," depicts man helpless and bewildered in the hands of chance, at the mercy of unknown forces both within and outside himself. Material was selected in terms of these categories, and for the last three groups was available in abundance throughout native Africa. For the first group this was not found to be so, for true creation myths are uncommon.

A glossary and an accounting of the sources of the tales will be found following the tales themselves.

The following publishers have kindly granted permission to reprint tales from works published by them: GEORGE ALLEN AND CO.: W. H. I. Bleek and L. C. Lloyd, *Specimens of Bushman Folklore* (1911); EDWARD ARNOLD: W. S. and K. Routledge, *With a Prehistoric People* (1910); CLARENDON PRESS, OXFORD: R. S. Rattray, *Akan-Ashanti Folk-tales* (1930); F. Posselt, *Fables of the Veld* (1929); Sir Claude Hollis, *The Masai* (1905); M. W. H. Beech, *The Suk* (1911); G. H. DORAN and WM. HEINEMANN: P. A. Talbot, *In the Shadow of the Bush* (1912); KEGAN PAUL, TRENCH, TRUBNER AND CO.: J. Torrend, *Specimens of Bantu Folk-lore* (1921); LONGMANS, GREEN AND CO.: Elphinstone Dayrell, *Folk-stories from Southern Nigeria* (1910); MACMILLAN AND CO.: J. Roscoe, *The Baganda* (1911); E. W. Smith and A. M. Dale, *The Ila-Speaking Peoples of Northern Rhodesia* (1920); H. A. Junod, *The Life of a South African Tribe* (1913); OXFORD UNIVERSITY PRESS: A. W. Cardinall, *Tales Told in Togoland* (1931); Ray Huffman, *Nuer Customs and Folk-lore* (1931); H. A. Stayt, *The Bavenda* (1931); THE STAPLES PRESS: A. J. N. Tremearne, *Hausa Superstitions and Customs* (1913).

Acknowledgments of the photographs of sculpture will be found in the catalogue of plates. The editor of the sculpture section wishes particularly to thank the following for their help: William Fagg, British Museum, London; Marcel Griaule and Michel Leiris, Musée de l'Homme, Paris; Dr. Frans Olbrechts, Musée de Tervueren, Belgium; Mr. and Mrs. Webster Plass, London; Frederick Pleasants, Brooklyn Museum; Charles Ratton, Paris; Basil Taylor, London.

Usage in the spelling of African tribal names varies considerably. This volume follows, in general, the preferences indicated in the *Anthropological Bibliography of Native Africa*, edited by H. A. Wieschoff (American Oriental Series, Vol. XXIII; New Haven, 1948).

II. The Animal and His World

Table of Contents

NATIVE AFRICAN FOLKTALES

1. The Universe and Its Beginnings

III. The Realm of Man

IV. Man and His Fate

AFRICAN NEGRO SCULPTURE

CONTENTS

xxi

NATIVE AFRICAN FOLKTALES

Introduction

ABOUT FEW PEOPLES are there more misconceptions in the minds of Western Europeans than there are about the aboriginal inhabitants of Africa. The reasons are, perhaps, easy to explain. African cultures belong to those which laymen, particularly in the United States and England, have been accustomed for generations to regard as primitive in every sense of that much-abused term. They are supposed to possess all those characteristics which laymen, and not a few scientists brought up under the influence of the evolutionary theory as formulated by Herbert Spencer in the last three decennia of the nineteenth century, predicated for societies belonging to the lower stages of man's development. However, another fact of perhaps greater import is involved here. These cultures belong to a race that from the fifteenth to well into the nineteenth century had been enslaved. And even where members of this race had been freed, it was their fate to be forced into a position of social inferiority. They were segregated from the white population and relegated to the most menial tasks; in short, they were compelled to live a life impoverished economically, spiritually, and intellectually.

Under these circumstances it is not surprising that incredulity and scepticism greeted the appearance of the early collections of native African folktales, for they gave the most clear-cut evidence that their creators were not primitive. It is a tribute to the missionaries who compiled these collections that they themselves remained open-minded, at least to the extent of equating these native folktales with our own *Märchen* and nursery tales. One man in particular must be singled out, Bishop Callaway, who in two famous works, *Nursery Tales, Traditions, and Histories of the Zulus* (1868) and *The Religious System of the Amazulu* (1870), laid the foundations for the scientific study of native African religion and folklore.

Many otherwise open-minded people find it difficult to believe that the Negroes, of all aboriginal peoples, should possess an oral literature of any artistic distinction which could be equated in many respects with our own folktales. The well-known German Africanist, Carl Meinhof, relates,[1] for in-

1. *Die Dichtung der Afrikaner* (Berlin, 1911).

I

stance, that when a collection of folktales from the Cameroons was published in Germany in 1888, many of the white people who had lived in daily contact with the natives for many years protested quite vigorously and indignantly and insisted that no Negro could possibly have composed them.

Today, of course, no serious person not totally bound by prejudice or too hopelessly conditioned academically can close his eyes to the high quality of the oral literatures of aboriginal peoples. Yet in many quarters a belief is still prevalent that the peculiarities of native African mythologies, as contrasted, for instance, with Polynesian, Indonesian, and American Indian mythologies, are due not to special historical and cultural conditions but rather to certain innate deficiencies of the Negro mind. The implication here is that the Negro mind is more primitive than that of other aboriginal peoples. The German anthropologist, Hermann Baumann [2]—and many of his fellow anthropologists throughout the world would be in agreement—actually insists that the Negro is devoid of the gift for true myth-making and that this is evidenced by the absence in his folk literature of true cosmological myths.

Now in so far as this statement is simply the reflection of Baumann's views concerning the correlation of a given type of mentality with a given race, we need pay no attention to it. Few theories have now been so thoroughly exploded as this one. However, as it is a fact that cosmological myths—for instance, myths dealing with the origins of the heavens and of the celestial bodies —are rarely encountered in Africa, an explanation is called for. An explanation is, indeed, all the more urgent because of the fascination exercised on our minds by the cosmological myths and speculations of the Polynesians and the American Indians as embodied in their highly imaginative folk literatures. Explanation accordingly there must be, but it must in no way differ in kind from that which we seek when we attempt to account for the special traits of any mythologies.

Only an adequate knowledge of the historical development of a people can, of course, give us a full explanation; this, in the absence of all written records for aboriginal civilizations, we can never obtain. Yet the situation is not completely hopeless. We now possess unusually rich data for a study of comparative folklore and a reasonable knowledge of a large number of cultural sequences—enough information, I feel, to justify our hazarding certain assumptions of fundamental significance for the development of mythologies and of literatures.

Briefly stated, these assumptions are the following: All peoples are endowed in equal degree with the mythopoeic imagination. The type of mythology found today is not necessarily, nor even probably, the only type a given people ever possessed. Myths and *Märchen* have changed as the social-economic structure of a civilization and the ideas developed in connection with it have changed. The changes in their content and style may be ascribed primarily to

2. *Schöpfung und Urzeit des Menschen im Mythus der afrikanischen Völker* (Berlin, 1936).

two factors: the extent to which transformations in the social-economic structure have enabled the specific ideologies flowing from and accompanying such structures to become dominant, and the extent to which the old cultural traditions and background have been reorganized, reinterpreted, and given new forms, particularly by artistically gifted individuals. All the evidence at our disposal today—and it is not inconsiderable—justifies our assuming that, from the very beginning of man's history, artistically gifted individuals have existed among all peoples.

Now for the great historic civilizations of Asia and Europe, it has been contended by some theorists [3] that the mythopoeic imagination has been most profoundly stirred and has found its richest expression at three historic periods and in three specific areas, India, Greece, and Christian Europe of the Middle Ages. It is always dangerous to hazard precise dates, but I do not think it would be far from wrong to assign the Indian period to somewhere in the early part of the second millennium B.C., the Greek to the early part of the first millennium B.C. Moreover, according to the same theorists, it is not really of much importance whether or not the plots, themes, and motifs found among the Greeks and in the Christian Middle Ages did or did not come ultimately from India, as the great scholar Benfey [4] once contended. What is important is the nature and the intensity of a people's preoccupation with them.

That reputable folklorists and culture-historians should have taken it upon themselves thus to limit and restrict this stirring of the so-called mythopoeic imagination to just a few periods in the history of specific peoples is almost incomprehensible. Possibly it can be explained by the well known limitations of the academic mind and the narrowness of its vision. Needless to say, nothing is actually further from the truth.

On the basis of data obtained in the nineteenth and twentieth centuries concerning the unwritten literatures of aboriginal peoples, it is now quite clear that at certain periods in their history, the mythopoeic imagination had been as vitally stirred and had expressed itself among them as richly and voluminously as was ever the case in Greece, India, and Christian medieval Europe. It would be erroneous, however, to suppose that the mythopoeic imagination has been at work among aboriginal peoples from the beginning of their history and that it was still in evidence when they were discovered by the Europeans. This would be a dangerous illusion. No aboriginal tribe exists that does not assign its mythmaking to an earlier and very distant epoch in its history.

Yet although myths and *Märchen* exist among all tribes, their number and the manner in which they function varies materially in different areas. In the two Americas, until quite recently, their number was very large, as compared to that of other types of prose fiction, and their function of vital significance

3. Especially by the members of the Finnish school of folklore.

4. Theodor Benfey, introduction to his translation: *Pantschatantra* (Leipzig, 1859).

to the community. This held as well for Polynesia. But in other areas the situation was quite different. Among the Eskimo and among a few tribes in the United States, and in most of Melanesia and in practically all of Africa (the Bushmen and the Hottentots always excepted), the number of what can be properly designated as myths and *Märchen* is actually quite small. In the comparatively few places where true myths are found, they tend to become the life-histories of gods or divine beings, and *Märchen* to become fables in the strict sense, where they have not developed into animal-novelettes.

However, we are not interested here in trying to explain how this transformation has come about, but rather in pointing out that native Africa is not a unique case if true myths and *Märchen* are comparatively rare there.

It is in the perspective of what has been said above that we must approach the study of the folk-literature of that vast continent.

Bearing this in mind, let us now turn to our subject proper, the specific nature of native African folk-literature.[5] The first salient trait to be stressed is that native African folk-literature constitutes a single unit. Of no other region of comparable size in the world does this hold true. The similarities extend not merely to the types of plot-construction and to specific subject-matter, but to literary devices as well—for example, the role played by the songs in the prose text, the frequency of moralistic endings, and the marked prevalence of etiological explanations.

But even more striking and more fundamental than the similarities just mentioned are the stark realism, the insistent emphasis upon man in all his moods, the emphasis upon the contemporary scene, and the high degree of sophistication pervading the whole of native African oral literature. Rarely has man been depicted as more completely and inextricably anchored in this world, more obsessively earthbound. Contrary to the belief widespread throughout the world, man in aboriginal Africa is never thought of as having once possessed a portion of divinity and having subsequently lost it. Even in the few myths that deal with the so-called high gods and the heavenly deities, one detects an almost obsessive geocentrism. Man does not, for instance, ascend to heaven to have intercourse with the gods; the gods descend to earth. In some myths the gods once resided on earth and were forced for various reasons to ascend to the skies. The gods of native Africa, it may be said, must lose their earthly constituent, their earthly adhesions, before they can become properly divine.

The first six myths in this collection deal with this theme. It is perhaps best illustrated by the myth "The Separation of God from Man" (No. 2), found among the Krachi, of Togoland, west Africa, and the one here [6] entitled "The Sun and the Children" (No. 6), found among the Bushmen, of the extreme

5. Cf. Meinhof, *op. cit.*; Alice Werner, "African Mythology," in *The Mythology of All Races*, Vol. VII (Boston, 1925); and other authorities on this folk-literature.

6. The title as given by W. H. I. Bleek and L. C. Lloyd, in *Specimens of Bushmen Folklore* (London, 1911), is "The Children Are Sent to Throw the Sleeping Sun into the Sky."

southern portion of the continent. That the Bushmen should possess a myth with this theme is an indication of its universal distribution in Africa, for in most other respects their myths and *Märchen* are distinct and separate.

In the Krachi myth, the sky-god, Wulbari, is represented as residing on earth—as lying directly upon Mother Earth. There is, in consequence, very little room to move about. In the Bushmen myth, the Sun is lying on the ground and the children, who are the heroes of the myth, are being admonished by their mother to lift up the Sun's armpit. "Children," she says, "you must wait for the sun, who is making us so cold, to lie down to sleep. Then approach him gently and, all together, lift him up and throw him into the sky."

Now the theme of the close union of heaven and earth as the primary stage in the evolution of the cosmos is fairly widespread. It was known to the Greeks, the Japanese, the ancient Aztecs, and the Polynesians, to give but a few instances. In all those mythologies the sky-god is pictured as dwelling on high. In the Polynesian version [7] man, to survive and properly function (for he then dwelt in darkness, within the embrace of his parents—and this is true for the Greek version as well), must castrate his divine parent, push him farther upward into the dome of heaven, and after innumerable adventures and tribulations, finally make his way to freedom. In the African counterpart, the separation of Wulbari from the Earth is fundamentally different. Wulbari rises to the sky, our Togo narrator tells us, because of the many indignities he has suffered at the hands of man. "The divinity . . . in disgust . . . rose up to the present place where one can admire him but not reach him."

I know of nothing even remotely similar to this myth in any other mythology. A long and peculiar history must lie behind such realism, such geocentrism and such cynicism.

However, African realism is not always nor generally accompanied by cynicism. It can deal with more pleasant subjects, with the joys of daily life, the love of parents and children, with loyalties, duties well-performed and properly rewarded. The Routledges, in their book *With a Prehistoric People*,[8] recount the tale of a brother whose love for his sister was so great that when, largely through his own negligence, she is abducted, he sets out in search of her and endures untold hardships and sufferings until he has found her. Since she no longer resides on earth he cheerfully renounces his kinsmen and the joys of earth to stay with her. The story of Kintu (No. 16) stresses the tests to which a man will submit in order to obtain the woman he loves.

Yet, in the main, little romanticism is found in African myths and definitely no sentimentality. It is emphatically not a literature in which wish-fulfilment plays a great role, not one where we can assume that the hero will triumph at the end or that wrongs will always be righted. How are we to explain this?

7. Given in Paul Radin, *Primitive Man as Philosopher* (New York, 1927), pp. 305 ff.

8. W. S. and K. Routledge, *With a Prehistoric People: The Akikuyu of British East Africa* (London, 1910).

Here again we must be very careful not to make hasty and unwarranted assumptions and generalizations though, regrettably, this is a field where they are always made, particularly by historians of literature. Even a man of such astounding depth of knowledge and understanding as Wilamowitz-Moellendorff succumbed. According to him,[9] it was only the Ionians of the sixth century B.C. who possessed the capacity for composing a realistic tale (*Novelle*), because only the Ionians had learned to depict man in proper human terms. This knowledge they had obtained, he contended, from the Orient, for it is of the Orient we always think when we speak of realistic tales and their narrators.

If such evaluations are made as between different members of the great historic cultures, it is not strange that they should be made where the difference is so great as that between the historic and the aboriginal cultures. Yet nothing is more erroneous than to describe one people as being more realistic, as such, or more imaginative, as such, than another. The Negro, in short, is no more nor less realistic than is any other race.

That we find a free, unhampered play of fantasy and imagination among the ancient Greeks, the ancient Japanese, the Polynesians, and most American Indian tribes does not make them specially gifted in this regard. The presence or absence of specific plots and themes, a realistic or non-realistic handling of a plot, merely signifies that the culture and literary tradition in question tends to exclude the one and include the other. These literary traditions are often unbelievably rigorous. Among the Eskimo, for instance, few animal tales exist. The hero of a tale is generally a human being, and the subject-matter is as unmitigatingly realistic as that of the tales from Africa. Among the Winnebago of Wisconsin and Nebraska, on the other hand, the literary tradition is different. There we find a division into myths and *Märchen* on the one hand and novelettes on the other, a twofold division clearly recognized as such, and having special designations. In the first category, we are dealing with a far distant past, and with a world and actors utterly different from those of today. All *Märchen* must end happily, with the hero triumphant and virtue rewarded. In the novelettes, on the contrary, we are dealing with the contemporary or at least the historic scene. The *dramatis personae* are always human beings, the heroes face realities and the vicissitudes of human existence, and the dénouement is always tragic. On the other hand, among the Polynesians no such division of tales exists and no one type of ending is prescribed.

Nor should we be too arbitrary in our concept of what constitutes fantasy and imagination. There has always been a tendency in the Germanic countries (this includes England and the United States), since the beginning of the Romantic period of the early nineteenth century, to define these notions too narrowly—to conceive them largely in terms of Shakespeare's and Aeschylus's imagery. But this is simply a form of provincialism owing to the influence of

9. Ulrich von Wilamowitz-Moellendorff, "Die griechische Literatur des Altertums," in: Wilamowitz-Moellendorff and others, *Die griechische und lateinische Literatur und Sprache* (3rd ed., Berlin, 1912; Die Kultur der Gegenwart, I, 8), p. 56.

our own literary conventions. There are many kinds of imaginative play and fantasy; the tales in this collection, we shall see, are replete with them. In Navaho mythology, which all anthropologists regard as notably rich in the kind of imagery to which we assign so high a value, I can think of nothing superior in imaginative quality to the short narrative prologue to the tales in this book. There we have the figure of a mouse scurrying from house to house, watching the doing of secret things, burrowing from one treasure-chamber to another, and then creating out of her experiences "story-children" which she clothes in different colours and which she adopts because she has no children of her own. Now this is a type of imaginative play and symbolism of a high order. It implies a type of cultural maturity and a sophistication conspicuously absent in most aboriginal societies and strangely reminiscent of the more complex Oriental civilizations.

To sum up briefly. The subject-matter of myths and folktales is not determined by the psyche of a people, as has so frequently been contended directly or indirectly by so many social theorists. There is no such psyche. Nor are matters at all helped by having recourse to pseudo-substitutes for a tribal or national psyche, like culture-patterns or configurations. The subject-matter of myths and folktales is determined by historical circumstances, by the selectivity that a more or less fixed and concrete literary tradition and fixed literary conventions impose upon it, and by the transformations and reinterpretations to which it is subjected by specially gifted individuals. These individuals do not live in a vacuum, nor are they interested in art for art's sake.

All this must be duly remembered before we embark on the somewhat adventurous journey of trying to explain why African folktales have acquired their particular and peculiar physiognomy, why certain themes and motifs are present and others absent, why certain stylistic treatments are accepted and others rejected.

II

THE intercommunicability of the different parts of Africa has frequently been commented upon. To so competent an Africanist as Alice Werner, this is of vital importance for the study of native African culture. She insists that "whether one studies Africa geographically, ethnologically or psychologically, one feels the absence of definite frontiers more and more as one goes on." [10] However, while this intercommunicability and the absence of frontiers are facts to be given due significance, by themselves they really explain very little. To understand the cultural physiognomy of aboriginal Africa it is far more

10. Werner, *op. cit.*, p. 111.

fruitful to turn to the political events of the last two thousand years. Throughout this long period, native Africa has been in a state of profound turmoil and unrest, because of the repeated and persistent influences that have come from the more complexly organized civilizations of the Mediterranean in general and northeastern Africa in particular. We are not dealing here with the spread of individual or even multiple cultural traits only by peaceful means but also, and more generally, with their dissemination by force and brutal conquest. We can safely assume likewise, that influences of a vital and transforming nature came to Africa from ancient Egypt, even if only indirectly and marginally, possibly as early as 2000 B.C.

While it would be incorrect to regard all these influences as directly responsible for the types of societal structure encountered among the majority of the west African and Nilotic tribes and not a few of the south central and southeastern Bantu groups, they clearly played a not insignificant part in their creation and crystallization. The native African civilizations just mentioned, in the form in which we find them today, are probably not more than six or seven hundred years old. They betray their mixed origin in innumerable ways, perhaps in none more markedly than in the multiple facets and the lack of integration of their political and ceremonial organization and religious beliefs. This lack of integration, often bordering on chaos, probably goes much farther back than A.D. 1300. The explanation for this confusion must be sought in the repeated impact upon aboriginal Africa of peoples on a much higher economic and technological level and with correspondingly more complex ideological superstructures. This impact thwarted, where it did not nullify, all efforts at unification. That attempts at unification must have been made our data indicate only too clearly. That they were frustrated at different stages of success, this, too, our data indicate just as definitely. It was not only because each invasion of foreign ideas and peoples arrived before the impact of a previous one had spent itself. The old and the new cultural traits were so different in kind and so antagonistic that the process of harmonizing and welding them into a new whole was an almost hopeless task.

Specific and local developments are to be found in abundance. In some places, right in the centre of the major west African cultures in fact, the older political and economic structure showed amazing powers of resistance. This holds true to an even greater extent among the southern Bantu and, of course, among such peoples as the Congo Pygmies, the Bushmen, and the Hottentots. But the general picture certainly is one of civilizations in a state of confusion and bewilderment, and at loose ends.

It goes without saying that the conflict and disorganization engendered in people by a forced acculturation extending over so many centuries would leave a permanent residue in their oral literature. Folktales which were predominantly wish-fulfilment fantasies—the *Märchen* proper, in short—were pushed into the background. Human heroes with plots taken from purely human situations forged to the front. In the latter, with uncompromising realism, man was pitted against man, as is inevitably the case when individuals are living in an economically and politically disturbed and insecure world.

Assuredly we have the right to infer that it is largely because these people are living in an insecure and semi-chaotic world, with its loss of values and its consequent inward demoralization, that cruelty and wanton murder loom so large in many of their tales. So it does among the Eskimo, where the environment is so persistently inimical, and so it did in the Russia of the nineteenth century. Yet to judge from the very tales where cruelty and murder are the main themes, so strong in these cultures was the resistance to personal and cultural disintegration that the teller of the tales, the author-raconteur, felt it necessary to attach to them a clear-cut moral to the effect that death is the inevitable fate of those who fail to resist disorganization, and that outward disorganization is followed remorselessly by inward disintegration. This is brought out with remarkable sharpness in our tale entitled "How an Unborn Child Avenged Its Mother's Death" (No. 49). It is brought out in an even more symbolical and poetical form in a Bantu (Baila) tale, "Let the Big Drum Roll." [11]

The plot is simplicity itself. A young king joins some people on a trading expedition. He brings back a large amount of goods and is killed by persons jealous of his good fortune. His body is thrown into the bush and the murderers go on their way apparently unconcerned. But the king changes into a little bird and he perches on the top of a tree in front of the murderers and sings:

> "Let the big drum roll! Let the big drum roll!
> It flaps the wings,
> The little bird that has come out from the deep river,
> From the great river of God. Let the big drum roll!
>
> Let the big drum roll! Let the big drum roll!
> At the great river of beads and pearls I have found
> fools which pound,
> Using mortars hewn from blood-trees.[12]
>
> Let the big drum roll! Let the big drum roll!
> Using mortars hewn from the blood-trees,
> Their beads are all white.
> Here! Nemba,[13] where are you?
>
> Let the big drum roll! Let the big drum roll!
> Here! Nemba, where are you?
> Start threading pearls,
> Brilliant pearls.[14]

11. J. Torrend, *Specimens of Bantu Folklore from Northern Rhodesia* (London and New York, 1921), pp. 24–26.

12. That is, "crying vengeance for the blood spilt."   13. The king's sister.   14. To be put on for mourning.

Let the big drum roll! Let the big drum roll!
Start threading pearls,
Brilliant pearls,
From the land where I-wash-the-wrongs.[15]

Let the big drum roll! Let the big drum roll!
The land where I-wash-the-wrongs!
It is far here where you have brought me,
Me who have no feet."

The murderers hear the song and kill the bird. Hardly have they resumed their march than they see the bird again. Once more he sings his song; once more he is killed. Finally, the bird perches on top of the royal house. The retainers of the king see the bird and they hear him sing his song. The murderers have now approached the kraal. However, to get the full impact of the ending it must be given in the words of the narrator:

"*So you have reappeared!*" [The retainers are speaking.]
"*We have reappeared.*"
"*And the king, where have you left him?*"
"*On the road.*"
"*Really? On the road! Come and see a little bird which is on the roof of the royal house.*"
They at once said, "Let us kill it."
Meanwhile, some people are digging a hole in the ground. Then Nemba says, "No, don't kill it. Let us hear the news first."
Just then the little bird started its song again.
"*Go into the hut* [the retainers are speaking] *that you may explain to us exactly what the little bird sings.*"
They went and sat down in the hut on the mat spread there, but then powowowo, *they tumbled down into the hole. Boiling water was brought at once and poured on top of them. That is how they died.*

This emphasis upon man and the mundane contemporary scene did much more, however, than assure to the tales dealing with them a major place. It brought about a humanization of the animal stories as well as a reinterpretation and a new utilization of the *Märchen* themes and motifs proper. This emerges very clearly in the case of the animal tales. These are assuredly very common in Africa. Yet I doubt whether they are any commoner there than in other aboriginal tribes. There are, in fact, areas in Africa where animal tales are quite rare. Torrend,[16] one of the outstanding authorities on African folk literature, states, for instance, that among certain tribes of Northern Rhodesia, as well as among such important tribes as the Xosa and Zulu, tribes who do not remember ever having been enslaved, the number of animal tales is insignificant and evidently borrowed.

15. The land of the dead.   16. *Op. cit.*, p. 6, note 2.

If a belief to the contrary exists among laymen and many students of folk-lore, this is due to the comparative ease with which animal tales are obtained and the new uses to which they have been put. It is not the number of such tales that the folklorist should stress for Africa, but the process by which the animal has been, or is still in the process of being, transformed into a human hero and the manner in which adventures and behaviour supposedly peculiar to animals have been remodelled and converted into ones authentically human. Even Hare, who seems to have kept his original identity more tenaciously than other animals, has, among the Zulu, at times been fused with a quasi-human being named Hlakayana.[17] In parts of eastern Africa he has even been confused with an historical personage, the Arab poet Abu Nuwas (756?–810), "the hero," Miss Werner tells us, "of many more or less discreditable adventures." [18] We are not dealing here with anthropomorphization but with a humanization of animals, which has a certain family resemblance to what developed in medieval Europe.

However, a knowledge of the background, political and social-economic, which led to displacement of one type of folktale by another, like the inter-communicability of the various parts of Africa, will give us only a partial answer to our question. It presents us with a matrix within which this change was brought about, but it tells us nothing about the men and women who directed it and gave it the imprint of their genius. But before we can profitably consider them it will be necessary to review briefly some of the views held by scholars, both anthropologists and non-anthropologists, concerning the existence of such gifted individuals in aboriginal societies, as well as the larger question as to whether true literatures exist there.

The anthropologists and the laymen who have collected aboriginal folk-tales tell us, as a rule, very little about their informants except that some have the reputation of knowing more, some of knowing fewer narratives, and that some are good, some poor narrators. This dearth of information is not accidental. It flows from two assumptions that the collectors make, often consciously. One is to the effect that there is no true individual authorship; the other, that there is no true literature in the strict sense of the term. Most of these collectors are profoundly ignorant, let me add, of the conclusions to which representative students of the European folktale and *Märchen* have come.

Yet, while these last-mentioned students are now convinced that the European-Asiatic *Märchen* represents a true art-form and must be studied as we study all literary expressions, they unfortunately are still under the illusion that American Indians, Negroes, Malays, Polynesians, and so on are really primitive peoples in the older, simple, naïve, and uncomplicated evolutionary sense. There are a few, of course, who know better, notably Louise Pound.[19] Most of the German folklorists, however, would accept Robert Petsch's state-

17. G. McCall Theal, *Kaffir Folk-lore* (London, 2nd edition, 1886), pp. 89 ff.
18. Werner, *op. cit.*, p. 292.

19. *Poetic Origins and the Ballad* (New York, 1921).

ments in his well-known work, *Wesen und Formen der Erzählkunst.*[20] For him the folktales of aboriginal peoples are simply antecedent forms of the narrative art. *Vorformen,* he calls them. They are concerned exclusively with descriptions of what transpires before one's eyes and have as their ultimate purpose, primarily, the heightening of the sense of existence. No constructive imagination is involved. They serve a purely practical function, and aesthetic functions, at best, only marginally and inconsistently.

Petsch's viewpoint is shared by a considerable number of well-known anthropologists who have probably never heard his name. All the members of the so-called functionalist school share it—for instance, particularly, Malinowski. They admit grudgingly enough, Malinowski excepted, that some rudimentary delight in the telling of a story for its own sake may exist among preliterate peoples. But such tales, they claim, are not free. They possess practical entanglements of numerous disturbing kinds. Petsch (and the functionalists, if they are at all to be consistent with themselves, must here acquiesce) contends that only the great historical civilizations could rise to the artistic height of telling a story for its own sake. In other words, only among them can we expect to find the *Märchen,* the *Urform* of all true literature.

Nothing could be more erroneous. Every field-worker in anthropology who has the slightest understanding of literature knows today that literary artists exist in every preliterate community, that they are recognized as such by the community, and that, moreover, fictional and semi-historical narratives are told for the sheer delight of telling them. That presupposes, of course, an audience willing to listen and able to evaluate and appreciate. Petsch and the innumerable anthropologists who follow him, in fact if not in theory, would do well to read a little book written many years ago, the posthumous work of a great historian of literature, Wilhelm Scherer's *Poetik.*[21] They might also take to heart the consensus of a representative number of American and English poets and literary critics,[22] excluding those who, like I. A. Richards [23] and T. C. Pollock,[24] have been misled by Malinowski's verbal felicity.

But to return to the literary artist in aboriginal society. Sometimes it is comparatively easy to segregate him from the rest of the population. Among the Polynesians, for instance, it is clear that he belonged to the upper caste and that he was, on the whole, freed from many of his civic obligations so that he could have leisure to devote to his art. He is, to all intents and purposes, a professional bard and narrator. Because of the taboos of Polynesian society, his audience must have been limited to members of his own caste. In other tribes he is not so strictly set apart, and the whole group constitutes the audience. Yet, always, he is a specially qualified individual. At all times, social

20. Halle, 1934. Cf. particularly Chapter I, "Wesen und Werden der Erzählkunst."

21. Berlin, 1888.

22. For example, Christopher Caudwell, *Illusion and Reality* (London, 1937).

23. *Principles of Literary Criticism* (New York, 1924).

24. *The Nature of Literature* (Princeton, 1942). Cf. particularly pp. 57 ff.

position, membership in certain rituals, and specific theories of ownership and rights determine who may and who may not narrate a given myth or tale. All these factors necessarily bring about changes and introduce innumerable secondary stresses and nuances, over and above those flowing from the strictly personal interests and the personality of a given author-raconteur.

It has frequently been contended that the oral literature of preliterate peoples cannot claim to be counted true literature because it is never divorced from the major activities of the group and because, in the view of its creators or remodellers, as well as of its audience, it has practical purposes to fulfil. It has practical purposes to fulfil quite frequently. But this holds for every literature when it is functioning most significantly. Many folklorists and anthropologists, we know, are shocked by what to them appear to be the magical adhesions of aboriginal literature. The partly or wholly utilitarian conditions to which such myths and tales have to conform, they insist, take them out of the realm of literature. They are subscribing here, wittingly or unwittingly, to a crude form of the mid-Victorian "art for art's sake" theory. By this criterion they would have to exclude almost all lyric poetry and, most certainly, the whole of the classic Greek drama. I cannot imagine a more specifically magical-religious framework than that within which the great plays of Aeschylus matured. It is becoming increasingly evident, furthermore, that the *Oresteia* contains innumerable social and political implications,[25] as do, apparently, Shakespeare's historical plays. Aeschylus would probably have been the first to resent the vacuum in which the great classical scholars of the nineteenth and twentieth centuries have placed him.

What matters is not whether a particular poem-song or prose narrative has practical functions or a magical setting, or what the nature of its subject is, but whether an artist has worked on it. It is this we must determine. We shall, of course, always have to bear in mind that, in aboriginal societies as in our own, artists work with specific, traditional materials and in a limited number of styles. Only the supreme artists and craftsmen are moderately free and strike out in new and untried fields.

When, consequently, an eminent Africanist like Gerhard Lindblom [26] stresses the fact that the Akamba, in common with many other aborigines, will not tell stories in the daytime, no more significance should be attached to this custom, as such, than to the fact that Aeschylus composed his dramas in connection with specific and set ritualistic occasions. The east Africans believe that an infraction of this custom will cause their cattle to be attacked by wild beasts. Very well, it might be retorted, the Greeks too would doubtless have insisted that dire consequences would befall the community if dramas were performed at any but the prescribed time. Professor Lindblom adds, as though it were a peculiarity of the Akamba, that to them story-telling is not

---

25. George Thomson, *Aeschylus and Athens* (London, 1941).

26. "Kamba Tales of Animals" in his *Kamba Folklore* (Uppsala, 1928; Archives d'Études Orientales, XX, 1), p. vi.

only a diversion but something in the nature of a magical act and that mystical power is attributed to those tales that refer to their forefathers. "They are part of the homage which is paid to the ancestral spirits, and contribute to make them favourably disposed towards descendants now alive." [27] Even the Greeks of Aeschylus's time, not to speak of the century preceding, would have found nothing extraordinary in such a belief.

We are now prepared to put to ourselves the fundamental question: In what fashion, if any, did the African author-raconteur differ from his colleagues in other preliterate civilizations? We must seek the answer in strictly historical terms despite the inadequacies of our sources.

There is little evidence for assuming that in Africa author-raconteurs were ever a special and privileged class as in Polynesia. There is, however, ample evidence for believing that two general types of professional author-raconteurs existed there, one type attached rather closely to a leader or "monarch," [28] the other free. The function of the first was to extol the regime and the *status quo*. They were the official "historians," the "laureates," of the ruling class. They dealt, in consequence, primarily with contemporary events and with actual men and women. In all probability they were not recruited to an overwhelming degree from the ranks of the ruling class, however. We can be certain that many of them were priests. That they were steeped in the traditional oral literature of the tribe is certain. Their official preoccupation with the human scene and their particular relation to the governing minority determined much of the subject-matter they selected and the manner in which it was stressed and reinterpreted.

Plots with human heroes were to loom large; and, as pointed out before, animals were to be thoroughly humanized. Since considerable prestige attached to their artistic formulations, these spread to areas where tribal society was organized on entirely different and much simpler political-economic principles, that is, throughout southern Africa. Moreover, since one of the tasks of these author-raconteurs was to account realistically for the origin of earthly rulers and of tribal institutions, cosmological myths were pushed into the background. There is considerable evidence pointing to the former existence of such myths in many parts of Africa, particularly among the Nilotic and west African tribes. Yet it must always be remembered that speculative concern with the origin of the universe or of celestial objects and deities is not a preoccupation of the layman. It is always the product of the thinking and the imagination of the priest-philosopher. Here in Africa, if we can regard the Ewe of Togoland or the Baila of Northern Rhodesia as at all typical, this thinking has apparently been directed into slightly different channels. Instead of speculating upon the origin of the world and of the gods, philosopher-priests cogitate upon the nature of the world and the attributes and powers of the gods.

27. *Ibid.*
28. This is particularly true of west Africa, but is found among the Bantu Baganda as well.

The general principles according to which these author-raconteurs reorganized and reinterpreted the animal tale in terms of human beings and the human scene have already been touched upon. It only remains now to illustrate concretely the processes involved, by discussing one of the stories in our collection—a tale of the Spider-Ananse cycle of the Ashanti, "How Spider Obtained the Sky-God's Stories" (No. 1).

This is an old animal tale containing elements of very wide distribution. It has the simplest of plots: how little Spider beguiles dangerous animals by means of cunning stratagems and then captures them. Originally the plot must have stood by itself. In the Ashanti version the original plot has been retained, but it has been completely subordinated to a special theme of a strange kind, namely a wager between a thoroughly humanized spider and an equally humanized sky-god. Spider is represented as approaching the sky-god in order to buy the sky-god's stories. To his request the sky-god replies, "Great and powerful towns . . . have come but they were unable to purchase them, and yet you who are but a mere masterless man, you say you will be able [to do it]?" Then he gave the price. Spider must bring the sky-god a python, some hornets, a leopard, and a fairy. The wager is accepted. Boastfully Spider assures him he will bring them all. "I will add my old mother . . . to the lot," he exclaims. The account of how the animals and the fairy are captured then follows.

Clearly, however, the interest is centred not on the prizes or the stratagems used to capture them but on the wager and the two main actors. In the final scene Spider is shown bringing his last two payments, the fairy and his mother. The sky-god then calls a council of elders and puts the matter before them. "Very great kings have come," the sky-god tells them, "and were not able to buy the sky-god's stories, but Kwaku Ananse, the spider, has been able to pay the price. . . . Sing his praise." And when they had done so the sky-god continued, "Kwaku Ananse, from today and going on forever, I take my sky-god's stories, and I present them to you. . . . My blessing, blessing, blessing."

A secondary consequence of the reorganization and reorientation of so many of the animal tales is the practical disappearance of the so-called trickster and culture-hero types of tale, in all those areas where the author-raconteur was essentially an official scribe. Both types are encountered all over the rest of the aboriginal world; they are developed most richly, perhaps, where assuredly political events were more than normally contributory. The existence and prominence of trickster and culture-hero tales among the Bushmen indicates that they must once have been found in other parts of Africa too. Indeed, those Bantu tribes where there is no division into stratified classes, where, in consequence, there is no tendency for the activities of the author-raconteur to become closely identified with the interests of a leader at times exalted to the rank of ruler, these do actually possess a trickster-culture-hero, namely, the Hare. His creative function has, it is true, disappeared. But this holds for many American Indian tribes as well.

In marked contrast to the role played by these more or less officially designated author-raconteurs is that of the story-teller proper. These story-tellers
are to be encountered in every group, in every village. Here in Africa, they
played a particularly important role at the great gatherings and markets where
goods were exchanged, and where, incidentally, stories passed readily from
tribe to tribe. While these story-tellers are assuredly absent in no portion of
Africa, it is in the predominantly non-stratified societies of southern Africa
that we can best see them at work. They, too, reformulate and reorientate the
traditional subject-matter, but primarily in order to bring it up to date, to
make it understandable and palatable to a contemporary audience. This, in
fact, is their function in all aboriginal societies. However, because of the ra-
pidity with which, even in southern Africa, societies were transformed, this
meant much more than it meant in other parts of the aboriginal world. Thus,
for instance, while the actors of the animal stories have not escaped the process
of humanization, the plots have remained intact and persist in their older form.
But they have been reduced often to mere skeletons of their former selves.
Take, for example, the following from the Thonga, of southern Africa
(cf. No. 30): [29]

*One day the Hare said to the Grey Antelope: "Let us go and sow peas."
"I don't like peas, I prefer wild beans," said the Antelope. So the Hare went
by himself to sow peas. When they began to sprout, he noticed that they were
disappearing, so he hid himself in the field, and caught the Antelope digging
up his peas. "Aha!" said he. "You are a thief. Pay the fine!" She gave him a
hoe and he went off.*

*He met some women who were digging clay with sticks. He said to them:
"Haven't you got any hoes?" "No," they said, "we haven't a single one."
"Then take this one," said he, "you can give it back later on." When they had
finished, the last one who used the hoe broke it. Then the Hare sang the following words:*

*"Clay-diggers, give back my hoe, my friends.
My hoe which the Antelope gave me,
The Antelope who paid the fine for my peas."*

The tale concludes with the women each giving him a pot.
Here the animal plot is retained in its full form, but the animal hero has
been thoroughly humanized. In other instances where this holds true, either
the animal hero is displaced by a human hero or a human figure is introduced
who competes in importance with him.
Analogous transformations took place in the forms given to older myths and
Märchen of southern Africa. Despite their more conservative tendencies and
their very close relationship to the older traditional folktales, the southern

29. Henri A. Junod, *The Life of a South African Tribe*
(London, 1913), Vol. II, p. 223.

raconteurs, like their northern colleagues, were deeply affected by the chaos and disorganization which has characterized native African history of the last seven hundred years. The realistic tale, the novelette, came to the fore here as it did in the north. Indeed one gets the impression that the reflection of the political-economic background is more direct here, in southern Africa, than among the northern Bantu or the Nilotic and west African tribes. Human relations must have become unusually intense and unbearable to have produced a novelette like that entitled "How an Unborn Child Avenged Its Mother's Death" (No. 49). It is worth while commenting upon it, because it represents the work of an author-raconteur of unusual skill and acute psychological and philosophical insight.

The plot has a mature simplicity. A pitiless physical environment is pitted against a husband and prospective father. The man fails to meet the test and thereby isolates himself, internally and externally, from his social group. He stands before us, naked, stripped of all his moral values and standards. Punishment and retribution follow inexorably. The full realization of the crime he has committed is symbolized in a twofold fashion. A sudden accession of fear comes upon him and he must run, run from the dead body of the wife he has wantonly murdered and from himself. Then from the womb of the dead woman emerges her unborn child, who starts in rapid pursuit of the murderer to drive him back into the arms of the society from which he has cut himself off, and to his death.

At times we have incorporated in the novelette plots, themes, and motifs belonging to *Märchen*, which have been divorced from their older settings and employed secondarily and symbolically. As an example let me cite the very profound tale "The Wonder-Worker of the Plains" (No. 62).

Here we have a magical and supernatural animal transferred to a purely human, contemporary scene. This transference necessitates the complete transformation of the animal, a wonder-working buffalo. He is no longer a mere animal or a supernatural being but the symbol of that aspect of the external world upon which man must subsist. The human heroes in the tale refuse to conform to the traditional mores of their group. The boy will not permit his parents to select his wife; he will not marry within his own group; he will not permit his parents to visit the parents of the girl he finally selects as bride and bring them the bride-price in person. He is depicted as behaving in this fashion because of his excessive confidence in himself and because, ostensibly at least, he wishes to spare his bride the pain she might suffer from his parents' hard admonitions.

The girl refuses to conform, in a different but an equally egotistical fashion. Instead of accepting the woman helpers her parents place at her disposal, she demands the wonder-working buffalo. "Give me . . . the Wonder-Worker of the Plains. Let him serve me," she demands. Not only is her behaviour thus extremely antisocial, but she completely misunderstands man's relation to nature, to the external world. Nature is to be compelled to be subservient to her.

It is a very subtle touch of the author-raconteur that makes the buffalo visible only to her and not to her husband, when the two set out for their home.

The plot demands that the man be chastised for his recalcitrance and his false self-sufficiency. However, he is not represented as sinning against the elementary conditions of human existence and human happiness; he is not to be overwhelmed and destroyed in the final catastrophe; his punishment is to take another form. He is to be the instrument that is to bring about the final catastrophe.

The woman (as one might expect, in view of the nature of her demand upon her parents) is never quite to understand the nature of her sin and her profound misconception of reality. Her punishment, as well as the essential tragedy of the situation, lies precisely in this fact. In the scene where, weeping and full of remorse, she attempts to resuscitate the dead buffalo, some glimmering of the heinousness of her behaviour seems to dawn upon her, and she intones a mystical song:

"*Ah, my father, Wonder-Worker of the Plains,*
Indeed they have told me: You would go through the deep darkness; that in
all directions you would stumble through the night, Wonder-Worker of
the Plains;
You are the young wonder-tree plant, grown out of ruins, which dies before
its time, consumed by a gnawing worm. . . .
You made flowers and fruit fall upon your road, Wonder-Worker of the
Plains!"

Yet this awareness is never much more than a glimmering. The woman cannot, at bottom, be forgiven. No sooner has she restored the buffalo to life and he begins to move his limbs than the real world she has so flagrantly outraged intervenes, first in the person of her husband and second in that of her mother-in-law. And so the buffalo dies, in his death presaging the utter destruction of her people and herself.

This concept of tragedy as flowing from a misunderstanding of man's relation to nature is widespread among all aboriginal civilizations. It holds wherever man's attitude is ambivalent, wherever his control of the external world is inadequate, and where, in addition, societies are not organized on a class basis. I can find no expression of it, for instance, among the northern Bantu, the west African, or the Nilotic peoples.

An interesting variant of the theme of the Wonder-Worker of the Plains is found among the Bushmen in a tale entitled "The Young Man Who Was Carried Off by a Lion" (No. 41). It should be remembered that among the Bushmen *Märchen* and simple animal tales are still overwhelmingly dominant. The basic theme of this tale is that Nature can, after a fashion, misunderstand its relation to man just as man his relation to Nature.

The plot is the following: A young man falls asleep while hunting. A hungry lion seizes him. The man, to save his life, feigns death, and the lion, convinced that he is dead, carries him to a tree and forces his body tightly between its branches. Then he departs to quench his thirst. The man frees himself and flees to his home, where he begs his kinsfolk to hide him from the lion, who, he feels, is bound to trail him. His mother accordingly hides him. Soon the lion appears and threatens the community with destruction if the young man is not turned over to him. Arrows and spears are discharged at the lion, but all to no avail. As a last recourse, human beings are thrown to him to devour. He will have none of them. He insists upon recovering the young man he had seized and who had duped him by feigning death. Finally the community, in desperation, demands that the mother deliver her son to the lion so that the others may be saved. This is done. But the lion, too, must die, for he has made an unwarranted demand, one lying beyond his rights. Thus, we are taught, Nature can transgress and must be brought to terms as best one can. That is what the words of the youth's mother imply when at the end she acquiesces and says: "Be it so. Give my child to the lion. In no wise, however, must you allow the lion to eat him, in no wise must you allow the lion to continue walking about here. You must kill him and lay him upon my child. Let the lion die and lie upon my son."

And now to conclude. If what I have said is even moderately correct, it is erroneous to equate the prose literature of aboriginal Africa with that of other aboriginal peoples except in the most general manner, excluding, of course, Polynesia. The other myths, *Märchen*, and tales no more resemble the African folktale in its original form than do the conscious literary reworkings of Greek mythology resemble theirs. In fact they are on a higher level, I feel, than those reworkings. We are, essentially, in the presence of a true art form, often possessing a high degree of sophistication and formalism. The creators of African literature can at times be as sceptical and ironical as the Greeks. It would be difficult, indeed, to find a match for irony and sophistication comparable to the traditional beginning of an Ashanti tale:

"We do not really mean, we do not really mean, that what we are going to say is true."

Or the traditional ending:

"This, my story which I have related, if it be sweet or if it be not sweet, take some elsewhere and let some come back to me."

PAUL RADIN

Prologue

MOUSE GOES everywhere. Through rich men's houses she creeps, and she visits even the poorest. At night, with her bright little eyes, she watches the doing of secret things, and no treasure chamber is so safe but she can tunnel through and see what is hidden there.

In olden days she wove a story child from all that she saw, and to each of these she gave a gown of a different colour—white, red, blue, or black. The stories became her children and lived in her house and served her because she had no children of her own.

[EKOI]

We do not really mean, we do not really mean
that what we are going to say is true

I

The Universe and Its Beginnings

1

How Spider Obtained the Sky-God's Stories

KWAKU ANANSE, the spider, once went to Nyankonpon, the sky-god, in order to buy the sky-god's stories. The sky-god said, "What makes you think *you* can buy them?" The spider answered and said, "I know I shall be able." Thereupon the sky-god said, "Great and powerful towns like Kokofu, Bekwai, Asumengya, have come, but they were unable to purchase them, and yet you who are but a mere masterless man, you say you will be able?"

The spider said, "What is the price of the stories?" The sky-god said, "They cannot be bought for anything except Onini, the python; Osebo, the leopard; Mmoatia, the fairy; and Mmoboro, the hornets." The spider said, "I will bring some of all these things, and, what is more, I'll add my old mother, Nsia, the sixth child, to the lot."

The sky-god said, "Go and bring them then." The spider came back, and told his mother all about it, saying, "I wish to buy the stories of the sky-god, and the sky-god says I must bring Onini, the python; Osebo, the leopard; Mmoatia, the fairy; and Mmoboro, the hornets; and I said I would add you to the lot and give you to the sky-god." Now the spider consulted his wife, Aso, saying, "What is to be done that we may get Onini, the python?" Aso said to him, "You go off and cut a branch of a palm tree, and cut some string-creeper as well, and bring them." And the spider came back with them. And Aso said, "Take them to the stream." So Ananse took them; and, as he was going along, he said, "It's longer than he is, it's not so long as he; you lie, it's longer than he."

The spider said, "There he is, lying yonder." The python, who had over-heard this imaginary conversation, then asked, "What's this all about?" To which the spider replied, "Is it not my wife, Aso, who is arguing with me that this palm branch is longer than you, and I say she is a liar." And Onini, the python, said, "Bring it, and come and measure me." Ananse took the palm branch and laid it along the python's body. Then he said, "Stretch yourself out." And the python stretched himself out, and Ananse took the rope-creeper and wound it and the sound of the tying was *nwenene! nwenene! nwenene!* until he came to the head.

Ananse, the spider, said, "Fool, I shall take you to the sky-god and receive the sky-god's tales in exchange." So Ananse took him off to Nyame, the sky-god. The sky-god then said, "My hand has touched it, there remains what still remains." The spider returned and came and told his wife what had happened, saying, "There remain the hornets." His wife said, "Look for a gourd, and fill it with water and go off with it." The spider went along through the bush, when he saw a swarm of hornets hanging there, and he poured out some of the water and sprinkled it on them. He then poured the remainder upon himself and cut a leaf of plantain and covered his head with it. And now he addressed the hornets, saying, "As the rain has come, had you not better come and enter this, my gourd, so that the rain will not beat you; don't you see that I have taken a plantain leaf to cover myself?" Then the hornets said, "We thank you, Aku, we thank you, Aku." All the hornets flew, disappearing into the gourd, *fom!* Father Spider covered the mouth, and exclaimed, "Fools, I have got you, and I am taking you to receive the tales of the sky-god in exchange."

And he took the hornets to the sky-god. The sky-god said, "My hand has touched it; what remains still remains."

The spider came back once more, and told his wife, and said, "There remains Osebo, the leopard." Aso said, "Go and dig a hole." Ananse said, "That's enough, I understand." Then the spider went off to look for the leopard's tracks, and, having found them, he dug a very deep pit, covered it over, and came back home. Very early next day, when objects began to be visible, the spider said he would go off, and when he went, lo, a leopard was lying in the pit. Ananse said, "Little father's child, little mother's child, I have told you not to get drunk, and now, just as one would expect of you, you have become intoxicated, and that's why you have fallen into the pit. If I were to say I would get you out, next day, if you saw me, or likewise any of my children, you would go and catch me and them." The leopard said, "O! I could not do such a thing."

Ananse then went and cut two sticks, put one here, and one there, and said, "Put one of your paws here, and one also of your paws here." And the leopard placed them where he was told. As he was about to climb up, Ananse lifted up his knife, and in a flash it descended on his head, *gao!* was the sound it made. The pit received the leopard and *fom!* was the sound of the falling. Ananse got a ladder to descend into the pit to go and get the leopard out. He got the leopard out and came back with it, exclaiming, "Fool, I am taking you to exchange for the stories of the sky-god." He lifted up the leopard to go and give to Nyame, the sky-god. The sky-god said, "My hands have touched it; what remains still remains."

Then the spider came back, carved an Akua's child, a black flat-faced wooden doll, tapped some sticky fluid from a tree and plastered the doll's body with it. Then he made *eto*, pounded yams, and put some in the doll's hand. Again he pounded some more and placed it in a brass basin; he tied string round the doll's waist, and went with it and placed it at the foot of the odum tree, the place where the fairies come to play. And a fairy came along. She said, "Akua, may I eat a little of this mash?" Ananse tugged at the string, and the doll nodded her head. The fairy turned to one of the sisters, saying, "She says I may eat some." She said, "Eat some, then." And she finished eating, and thanked her. But when she thanked her, the doll did not answer. And the fairy said to her sister, "When I thank her, she does not reply." The sister of the first fairy said, "Slap her crying-place." And she slapped it, *pa!* And her hand stuck there. She said to her sister, "My hand has stuck there." She said, "Take the one that remains and slap her crying-place again." And she took it and slapped her, *pa!* and this one, too, stuck fast. And the fairy told her sister, saying, "My two hands have stuck fast." She said, "Push it with your stomach." She pushed it and her stomach stuck to it. And Ananse came and tied her up, and he said, "Fool, I have got you, I shall take you to the sky-god in exchange for his stories." And he went off home with her.

Now Ananse spoke to his mother, Ya Nsia, the sixth child, saying, "Rise up, let us go, for I am taking you along with the fairy to go and give you to the sky-god in exchange for his stories." He lifted them up, and went off there to where the sky-god was. Arrived there he said, "Sky-god, here is a fairy and my old woman whom I spoke about, here she is, too." Now the sky-god called his elders, the Kontire and Akwam chiefs, the Adonten, the Gyase, the Oyoko, Ankobea, and Kyidom. And he put the matter before them, saying, "Very great kings have come, and were not able to buy the sky-god's stories, but Kwaku Ananse, the spider, has been able to pay the price: I have received from him Osebo, the leopard; I have received from him Onini, the python; and of his own accord, Ananse has added his mother to the lot; all these things lie here." He said, "Sing his praise." "*Eee!*" they shouted. The sky-god said, "Kwaku Ananse, from today and going on for ever, I take my sky-god's stories and I present them to you, *kose! kose! kose!* my blessing, blessing, blessing! No more shall we call them the stories of the sky-god, but we shall call them spider-stories."

This, my story, which I have related, if it be sweet, or if it be not sweet, take some elsewhere, and let some come back to me.

[ASHANTI]

2

The Separation of God from Man

I N T H E B E G I N N I N G of days Wulbari and man lived close together and Wulbari lay on top of Mother Earth, Asase Ya. Thus it happened that, as there was so little space to move about in, man annoyed the divinity, who in disgust went away and rose up to the present place where one can admire him but not reach him.

He was annoyed for a number of reasons. An old woman, while making her *fufu* outside her hut, kept on knocking Wulbari with her pestle. This hurt him and, as she persisted, he was forced to go higher out of her reach. Besides, the smoke of the cooking fires got into his eyes so that he had to go farther away. According to others, however, Wulbari, being so close to men, made a convenient sort of towel, and the people used to wipe their dirty fingers on him. This naturally annoyed him. Yet this was not so bad a grievance as that which caused We, the Wulbari of the Kassena people, to remove himself out of the reach of man. He did so because an old woman, anxious to make a good soup, used to cut off a bit of him at each mealtime, and We, being pained at this treatment, went higher.

Established in his new setting, Wulbari formed a court in which the animals were his chief attendants. Everything seemed to run smoothly for a time until one day Ananse, spider, who was Captain of the Guard, asked Wulbari if he would give him one corncob. "Certainly," Wulbari said, but he wanted to know what Ananse wished to do with only one corncob.

And Ananse said, "Master, I will bring you a hundred slaves in exchange for one corncob."

At this, Wulbari laughed.

But Ananse meant what he said, and he straightway took the road from the sky down to the earth, and there he asked the way from Krachi to Yendi. Some men showed him the road and Ananse set out. That evening he had gone as far as Tariasu. There he asked the chief for a lodging, and a house was shown him. And when it was time to go to bed, he took the corncob and asked the chief where he could put it for safe keeping. "It is the corn of Wulbari; he has sent me on a message to Yendi, and this corncob I must not lose."

So the people showed him a good place in the roof, and everyone went

28

to sleep. But Ananse arose in the night and gave the corn to the fowls and, when day broke, he asked for the cob and lo! it was all eaten and destroyed. So Ananse made a great fuss and was not content till the people of Tariasu had given him a great basket of corn. Then he continued on his way and shortly sat down by the roadside, as he was weary from carrying so great a load.

Presently there came along a man with a live fowl in his hand which he was bringing back from his field. Ananse greeted him and they soon became friends. Ananse said that he liked the fowl—in fact, he liked it so much that he would give the whole of his load of corn in exchange if the man would agree. Such a proposal was not to be met with every day; the fellow agreed, and Ananse went on his way carrying the fowl with him.

That night he reached Kpandae, and he went and saluted the chief from whom he begged a night's lodging. This was readily granted and Ananse, being tired, soon went to bed. First, however, he showed his fowl to the people and explained that it was the fowl of Wulbari and that he had to deliver it to Yendi. They were properly impressed with this information and showed Ananse a nice, quiet fowl-house where it would be perfectly safe. Then all went to bed.

But Ananse did not sleep. As soon as he heard every one snoring, he arose and took his fowl and went outside the village and there sacrificed the poor bird. Leaving the corpse in the bush and placing some of the blood and feathers on the chief's own doorpost, he went back to bed.

At cock-crow Ananse arose and began shouting and crying out that the fowl of Wulbari was gone, that he had lost his place as Captain of the Guard, and that the unfortunate village of Kpandae would most certainly be visited by misfortune. The hullabaloo brought everyone outside, and by this time it was daylight. Great indeed was the clamour when the people learned what the fuss was about, and then suddenly Ananse pointed to the feathers and blood on the chief's doorpost.

There was no use denying the fact—the feathers were undoubtedly those of the unfortunate fowl, and just then a small boy found its body. It was evident to all that their own chief had been guilty of a sacrilege too dreadful to think about. They, therefore, one and all, came and begged Ananse to forgive them and to do something or other to divert the approaching calamity, which everyone thought must be inevitable.

Ananse at last said that possibly Wulbari would forgive them, if they gave him a sheep to take to Yendi.

"Sheep!" cried the people. "We will give you any number of sheep so long as you stop this trouble."

Ananse was satisfied with ten sheep and he went his way.

He had no further adventures until he reached the outskirts of Yendi with his sheep. He was a little tired, however, and sat down outside the village and allowed his sheep to graze. He was still resting when there came toward him a company of people, wailing and weeping. They bore with them a corpse, and when Ananse saluted them and asked what they were doing, they said that a young man had died and that they were now carrying him back to his village for burial.

Ananse asked if the village was far, and they said it was far. Then he said that it was more than likely that the body would rot on the road, and they agreed. He then suggested that they should give him the corpse and in exchange he would give them the ten sheep. This was a novel kind of business deal, but it sounded all right and, after a little while, the company of young men agreed and they went off with the sheep, leaving their dead brother with Ananse.

The latter waited until nightfall and then walked into the town, carrying with him the corpse. He came to the house of the chief of Yendi and saluted that mighty monarch, and begged for a small place where he could rest. He added:

"I have with me as companion the son of Wulbari. He is his favourite son, and, although you know me as the Captain of Wulbari's Host, yet I am only as a slave to this boy. He is asleep now, and as he is so tired I want to find a hut for him."

This was excellent news for the people of Yendi and a hut was soon ready for the favourite son of Wulbari.

Ananse placed the corpse inside and covered it with a cloth so that it seemed verily like a sleeping man. Ananse then came outside and was given food. He feasted himself well and asked for some food for Wulbari's son. This he took into the hut where, being greedy, he finished the meal and came out bearing with him the empty pots.

Now the people of Yendi asked if they might play and dance, for it was not often that a son of Wulbari came to visit them. Ananse said that they might, for he pointed out to them that the boy was an extraordinarily hard sleeper and practically nothing could wake him—that he himself, each morning, had had to flog the boy until he woke, and that shaking was no use, nor was shouting. So they played and they danced.

As the dawn came, Ananse got up and said it was time for him and Wulbari's son to be up and about their business. So he asked some of the chief's own children who had been dancing to go in and wake the son of Wulbari. He said that, if the young man did not get up, they were to flog him, and then he would surely be aroused. The children did this, but Wulbari's son did not wake. "Hit harder, hit harder!" cried Ananse, and the children did so. But still Wulbari's son did not wake.

Then Ananse said that he would go inside and wake him himself. So he arose and went into the hut and called to Wulbari's son. He shook him, and then he made the startling discovery that the boy was dead. Ananse's cries drew everyone to the door of the compound, and there they learned the dreadful news that the sons of their chief had beaten Wulbari's favourite child to death.

Great was the consternation of the people. The chief himself came and saw and was convinced. He offered to have his children killed; he offered to kill himself; he offered everything imaginable. But Ananse refused and said that he could think of nothing that day, as his grief was too great. Let the people bury the unfortunate boy and perhaps he, Ananse, would devise some plan by which Wulbari might be appeased.

So the people took the dead body and buried it.

That day all Yendi was silent, as all men were stricken with fear.

But in the evening Ananse called the chief to him and said, "I will return to my father, Wulbari, and I will tell him how the young boy has died. But I will take all the blame on myself and I will hide you from his wrath. You must, however, give me a hundred young men to go back with me, so that they can bear witness as to the boy's death."

Then the people were glad, and they chose a hundred of the best young men and made them ready for the long journey to the abode of Wulbari.

Next morning Ananse arose and, finding the young men ready for the road, he went with them back to Krachi and from there he took them up to Wulbari.

The latter saw him coming with the crowd of youths and came out to greet him. And Ananse told him all that he had done and showed how from one single corncob Wulbari had now got a hundred excellent young slaves. So pleased was Wulbari that he confirmed Ananse in his appointment as Chief of his Host and changed his name from Anyankon to Ananse, which it has remained to the present day.

Now Ananse got very conceited over this deed and used to boast greatly about his cleverness. One day he even went so far as to say that he possessed more sense than Wulbari himself. It happened that Wulbari overheard this, and he was naturally annoyed at such presumption. So, next day, he sent for his captain and told him that he must go and fetch him *something*. No further information was forthcoming, and Ananse was left to find out for himself what Wulbari wanted.

All day Ananse thought and thought, and in the evening Wulbari laughed at him and said, "You must bring me *something*. You boast everywhere that you are my equal, now prove it."

So next day Ananse arose and left the sky on his way to find *something*. Presently he had an idea and, sitting down by the wayside, he called all the birds together. From each one he borrowed a fine feather and then dismissed them. Rapidly he wove the feathers into a magnificent garment and then returned to Wulbari's town. There he put on the wonderful feather robe and climbed up the tree over against Wulbari's house. Soon Wulbari came out and saw the garishly coloured bird. It was a new bird to him, so he called all the people together and asked them the name of the wonderful bird. But none of them could tell, not even the elephant, who knows all that is in the far, far bush. Someone suggested that Ananse might know, but Wulbari said that, unfortunately, he had sent him away on an errand. Everyone wanted to know the errand and Wulbari laughed and said, "Ananse has been boasting too much and I heard him say that he has as much sense as I have. So I told him to go and get me *something*." Everyone wanted to know what this *something* was, and Wulbari explained that Ananse would never guess what he meant, for the *something* he wanted was nothing less than the sun, the moon, and darkness.

The meeting then broke up amid roars of laughter at Ananse's predicament and Wulbari's exceeding cleverness. But Ananse, in his fine plumes, had heard what was required of him and, as soon as the road was clear, descended from his tree and made off to the bush.

There he discarded his feathers and went far, far away. No man knows quite where he went, but, wherever he went, he managed to find the sun and the moon and the darkness. Some say that the python gave them to him, others are not sure. In any case, find them he did and, putting them into his bag, he hastened back to Wulbari.

He arrived at his master's house late one afternoon and was greeted by Wulbari who, after a while, asked Ananse if he had brought back *something*.

"Yes," said Ananse, and went to his bag and drew out darkness. Then all was black and no one could see. Thereupon he drew out the moon and all could see a little again. Then last he drew out the sun, and some who were looking at Ananse saw the sun and they became blind, and some who saw only a little of it were blinded in one eye. Others, who had their eyes shut at the moment, were luckier, so they lost nothing of their eyesight.

Thus it came about that blindness was brought into the world, because Wulbari wanted *something*.

[KRACHI]

3

The Creator Nyame and His Four Wives

NYAME WAS MARRIED to Akoko, the barn-door fowl, but after a while he took to himself four other wives. Akoko, of course, retained her rights as the head wife, and the other four wives obeyed her.

One day Nyame called the four newcomers together and asked each one what present she would give him in return for his having raised her above other women in the tribe. The first one promised that she would always sweep his compound for him and keep the place neat and tidy; the second said she would always cook for him and never complain when there were many visitors; the third agreed to spin cotton for him and to bring him all the water he might require; and the fourth one said that she would bear him a child of gold.

This last promise pleased Nyame, and every day he killed a sheep for this woman. But the child was long in coming. Just when Nyame's patience was giving out, the woman conceived, and Nyame detailed Akoko to tend and care for her.

So Akoko took the woman into her hut and, when the time of delivery was at hand, Akoko told her that, whatever else she did, she was to be sure to shut her eyes when the child was born and not to open them until she was told to do so. The woman obeyed, and Akoko hurried out and brought back a big pot.

Now it happened that the woman bore twins. The first one to be born was made entirely of silver, and Akoko at once took the babe and placed it in the pot. The second child was of gold, and Akoko placed it in the pot. Then she hurried outside and found two frogs. Returning with these, she placed them on the couch and then told the mother to open her eyes and see her children.

Then Akoko hastened out of the hut with the pot and ran with it as fast as she could to the far, far bush, where she found a dead odum tree. There she hid the pot with the two babies and then returned swiftly to Nyame's compound, passing by his hut on the way. She told her husband that the children had been born and asked him to go with her to see his offspring.

Nyame at once arose and went to the hut where the mother was lying. To his consternation and anger, he found two frogs instead of the expected child of gold. He gave orders that the frogs were to be killed at once and that the woman should be sent into the farthermost corner of his kingdom.

Now it chanced that Nyame had a certain hunter whose hut was situated in the far bush. He happened to be out hunting on the day the children were born and his chase led him to the odum tree. There his eye was attracted by the glitter of the golden child and he cried out, "Why, what is this?"

The children answered him, "We are the children of Nyame." But he could not believe that.

He took some of the dust that had fallen from their bodies, however, and put it into his bag. Then he took up the children and carried them to his hovel. There he kept them secretly, nor did he tell any man of what he had found.

And every time the hunter wanted money he would gather some of the children's dust. Thus he became a very rich man. Instead of having a solitary hovel in the bush, he built a huge compound and round him there gathered a great town.

Now not very far away there lived Ananse. One day he went out into the bush to gather some white ants for his fowls and he came across the new town. He was astounded to see that in the place where he expected a hovel there was so much wealth and so many people. His curiosity aroused, Ananse entered the town to learn how the change had come about. By sheer accident he espied the former hunter playing with the children. At once Ananse knew that the latter were the lost children of Nyame, and he hurried back home to send a message to their father. But the hunter had also seen Ananse, and he knew full well that that busybody would betray his secret. Therefore he called the children and told them that, as they claimed they were the children of Nyame, he proposed to take them to Nyame.

The next morning he prepared hammocks and fine clothes for the children and proceeded on the way to Nyame. On the road the children called their foster-father and told him that he must collect some stones with which to play *wari*, as they themselves could not speak to their father, but that the stones would tell him the whole story.

The man did so, and they arrived before Nyame. There the hunter placed stools and asked Nyame if he would play a game of *wari* with him. Nyame agreed, but the silver child said, no, he himself wished to play, that the stones would tell the story for which they had come.

Then the silver child and Nyame sat down to the game and, as the stones went round and round the board, the golden child sang the story of their adventures from the time of their mother's promise until their birth; he sang of the baseness of Akoko and of the kindness of the hunter who had fed them instead of killing them for their silver and gold.

Then Nyame knew them to be his children, and he sent straightway into the far, far bush to call back the woman whom he had exiled. When she arrived, she was dirty all over and her hair was uncut and unkempt. Nyame himself washed the woman, and when she was all clean and nice again he sent for Akoko.

Great was Nyame's wrath. He tied the evil fowl Akoko, his first wife, by her foot to a stick and cursed her. Then he threw her down from the sky and gave orders that every time the fowl wished to drink she would first have to raise her head to him and beg. Further, Nyame gave orders that every man would in the future sacrifice fowls as the ordinary sacrifices to the gods.

Are not these things done to this day?

As for the children—once every year they are washed, and dust from them falls upon the earth. Some falls on men, and these are the lucky ones who become wealthy.

[KRACHI]

4

How Abosom, the Lesser Gods, Came
into the World

THERE ONCE WAS a certain woman who bore eleven children. Every day when she got up and cooked food the children ate it all and the mother did not get any of it. She pondered long about the matter, and went off to the plantation and spoke to the silk-cotton tree, saying, "I shall send my eleven children to come beneath you here to pluck pumpkins; and when they come, pluck off eleven of your branches and kill those children of mine."

The silk-cotton tree said, "I have heard, and I shall do it for you."

The mother then went home and said to her children, "You must go to the plantation beneath the silk-cotton tree; there are pumpkins there. Go pick them and come back."

The children set off. They went and reached the silk-cotton tree. Number Eleven said, "Number One, stand still; Number Two, stand still; Number Three, stand still; Number Four, stand still; Number Five, stand still; Number Six, stand still; Number Seven, stand still; Number Eight, stand still; Number Nine, stand still; Number Ten, stand still; and I myself, Number Eleven, I have stood still."

Number Eleven then addressed them, saying, "Do you not know the sole reason why Mother said we must go and pick pumpkins?"

His brothers answered, "No."

Thereupon he said, "She has told this silk-cotton tree that, when we go there, he must pluck off branches and beat us. Therefore all of you cut sticks and throw them against this silk-cotton tree."

They cut the sticks and threw them against the silk-cotton tree. *Pim! pen! pim! pen!* was the sound they made. The silk-cotton tree supposed that the children had come. He took off eleven of his branches and let them fall to the ground. Little Number Eleven said, "You have seen—had we gone on there, the silk-cotton tree would have killed us."

They picked up the pumpkins and took them to their mother. She cooked them. And at once the children had eaten all! Their mother said, "Ah! as for this matter, I cannot bear it! I shall take these children and give them to the sky-god."

The next morning, when things became visible, she went and told the sky-god all about it, saying, "The children to whom I have given birth eat so fast and so much that when I wish to eat, I can't get anything. Hunger is killing me. Therefore, I implore you, let the children be brought and killed, so that I may get something to eat."

The sky-god said, "Is that really the case?"

The woman said, "I am speaking with a head, the inside of which is white."

So the sky-god picked out messengers, and they went and dug a large pit in which they placed broken bottles. The sky-god himsef went and fetched a snake and a leopard, put them in the pit, and covered it over. And now the messenger went to call the children.

No sooner did they reach the place where the pit lay, than Number Eleven said, "Number One, stand still; Number Two, stand still; Number Three, stand still; Number Four, stand still; Number Five, stand still; Number Six, stand still; Number Seven, stand still; Number Eight, stand still; Number Nine, stand still; Number Ten, stand still; and I myself, little Number Eleven, I have stood still. You must pass here, but you must not pass there."

His brothers said, "Why, when a wide path lies there, must we pass through the bush?"

Now, as they were going along, they all carried clubs. Number Eleven said, "Throw one of these clubs upon this path." They threw a club upon the path, and it fell through into the pit. *Yiridi* was the sound of its fall. Number Eleven said, "There you are! You see! Had we passed there, we should all of us have died."

So they took a bypath and went off to meet the sky-god. The sky-god had caused holes to be dug, covered over, and stools placed upon them, so that when the children came to sit on them, they would fall into the holes. Soon the children arrived before the face of the sky-god. He spoke to them: "Stools are set there. You may go and be seated upon them."

Then Number Eleven said, "Who are we that we should be able to sit upon such very beautiful stools? So, sire, we are going to sit aside here."

Thereupon the sky-god gazed at the children and he said to himself, "I shall send these children to Death's village."

The next morning, when things became visible, he called the children and said, "You must go to Death who lives yonder and receive from her a golden pipe, a golden chewing-stick, a golden snuffbox, a golden whetstone, and a golden fly-switch."

Number Eleven said, "You are our master, wherever you will send us, we shall go."

The sky-god said, "Be off!"

So the children set out for Death's village. When they arrived there, Death said, "Why, when no one must ever come here, have you come here?"

They replied, "We were roaming about and came here quite by chance."

Death said, "Oh, all right then."

Now Death had ten children. With herself added, they made eleven. When things began to disappear—that is, when it became dark—Death divided up the children one by one and gave one to each of her children, while she herself and Number Eleven went to rest. When it was dark, Death then lit up her teeth until they shone red so that she might seize Number Eleven with them.

Number Eleven said, "Death, I am not yet asleep."

Death said, "When will you be asleep?"

Number Eleven said, "If you were to give me a golden pipe to smoke for a while, then I might fall asleep."

And Death fetched it for him.

A little while later, Death again lit up her teeth in order to go and seize Number Eleven with them.

Number Eleven said, "Death, I am not yet asleep."

Death said, "When will you be asleep?"

Number Eleven said, "If you were to bring me a golden snuffbox, I might go to sleep."

And Death brought it to him.

Again, soon afterward, Death was going to seize Number Eleven.

Number Eleven said, "I am not yet asleep."

Death said, "When will you be asleep?"

Number Eleven said, "If you were to go and fetch a golden chewing-stick for me so that I might chew it for a while, then I might fall asleep."

Death fetched it for him. A short time passed, and Death was about to seize him.

Number Eleven said, "Grandmother, I am not yet asleep."

And Death said, "Then when will you be asleep?"

Number Eleven said, "Grandmother, if you were to go and bring me a golden whetstone, then I might sleep."

And Death went and brought it. Again, soon afterward, Death rose up once more.

Number Eleven said, "Oh, Grandmother, I said I was not yet asleep."

Death said, "And what will be the day when you will be asleep?"

Number Eleven said, "If you were to go and take a calabash full of holes and go and splash water in it and boil some food for me to eat, then I might sleep."

Death lifted up a strainer and went off to the stream. When she splashed the water into it, the holes in the strainer let it pass through. Now Number Eleven said to his brothers, "Rise up and flee away." Then they rose up and fled, and Number Eleven went and cut plantain stems and placed them where his brothers had lain and took cloths and covered them over.

Now Death was at the stream splashing water. And Male Death called to Female Death, saying, "Ho there, Death!"

She replied, "*Adwo.*"

He said, "What are you doing?"

She replied, "Alas, is it not some small child whom I have got! When I am about to catch him, he says, 'I am not yet asleep.' He has taken all my things, and now he says I must take a strainer and splash water."

Male Death said, "Ah, are you a small child? If you pluck leaves and line the inside of the strainer and then splash water, would it not be all right?"

Female Death said, "Oh, how true!"

She plucked leaves, placed them inside, and splashed the water and went off. Number Eleven said, "Death, you have come already? Boil the food." Death cooked the food; she lit up her teeth in order to kill Number Eleven's brothers and cook them for food. When she went, she did not examine them carefully, and she herself killed all her own ten children.

The next day, very, very early, when things became visible, Death rose up and sat there by the fire. Number Eleven said, "Grandmother, a tsetse fly is sitting on your breast."

Death said, "Fetch the fly-switch which is lying there and kill it for me."

Number Eleven said, "Good gracious me! A person of your consequence —when a tsetse fly settles on you and a golden fly-switch lies there—you would use this old thing! Let me fetch the golden fly-switch and come and kill it."

Death said, "Go and fetch it from the room."

Number Eleven went and brought it. He purposely drove the fly away; he didn't kill it. Number Eleven said, "Oh, today, where this tsetse fly will rest, there I shall rest with him."

Then Number Eleven went to the room and took his bag in which lay the golden pipe and all the things. He said, "Grandmother Death, nothing will suffice save that I get the tsetse fly, put it in this bag, and bring it to you."

Number Eleven set off—*yiridi! yiridi! yiridi!* He reached the end of the town and said, "Ho, there, Grandmother Death! Pardon my saying so, but if you were not a perfect fool, could I have relieved you of all your things, could my brothers with whom I came have found a way of escape, and could I have made you also kill all your ten children? As for me, I am going off."

Death said, "You, a child like this! Wherever you rest, there I shall rest!"

Number Eleven leaped off—*yiridi! yiridi! yiridi!* and Death, too, went to chase him.

As Number Eleven was going, he overtook his brothers who were sitting on the path. They were making a bird-trap. Number Eleven said, "Have you not gone yet? Death is coming, so let us find some way to escape."

Now Death came upon them. Number Eleven took medicine and poured it on his brothers, and they went on top of a silk-cotton tree. And Death stood at the foot of the silk-cotton tree. She said, "Just now I saw those children, and where have they gone?"

Number Eleven was sitting above. He said to his brothers, "I am going to make water upon her."

His brothers said, "*E!* she is seeking us to catch us, and we have fled and come and sit here and yet you say, 'I am going to make water on her.' "

Number Eleven would not listen, and he made water over Death.

Death said, "Ah, there you are! Today you have seen trouble." Death said, "You, child, who are sitting up there, *Kyere-he-ne, Kyere-he-ne!*" Thereupon one of the children fell down. "*Kyere-he-ne!*" a second one fell down. Soon there remained only Number Eleven.

Death said, "Child, *Kyere-he-ne!*" and Number Eleven leaped and descended on the ground, *kirim!* And Death then went on top of the silk-cotton tree.

Number Eleven said, "You, great big woman, you too, *Kyere-he-ne!*"

And Death, also, came down, *tum!* She was dead.

Number Eleven went and plucked medicine, rolled it between his palms, and sprinkled it on his brothers, and they rose up. Number Eleven was going to throw the medicine away, when some of it dropped on Death, and Death awoke. She said, "You have killed me, and you have also awakened me. Today you and I will have a chase."

Then they all started to run off at once, *kiri! kiri! kiri!* Now Death was chasing them. As they were going, there lay before them a big river in flood. When Number Eleven and his brothers reached it, the brothers knew how to swim and they swam across. Number Eleven alone did not know how to swim. The children stood on the other side; they cried and cried and cried; their mouths became swollen up. As for Number Eleven, he turned into a stone.

Death reached the river. She said, "Oh, these children! You stand there! Let me get a stone to throw and hit your swollen mouths." Death, when she looked down, saw a stone lying there. She picked it up and threw it. As the stone was travelling, it said, "Winds take me and set me on the other side." It alighted on the other side. Number Eleven said, "Here I am!"

Death said, "Ah, that child! I have no further matter to talk to you about. All I have to say to you is this: Go and remain at home and change into one of the lesser gods, and, if anyone whom I wish to take comes to where you are, do you inform me. If I so desire, I will leave him and make you a present of him; but what I wish in exchange you must receive it for me."

That is how the Abosom, the lesser gods, came into the world. They are descended from the small child Number Eleven.

[ASHANTI]

5

Why the Sun and the Moon Live in the Sky

MANY YEARS ago the sun and the water were great friends, and both lived on the earth together. The sun very often used to visit the water, but the water never returned his visits. At last the sun asked the water why it was that he never came to see him in his house. The water replied that the sun's house was not big enough, and that if he came with his people he would drive the sun out.

The water then said, "If you wish me to visit you, you must build a very large compound; but I warn you that it will have to be a tremendous place, as my people are very numerous and take up a lot of room."

The sun promised to build a very big compound, and soon afterward he returned home to his wife, the moon, who greeted him with a broad smile when he opened the door. The sun told the moon what he had promised the water, and the next day he commenced building a huge compound in which to entertain his friend.

When it was completed, he asked the water to come and visit him the next day.

When the water arrived, he called out to the sun and asked him whether it would be safe for him to enter, and the sun answered, "Yes, come in, my friend."

The water then began to flow in, accompanied by the fish and all the water animals.

Very soon the water was knee-deep, so he asked the sun if it was still safe, and the sun again said, "Yes," so more water came in.

When the water was level with the top of a man's head, the water said to the sun, "Do you want more of my people to come?"

The sun and the moon both answered, "Yes," not knowing any better, so the water flowed in, until the sun and moon had to perch themselves on the top of the roof.

Again the water addressed the sun, but, receiving the same answer, and more of his people rushing in, the water very soon overflowed the top of the roof, and the sun and the moon were forced to go up into the sky, where they have remained ever since.

[EFIK-IBIBIO]

6

The Sun and the Children

ONCE SOME children, at their mother's behest, very gently approached the sun's armpit, as the sun lay sleeping. They were to lift up the sun's armpit.

At the same time, another woman ordered her children to do the same thing. She told them that if they approached ever so gently and drew up the sun's armpit, then the rice of the Bushmen would become dry, and the sun, as it proceeded from place to place across the sky, would cause everything to become bright. For this reason it was that the old woman, their mother, coaxed her children to do as she asked. "But, children," she said, "you must wait for the sun, who is making us so cold, to lie down to sleep. Then approach him gently and, all together, lift him up and throw him into the sky." Thus, indeed, did both of the old women speak.

And so the children approached the sun. They first sat down and looked at him in order to determine whether, as he lay there, he was looking at them. Finally they saw him lying there very quietly, his elbow lifted up so that his armpit shone upon the ground. Before the children prepared to throw him up into the sky they remembered what the old woman, their mother, had said: "O children, going yonder, you must speak to him when you throw him up. You must tell him that he must be the sun altogether, so that he will proceed forward while he feels that he is altogether the sun—the sun who is hot and who, as he passes along the sky, causes the Bushman rice to become dry—the sun who is hot as he stands above in the sky."

Thus had their mother, the old woman, whose head was white, spoken. They had listened and were going to obey her.

When all was in readiness, they took hold of the sun, all of them together, lifted him, raised him, even though he was hot to touch, and threw him up in the sky, addressing him as they threw him up: "O sun, you must altogether stand fast and you must proceed along your way—you must stand fast while you are hot."

Then the children returned to their mother, and one of them went to her and said, "Our companion, who is here, this one, took hold of him. So did I. Then my younger brother and my still younger brother, they all took hold of him. 'Grasp hold of him firmly,' I said, 'and throw him up. Grasp the old man firmly and throw him up.' Thus I spoke to them. Then the children threw him up, the old man, the sun."

Then another one of those who had been present—a youngster indeed—he also spoke to her and said, "Oh, grandmother, we threw him up, the sun, and we told him what you had told us, that he should altogether become the sun, the sun who is hot, for us who are cold. And we addressed him thus: 'O my grandfather, sun's armpit! Remain there at that place. Become the sun who is hot so that the Bushman rice may dry for us, so that you may make the whole earth light, that the earth may become warm in the summer, that you may altogether make heat. For that reason, you must shine everywhere. You must take away the darkness. You must come indeed so that the darkness will go away.' "

And thus it is. The sun comes, the darkness departs; the sun sets, the darkness comes and, then, at night the moon comes. The moon comes out; it brightens the darkness and the darkness then departs. It has taken the darkness away and now it moves along, continually brightening the darkness. And then the moon sets and the sun, following, comes out. The sun now drives away the darkness, indeed drives away the moon as it stands there. The sun actually pierces the moon with his knife and that is why it decays. Therefore the moon said, "O sun! leave the backbone for the children!" And the sun did so.

Then the moon painfully went away, painfully returned home. He went home to become another, a moon which is whole. He again comes to life although it had seemed that he had died. He becomes a new moon and feels as though he had put on a new stomach. He becomes large; he is alive again. Then he goes along at night, feeling that he is the moon once more. Indeed he feels he is a shoe, the shoe that Mantis threw into the sky, and ordered to become the moon.

That is what the sun has done—made all the earth bright. And thus it is that the people walk while the earth is light. Then people can see the bushes, can see other people. They can see the meat which they are eating. They can see the springbok, can hunt it in summer. It is when the sun shines, likewise, that they can hunt the ostrich. And so—because the sun brightens the earth, because he shines upon the path of men—the Bushmen steal up to the gemsbok, steal up to the kudu, travel about in summer, and go visiting one another. Because the sun shines hottest upon the path of men in summer, they always go shooting and hunting then, for they are certain to espy the springbok. It is in the summer that they lie contented in their little homes made of bushes, and they scratch up the earth. All this they do when the springbok comes.

The people of whom we are speaking were the first Bushmen, the men of the early race. It is they who first inhabited this earth and it was their children who worked with the sun, who threw the sun up and made him ascend so that he might warm the earth for them, and that they might be able to sit in the sun.

The sun, they say, was originally a man who lived on earth. In the beginning, he gave forth brightness for a space just around his own dwelling. As his shining was confined to a certain space just at and around his own house, the rest of the country seemed as if the sky were very cloudy—as it looks now, in fact, when the sun is behind thick clouds. This shining came from one of the sun's armpits as he lay with one arm lifted up. When he put down his arm, darkness fell everywhere; when he lifted it up again, it was as if day came. In the day, the sun's light used to be white, but, at night, it was red like a fire. When the sun was thrown up into the sky it became round and never was a man again.

The same is true of the moon. He, too, was once a man who could talk. But today neither the sun nor the moon talk. They just live in the sky.

[BUSHMEN]

7

The Brothers, Sun and Moon, and the Pretty Girl

HOW DID IT HAPPEN? A wife was pregnant, she bore a child, Moon, to begin with. She returned, became pregnant again, and this time bore Sun. Far in the wilderness was a man, and he had a pretty daughter.

Sun and Moon grew up and one day went for a stroll. In the wilderness they came upon the pretty daughter, and they asked her, "Where have you got your house? We live in that wilderness," they said to the girl. "Show us exactly where you live."

She replied to them, "We live in that wilderness. And there a great many dangerous animals."

Moon, the elder one of the brothers, said to the girl, "Do you like us? Shall we woo you?"

She said to them, "Yes, I am capable of liking you but may not."

Sun then asked, "Who is it that does not like us?"

She said, "It is my father."

Moon said to the girl, "Well, then, we shall wait for two days, and on the third we shall come to your village. We shall send our father's children."

They waited for two days, and on the third they sent the children, then they started out for the wilderness. And when they were quite close, they caught sight of the girl far off at the other edge of the jungle. They went to meet her and asked her, "Well, where is your village?"

She said, "Our village is here in the wilderness."

They asked her, "*I, I!* Are there people that live in the place where there is no hut?"

She said, "Yes, we live in the wilderness, we have no hut."

They said, "We wish that you would show us where you live."

The girl said, "All right, then." And she went on ahead to show them the way.

A big snake then appeared. Sun and Moon said, "Let us not be afraid!" They were not frightened, but went along on their way. When they had got as far as the foot of a certain tree, they found a number of snakes confronting them; but they went farther along and came upon a place full of hairs like horsehair, forming a sort of darkness before them. Nowhere were they able to see any path to take.

Sun said to the girl, "You! Have you brought **us** here so we should die at your place?"

She said to them, "No, but we have not yet arrived at our village."

And he, Moon, said to Sun, "Brother Sun, what are we to do now?" They said to the girl, "Tell us if you like us, and whether we are to woo you? We now wish to return home."

The girl said to them, "Go, and come back the day after tomorrow!"

They went away and returned home.

They reached their home. And Moon loved the girl very much, more than Sun did. The following morning Sun went to herd their father's cattle, and Moon hid himself from Sun and went alone out into the wilderness to seek the girl and take her to wife.

When he had got there, someone said to him, "Who is it?"

He said, "It is I."

He was asked, "Who are you?"

He answered, "It is I, Moon."

He was asked, "Whither are you going?"

He said, "I am coming hither."

The other one asked him, "From where have you come?"

Moon said to him, "I come from our village." And he added, "And you, what are you doing here?"

"I am not doing anything in particular," said the stranger.

"And I, neither am I doing anything in particular—I am just out for a walk," answered Moon.

The other asked him again, "Why have you come here?"

"Not for anything special."

The other man said to him, "*I, I?* Not for anything special?"

Moon replied, "*I, I!* I did not come here for anything special! *I*, I have come here without any purpose."

The strange man said, "Why do you ask *me* what I am seeking, but conceal and refuse to reveal your own business?"

Then Moon was frightened and said to himself, "I do not know these people, and they do not know me. I will return home!"

He returned home and said to Sun, "Brother, when I left you I saw a lot of queer things."

Sun said to Moon, "Well, let us go some day and you shall show me those things; just now I am busy tending the cattle."

Their mother said to them, "Go ye and find the girl, I will do the herding."

They went, and when they got to the wilderness, they saw swords appearing. They fought against the swords but saw no human being. The swords disappeared, and they went on farther and saw trees which grew so densely before them that there was no path. Sun drew his sword and cut down some of the trees. The trees then disappeared altogether, and they did not see them again. They went farther ahead and came to a pond; they were close to it. They saw teeth coming up out of the interior of the pond. They approached quite near. Two teeth passed right between them, one passed them to the left and another to the right. Moon fell back behind Sun; he was frightened.

Sun said to him, "I, I, Moon! Are you afraid? You are the elder one, go on ahead, let us walk on!"

"Yes, let us go on then! We are equally brave."

The teeth returned into the pond, and Sun and Moon walked on. When they had not got very far, they saw hairs coming up out of the pond. Moon looked at the girl's father, for it was he, and said to Sun, "My brother, here we shall perish!"

"It cannot be helped!"

The hairs returned, however, into the pond. When they had got close to the pond, again Sun sat down on a tree at the edge of the pond together with Moon. The beard of the girl's father came up to them but returned into the pond. Bones of dead people came up.

Moon said, "Oh! I am dying!" and suddenly he ran away.

Sun was left behind, alone there, sitting on the tree. The water rose, part of it came on one side of him and part of it on the other; it flowed all around him. He was sitting in the midst of the water, which presently returned to the pond. Sun did not budge from the spot. The water, however, returned to the river. Then smoke rose up out of the water. Sun said to himself, "I do not intend to die here, although my brother got frightened and ran away. I am going to remain, so that I may see that girl!" The smoke ceased, and the water flamed like fire. The fire, however, soon went out.

After that there came out of the water a human being—it was the girl. She came and took the young man by the hand and said to him, "Now we will go home to our place, and I shall give you food."

The girl said to the pond, "Get out of the way for this man! I am going to cook food for him." The water drew off to the side of the pond, went over to one side.

The girl went and cooked food which she brought and gave the young man, and he ate. She said to him:

"I, it is you that is to take me to wife, because you are a man who is not afraid of anything. And you, now you are my husband because you are not afraid of all the things that were shown you, but your elder brother ran away."

Then the girl's father said to Sun, "Take the girl. When you have gone home you are to tarry there with her for five days, and then you yourself and your father are to bring the girl back here!"

They started off. Moon had returned and sat down in the compound. He had a sword, and he said, "When Sun comes along with that girl, I shall kill him."

Then the girl approached, and Sun was walking in front of her. They came and found that Moon was in the compound. They asked him, "Moon, is there anyone at home in our village?"

"Sun, come here!"

Sun carried a sword. He went forward, and sat down. The mother came out and Sun said to her, "Mother, go and take that girl and conduct her into the village!"

The mother asked him, "This girl, is it you that have taken her to wife, or is it Moon?"

"She is my wife, Moon ran away." Sun repeated: "Moon ran away."

The latter grasped his sword. Sun looked up and saw the sword quite close to him, for Moon gave him a cut. And he, Sun, who also carried his sword, slashed Moon, and they fought. Sun was badly cut by Moon.

The mother cried a great deal. She took millet and other kinds of provisions and spoilt them for Moon. And she threw millet and all the other foodstuffs on the fire, saying, "You, Moon, have damaged Sun in this way. May you be destroyed in the same way!" And the mother took some milk, and she and her husband poured it into a calabash bowl along with millet and beer. Thereupon they blessed Sun, that he would shine brightly for mankind. The girl remained on in the village as Sun's wife, but Moon had no wife, and he who had formerly been more brilliant than Sun no longer was so.

Ever since that time and even now Moon avoids Sun; they will not agree to approach each other at the same fire, nor to eat food together. When Sun goes down, Moon comes out; when Sun comes out of the village, Moon rapidly runs away. Is not that a curse? Moon has become small, and Sun has become big.

[AKAMBA]

8

The Son of the Wind

THE SON OF THE WIND was once a man. When he was a man he used to go shooting and to roll a ball but later he became a bird and flew, no longer walking as he used to do when he was a man. When he had changed into a bird, he flew up and dwelt in a mountain hole. The mountain hole was his dwelling, and out of it he would fly every day and, later on, return. In this hole he slept and, awakening in the morning, he would leave in order to seek food. He sought it everywhere and he ate, ate, ate, until he had his fill. Then he would return to his mountain hole to sleep.

But when he was a man he had been quiet and still.

On one occasion when he was rolling his ball, he called out to Nakati, "Nakati, there it goes!" And Nakati exclaimed, "O comrade, truly there it goes!" He called him comrade because he didn't know the other's name. Yet it was truly he who is the wind, who had said, "Nakati, there it goes!"

Not knowing his name, however, Nakati went to his mother to question her. "Mother," he said, "do tell me the name of our comrade over there. He calls me by my name but I do not know his and I would like to know it when I am rolling the ball back to him."

"No, I will not at this moment tell you his name, that I will only do and let you utter it after Father has made a strong shelter for our hut. And then, when I tell you his name, the moment I have uttered it, you must at once scamper away and run home, so that you can seek the shelter of the hut."

Again Nakati went over to play with his companion and to roll the ball. When they had finished, Nakati went once more to question his mother, and she exclaimed, "He is *erriten-kuan-kuan*, he is *gau-gaubu-ti!*"

The next day Nakati again went to roll the ball with his companion. He did not, however, utter his playmate's name, for his mother had cautioned him to be silent on that matter, even when he was called by name. She had said, "When the time comes for you to utter his name, you must run home at once."

Now once more Nakati went to roll the ball with his friend, hoping and hoping that his father would finally finish making the shelter for their hut. At last he saw that his father had sat down, that he had indeed finished. Therefore, when he beheld this, he exclaimed, "There it goes, O *erriten-*

kuan-kuan! There it goes, O *gau-gaubu-ti!*" No sooner had he uttered it than he scampered away and ran home. His companion thereupon began to lean over, and then fall down. As he lay there he kicked violently upon the *vlei*. As he kicked, huts blew away, bushes vanished and the people could not see because of the dust. Thus was the wind blowing.

When the mother of the wind came out of her hut to grab him and set him on his feet again, he struggled with her for he wished to continue to lie down. However his mother took hold of him firmly and set him on his feet.

And so, because of all this, we who are Bushmen are wont to say, "The wind seems to be lying down, for it is blowing fiercely. When the wind stands on its feet then it is quiet and still. Thus it acts. The noise it makes comes from its knee; that is what makes the sound. I had wished that it might blow gently for us, that we might go out, that we might ascend the place yonder, that we might behold the river bed yonder, standing behind the hill. For we have driven the springbok from this place. They have gone to yonder dry river bed standing behind the hill."

[BUSHMEN]

9

How the Stars Came

EBOPP, THE LEMUR, and Mbaw, the dormouse, were making a tour in the bush. They looked for a good place to make a farm. When they found one, they cut down the trees and took two days to clear enough ground. After this, they went back to the town where the other animals lived.

The next morning Ebopp said, "Let us go back to our new farms and build a small house."

This they did. Ebopp made his, and Mbaw his.

Now, before a new town is begun, a little shed called *ekpa ntan* is always made where the Egbo house is to stand. Ebopp and Mbaw accordingly set to work and built an *ekpa ntan*. Then they went back to their old town and rested for two days.

On the third day they went to work again. Ebopp worked on his farm, Mbaw on his. That night they slept in the huts they had built and at dawn started to work once more. When night came, Ebopp lighted a lamp and said:

"I do not want to sleep here. If we sleep here we shall sleep hungry. Let us go back to our old town."

When they got there their wives cooked for them. Ebopp said to Mbaw, "Come and join together with me in eating." So his friend came and ate with him.

Afterwards Mbaw said, "Let us now go to my house and have food there too." So they went thither.

After they had eaten all that Mbaw had cooked, Ebopp went home.

The next morning he went to call for his friend and said, "Go and get young plantains to plant on the farm." Both of them collected a great basketful and went to the place where the new farms were—Ebopp to his, and Mbaw to his. They worked hard.

At midday, Ebopp said, "Let us rest a little while and eat the food we have brought." To this Mbaw agreed, and after some time they set to work again.

About five o'clock Ebopp called, "Let us go back now to the old town, for it is very far off."

So they left off working and went back, but before they could get there night fell.

The next morning they took more young plantains and, again, worked hard all day. When it was time to go back, Ebopp asked, "How many of the young plantains remain to be planted?"

Mbaw answered, "About forty."

Whereupon Ebopp said, "Of mine also there remain about forty."

At dawn, the next day, they went to their old farms to get some more plantain cuttings. Then they went back to the new farms and began planting.

As soon as Ebopp had finished, he said, "I have finished mine."

To this Mbaw replied, "Mine also are finished."

Ebopp said, "My work is done. I need come here only for the harvest."

Then they both went back to their old town and told their wives, "We have finished setting out the plantains. We hope that you will go and plant koko-yams tomorrow. Try, both of you, to get baskets full of koko-yams for the planting."

To this the women agreed and, when they had collected as many as were necessary, they set out for the new farms.

When they arrived, Mbaw's wife asked the wife of Ebopp, "Do you think we can finish planting all these today?"

Ebopp's wife answered, "Yes, we can do it."

All day they worked hard, and at night they went home and said, "We have finished planting all the koko-yams."

Ebopp said, "Good, you have done well."

Now the name of Ebopp's wife was Akpan Anwan. She and her sister, Akandem, were the daughters of Obassi Osaw. When she got home she started to cook the evening meal for her husband. As soon as it was ready, she placed it upon the table, set water also in a cup, and laid spoons near by.

They were eating together when a slave named Umaw ran in. He had just come from the town of Obassi Osaw. He said, "I would speak to Ebopp alone." When Akpan Anwan had left the room, the messenger said, "You are eating, but I bring you news that Akandem your sister-in-law is dead."

Ebopp cried out aloud in his grief and sent a messenger to call his friend Mbaw.

As soon as the latter heard, he came running and said, "What can we do? We are planting new farms and beginning to build a new town. There is hardly any food to be got. How then can we properly hold the funeral customs?"

Ebopp said, "Nevertheless, I must try my best."

When Umaw got ready to return, Ebopp said, "Say to Obassi Osaw, 'Wait for me for six days, then I will surely come.'"

The next morning he said to Mbaw, "Come now, let us do our utmost to collect what is necessary for the rites of my sister-in-law."

They went through the town and bought all the food which they could find. Then Ebopp went back and said to his wife, "I did not wish to tell you before about the death of your sister, but today I must tell you. Make ready. In five days' time I will take you back to your father's town to hold the funeral feast."

Akpan Anwan was very grieved to hear of this and wept.

Ebopp said to Mbaw, "We must get palm wine for the feast, also rum for the libations. How can we get these? I have no money, and you also have none."

Mbaw said, "Go round among the townsfolk and see if any of them will lend you some."

Ebopp said, "Good!" He then began to walk up and down, begging from all his friends, but none would give to him, although it was a big town. At last he went down to the place where they were making palm oil by the river. Quite nearby lived Iku, the water chevrotain. Ebopp told him his trouble and begged help, but Iku said, "I am very sorry for you, but I have nothing to give."

Ebopp was quite discouraged by now and, full of sorrow, turned to go away. When Iku saw this he said:

"Wait a minute, there is one thing I can do. You know that I have 'four eyes.' I will give you two of them, and with them you can buy all that you need."

From out of his head he took the two eyes with which he used to see in the dark. They shone so brightly that Ebopp knew they were worth a great price. He took them home and showed them to his wife and his friend Mbaw.

The latter said, "From today you are freed from all anxiety. With those you can buy all that is needed."

The next morning they gathered together all that had been collected, the plantains and the two shining eyes. Ebopp, Mbaw, and Akpan carried the loads between them. They set out for the dwelling place of Obassi Osaw.

When they arrived at the entrance of the town, Akpan Anwan began to weep bitterly. She threw down her burden and ran to the spot where her sister lay buried. Then she lay down on the grave and would not rise again.

Ebopp carried his own load into the house where the dead woman had dwelt. Then he went back and got his wife's load which she had left behind.

The townsfolk said to Ebopp, "You have come to keep your sister-in-law's funeral customs today. Bring palm wine. Bring rum also for the libations, and let us hold the feast."

Ebopp said, "I have brought nothing but plantains. All else that is necessary I mean to buy here."

Now there was a famine in Obassi Osaw's town, so Ebopp put all of his plantains in the Egbo House. The next day he sent a message to Obassi Osaw to bring his people, so that the food might be divided among them. Each man received one plantain.

Then Osaw said, "All that you have brought is eaten. If you cannot give us more, you shall not take my daughter back with you to your country."

Ebopp went to find his friend and told him what Obassi had said.

"Shall I sell the two eyes?" he asked. "They are worth hundreds and hundreds of plantains and many pieces of cloth, but if I sell them now, the people are so hungry they will only give a small price."

Mbaw said, "Do not mind. See, I will teach you how to get more sense.

"You hold one in your hand, and it is a big thing like a great shining stone; but if you put it in a mortar and grind it down, it will become, not one, but many stones, and some of the small pieces you can sell."

This Ebopp did. He ground up the great bright stones which had been Iku's eyes until they became like shining sand.

Then Ebopp and Mbaw went and procured a black cap which they filled with the fragments.

Mbaw said, "Now go and look round the town till you find someone who can sell what we need."

Ebopp did so, and in the house of Effion Obassi he saw great stores hidden —food and palm wine, palm oil in jars, and rum for the sacrifice.

Ebopp said to Effion, "If you will sell all this to me, I will give you in exchange something which will make all the townsfolk bow down before you."

Effion said, "I will not sell all, but half of what I have I will sell you."

So Ebopp said, "Very well. I will take what you give me, only do not open the thing I shall leave in exchange until I have returned to my own country. When you do open it, as I said before, all the townsfolk will bow down before you."

So the funeral feast was prepared, and the people were satisfied.

When the rites were finished, Obassi said, "It is good. You can go away now with your wife."

So Ebopp said to Mbaw and Akpan Anwan, "Come, let us go back to our own town. We must not sleep here tonight."

When they had reached home once more, Ebopp sent a slave named Edet to Effion Obassi with the message:

"You may now open the cap. I have reached my town again."

It was evening time, but Effion at once called the townspeople together and said, "I have a thing here which is worth a great price."

They cried, "Let us see it."

He answered, "My thing is a very good thing, such as you have never seen before."

He brought the cap outside and opened it before them. All the shining things fell out. As they fell, a strong breeze came and caught them and blew them all over the town. They lay on the roads and on the floors of the compounds, each like a little star.

All the children came round and began picking them up. They gathered and gathered. In the daytime they could not see them, but every night they went out and sought for the shining things. All that they picked up they put in a box. At length many had been gathered together and they shone like a little sun in the box. At the end of about a month nearly all had been collected. They could not shut down the lid, however, because the box was too full, so when a great breeze came by it blew all the shining things about again. That is why sometimes we have a small moon and plenty of stars shining around it, while sometimes we have a big moon and hardly any stars are to be seen. The children take a month to fill the box again.

When the sparkles were scattered about the town, Effion sent a messenger to Ebopp to ask: "Can you see the things shining from your town?"

At that time earth and sky were all joined together, like a house with an upstairs.

Ebopp went out and looked upward to the blue roof overhead. There he saw the small things sparkling in the darkness.

The next day he went to Iku and said, "Will you please go into a deep hole? I want to look at your eyes."

Iku went inside the hole. Ebopp looked at his eyes. They were very bright, just like the sparkles which shone in the sky.

The cause of all the stars, therefore, is Ebopp, who took Iku's eyes to Obassi's town.

Iku's eyes are like the stars.

The moon shines when all the fragments are gathered together. When it shines most brightly it is because the children have picked up nearly all the fragments and put them into the box.

[EKOI]

10

How the First Rain Came

ONCE, LONG AGO, a daughter was born to Obassi Osaw, and a son to Obassi Nsi. When both of them had come to marriageable age, Nsi sent a message and said, "Let us exchange children. I will send my son that he may wed one of your girls, and you send your daughter down to my town, that she may become my wife."

To this Obassi Osaw agreed. So the son of Nsi went up to the heavens, carrying many fine gifts, and Ara, the sky maiden, came down to dwell on earth. With her came seven men slaves and seven women slaves whom her father gave her to work for her, so that she should not be called upon to do anything herself.

One day, very early in the morning, Obassi Nsi said to his new wife, "Go, work on my farm!"

She answered, "My father gave me the slaves, so that they should work instead of me. Therefore send them."

Obassi Nsi was very angry and said, "Did you not hear that I gave my orders to you? You yourself shall work on my farm. As for the slaves, I will tell them what to do."

The girl went, though very unwillingly, and when she returned at night, tired out, Nsi said to her, "Go at once to the river and bring water for the household."

She answered, "I am weary with working on the farm. May not my slaves at least do this while I rest?"

Again Nsi refused and drove her forth, and she went backward and forward many times, carrying the heavy jars. Night had fallen long before she had brought enough.

The next morning Nsi bade her do the most menial services, and all day long he kept her at work, cooking, fetching water, and making fire. That night, again, she was very weary before she was allowed to lie down to rest. At dawn on the third morning Nsi said, "Go and bring in much firewood." Now the girl was young and unused to work, so as she went she wept, and the tears were still falling when she came back carrying her heavy burden.

As soon as Nsi saw her enter crying he called her. "Come here and lie down before me. . . . I wish to shame you in the presence of all my people. . . ." Thereupon the girl wept still more bitterly.

56

No food was given her until midday on the morrow, and then not enough. When she had finished eating all there was, Nsi said to her, "Go out and bring in a great bundle of fish poison."

The girl went into the bush to seek for the plant, but as she walked through the thick undergrowth a thorn pierced her foot. She lay down alone. All day long she lay there in pain, but as the sun sank she began to feel better. She got up and managed to limp back to the house.

When she entered, Nsi said to her, "Early this morning I ordered you to go and collect fish poison. You have stayed away all day and done nothing." So he drove her into the goat-pen, and said, "Tonight you shall sleep with the goats; you shall not enter my house."

That night she ate nothing. Early next morning one of the slaves opened the door of the goat pen and found the girl lying within with her foot all swollen and sore. She could not walk, so for five days she was left with the goats. After that her foot began to get better.

As soon as she could walk again, Nsi called her and said, "Here is a pot. Take it to the river and bring it back filled to the brim."

She set out, but when she reached the waterside, she sat down on the bank and dipped her foot in the cool stream. She said to herself, "I will never go back; it is better to stay here alone."

After a while one of the slaves came down to the river. He questioned her: "At dawn this morning you were sent to fetch water. Why have you not returned home?"

The girl said, "I will not come back."

When the slave had left her she thought, "Perhaps he will tell them, and they will be angered and may come and kill me. I had better go back after all." So she filled her pot and tried to raise it upon her head, but it was too heavy. Then she lifted it on to a tree trunk that lay by the side of the river and, kneeling beneath, tried to draw it in that way upon her head; but the pot fell and broke and, in falling, a sharp shard cut off one of her ears. The blood poured down from the wound, and she began to weep again, but suddenly thought, "My father is alive, my mother is alive; I do not know why I stay here with Obassi Nsi. I shall go back to my own father."

Then she set out to find the road by which Obassi Osaw had sent her to earth. She came to a high tree and from it saw a long rope hanging. She said to herself, "This is the way by which my father sent me."

She caught the rope and began to climb. Before she had gone halfway she grew very weary, and her sighs and tears mounted up to the kingdom of Obassi Osaw. Midway on her climb, she stayed and rested a while. Afterward she went on again.

After a long time she reached the top of the rope and found herself on the border of her father's land. Here she sat down almost worn out with weariness, and still weeping.

Now, one of the slaves of Obassi Osaw had been sent out to collect firewood. He chanced to stray from his path and came to a place near where the girl was resting. He heard her sobs mixed with broken words and ran back to the town, crying out, "I have heard the voice of Ara. She is weeping about a mile from here."

Obassi heard but could not believe, yet he said, "Take twelve slaves, and, should you find my daughter as you say, bring her home."

When they reached the place they found that it was indeed Ara. So they carried her home.

When her father saw her coming he called out, "Take her to the house of her mother."

There one of the lesser wives, Akun by name, heated water and bathed her. Then they prepared a bed and covered her well with soft skins and fine cloths.

While she was resting, Obassi killed a young kid and sent it to Akun, bidding her to prepare it for his daughter. Akun took it and, after she had washed it, cooked it whole in a pot. Obassi also sent a great bunch of plantains and other fruits, and these, too, were arranged in orderly fashion upon a table before the girl. Then they poured water into a gourd and brought palm wine in a native cup, and bade her to drink.

After she had eaten and drunk, Obassi came with four slaves carrying a great chest made of ebony. He bade them set it before her, opened it and said, "Come here; choose anything you will from this box."

Ara chose two pieces of cloth, three gowns, four small loincloths, four looking glasses, four spoons, two pairs of shoes, four cooking pots, and four chains of beads.

After this Obassi Osaw's storekeeper, named Ekpenyon, came forward and brought her twelve anklets. Akun gave her two gowns, a *fufu* stick, and a wooden knife.

Her own mother brought her five gowns, richer than all the rest, and five slaves to wait upon her.

After this Obassi Osaw said, "A house has been made ready for you; go there that you may be its mistress."

Then he went out and called together the members of the chief society of the town. This was named Angbu. He said to the men, "Go, fetch the son of Obassi Nsi. Cut off both his ears and bring them to me. Then flog him and drive him down the road to his father's town, with this message from me: 'I had built a great house up here in my town. In it I placed your son and treated him kindly. Now that I know what you have done to my child, I send your son back to you earless, in payment for Ara's ear and the sufferings which you put upon her.'"

When the Angbu society had cut off the ears of the son of Obassi Nsi, they brought them before Obassi Osaw and drove the lad back on the earthward road, as they had been ordered.

Osaw took the ears and made a great *juju,* and by reason of this a strong wind arose, and drove the boy earthward. On its wings it bore all the sufferings of Ara and the tears which she had shed through the cruelty of Obassi Nsi. The boy stumbled along, half blinded by the rain, and as he went he thought, "Obassi Osaw may do to me what he chooses. He has never done any unkind thing before. It is only in return for my father's cruelty that I must suffer all this."

So his tears mixed with those of Ara and fell earthward as rain.

Until that time there had been no rain on the earth. It fell for the first time when Obassi Osaw made the great wind and drove forth the son of his enemy.

[EKOI]

II

The Origin of Death

LONG, LONG AGO there was a great famine in the world, and a certain young man, while wandering in search of food, strayed into a part of the bush where he had never been before. Presently he perceived a strange mass lying on the ground. He approached and saw that it was the body of a giant whose hair resembled that of white men in that it was silky rather than woolly. It was of an incredible length and stretched as far as from Krachi to Salaga. The young man was properly awed at the spectacle, and wished to withdraw, but the giant, noticing him, asked what he wanted.

The young man told about the famine and begged the giant to give him some food. The latter agreed on condition that the youth would serve him for a while. This matter having been arranged, the giant said that his name was Owuo, or Death, and he then gave the boy some meat.

Never before had the latter tasted such fine food, and he was well pleased with his bargain. He served his master for a long time and received plenty of meat, but one day he grew homesick, and he begged his master to give him a short holiday. The latter agreed, if the youth would promise to bring another boy in his place. So the youth returned to his village and there persuaded his brother to go with him into the bush, and he gave him to Owuo.

In course of time the youth became hungry again and longed for the meat which Owuo had taught him to like so much. So one day he made up his mind to return to his master, and, leaving the village, he made his way back to the giant's abode. The latter asked him what he wanted, and when the youth told him that he wanted to taste once more of the good meat, the giant bade him enter the hut and take as much as he liked, but added that he would have to work for him again.

The youth agreed and entered the hut. He ate as much as he could and went to work at the task which his master set him. The work continued for a long time and the boy ate his fill every day. But, to his surprise, he never saw anything of his brother, and, whenever he asked about him, the giant told him that the lad was away on business.

Once more the youth grew homesick and asked for leave to return to his village. The giant agreed on condition that he would bring a girl for him, Owuo, to wed. So the youth went home and there persuaded his sister to go

60

into the bush and marry the giant. The girl agreed, and took with her a slave companion, and they all repaired to the giant's abode. There the youth left the two girls and went back to the village.

It was not very long after that he again grew hungry and longed for a taste of the meat. So he made his way once more into the bush and found the giant. The latter did not seem overpleased to see the boy and grumbled at being bothered a third time. However, he told the boy to go into the inner chamber of his hut and take what he wanted. The youth did so and took up a bone which he began to devour. To his horror he recognized it at once as being the bone of his sister. He looked around at all the rest of the meat and saw that it was that of his sister and her slave girl.

Thoroughly frightened, he escaped from the house and ran back to the village. There he told the elders what he had done and the awful thing he had seen. At once the alarm was sounded and all the people went out into the bush to see for themselves the dreadful thing they had heard about. When they drew near to the giant they grew afraid at the sight of so evil a monster. They went back to the village and consulted among themselves what they had best do. At last it was agreed to go to Salaga, where the end of the giant's hair was, and set a light to it. This was done, and when the hair was burning well they returned to the bush and watched the giant.

Presently the latter began to toss about and to sweat. It was quite evident that he was beginning to feel the heat. The nearer the flames advanced, the more he tossed and grumbled. At last the fire reached his head and for the moment the giant was dead.

The villagers approached him cautiously, and the young man noticed magic powder which had been concealed in the roots of the giant's hair. He took it and called the others to come and see what he had found. No one could say what power this medicine might have, but an old man suggested that no harm would be done if they sprinkled some of it on the bones and meat in the hut. This idea was carried out, and to the surprise of everyone, the girls and the boy at once returned to life.

The youth, who had still some of the powder left, proposed to put it on the giant. But at this there was a great uproar as the people feared Owuo might come to life again. The boy, therefore, by way of compromise, sprinkled it into the eye of the dead giant. At once the eye opened and the people fled in terror. But alas, it is from that eye that death comes, for every time that Owuo shuts that eye a man dies, and, unfortunately for us, he is forever blinking and winking.

[KRACHI]

12

The Origin of Death

AND HOW DID IT HAPPEN?
It is God who created men. And since God had pity, He said, "I do not wish men to die altogether. I wish that men, having died, should rise again." And so He created men and placed them in another region. But He stayed at home.

And then God saw the chameleon and the weaver-bird. After He had spent three days with the chameleon and the weaver-bird, He recognized that the weaver-bird was a great maker of words compounded of lies and truth. Now of lies there were many, but of the words of truth there were few.

Then He watched the chameleon and recognized that he had great intelligence. He did not lie. His words were true. So he spoke to the chameleon, "Chameleon, go into that region where I have placed the men I created, and tell them that when they have died, even if they are altogether dead, still they shall rise again—that each man shall rise again after he dies."

The chameleon said, "Yes, I will go there." But he went slowly, for it is his fashion to go slowly. The weaver-bird had stayed behind with God.

The chameleon travelled on, and when he had arrived at his destination, he said, "I was told, I was told, I was told. . . ." But he did not say what he had been told.

The weaver-bird said to God, "I wish to step out for a moment."

And God said to him, "Go!"

But the weaver-bird, since he is a bird, flew swiftly, and arrived at the place where the chameleon was speaking to the people and saying, "I was told. . . ." Everyone was gathered there to listen. When the weaver-bird arrived, he said, "What was told to us? Truly, we were told that men, when they are dead, shall perish like the roots of the aloe."

Then the chameleon exclaimed, "But we were told, we were told, we were told, that when men are dead, they shall rise again."

Then the magpie interposed and said, "The first speech is the wise one."

And now all the people left and returned to their homes. This was the way it happened.

And so men become old and die; they do not rise again.

[AKAMBA]

13

The Origin of Death

THE MOON, it is said, once sent an insect to men, saying, "Go to men and tell them, 'As I die, and dying live; so you shall also die, and dying live.'"

The insect started with the message, but, while on his way, was overtaken by the hare, who asked, "On what errand are you bound?"

The insect answered, "I am sent by the Moon to men, to tell them that as she dies and dying lives, so shall they also die and dying live."

The hare said, "As you are an awkward runner, let me go." With these words he ran off, and when he reached men, he said, "I am sent by the Moon to tell you, 'As I die and dying perish, in the same manner you also shall die and come wholly to an end.'"

The hare then returned to the Moon and told her what he had said to men. The Moon reproached him angrily, saying, "Do you dare tell the people a thing which I have not said?"

With these words the moon took up a piece of wood and struck the hare on the nose. Since that day the hare's nose has been slit, but men believe what Hare had told them.

[HOTTENTOT]

14

How Diseases Came to the Ashanti

Now there lived Kwaku Ananse, the spider, and he went to Nyankonpon, the sky-god, and said, "Grandsire, take your sheep called Kra Kwame, the one which you keep to sacrifice to your soul on a Saturday, and let me kill and eat it, that I may go and bring you a beautiful girl in exchange."

The sky-god gave him the sheep, and Ananse set out and returned to his village and killed the sheep and ate it. The spider then went to a certain village. In that village there was not a single male—all were women. Ananse married them all and he and they lived there.

One day, a hunter came and saw them. When he left, he went and said to the sky-god, "As for Ananse and that sheep of yours which he received, he has killed it and given it to some women to eat and then married them."

The sky-god said, "Is it true?"

The hunter said, "Grandsire, it is the truth."

The sky-god then sent messengers, telling them to go to that village and bring to him all the women who were there.

The messengers went off, met the women, and, with the exception of one woman who was ill, took them all to the sky-god.

Ananse said, "You who remain, what can I do with you? You can't do anything for me?"

The sick woman said, "Go and bring me a gourd cup." Ananse went and brought a gourd cup.

She said, "Bathe me, and take the water you have used and pour it into this gourd."

Ananse bathed her body and poured the water he had used into the gourd. She then became very beautiful; there was no woman like her in the tribe. Then Ananse married her again, although she was already his.

Now the hunter came again, and he saw this woman. He went off and reported to the sky-god, saying, "Ananse has made a fool of you, he sent you the ugly women and has kept the beautiful one for himself."

The sky-god sent messengers and directed them to go to the village where the spider was and to bring the woman to him.

They delivered the message of the sky-god to Ananse. He said, "Would he not like me to come also?"

The messengers said, "The sky-god said we must take the woman to him."
Ananse said, "That is she sitting there, take her away."

After she had been taken, Ananse went and got the gourd into which all the diseases he had taken from the woman had been poured, and he stretched a skin over the mouth of it. Then he stretched a skin over another gourd and gave it to his child, Ntikuma, and Ananse beat on the drum he had made and sang:

> "*Y'odende dende den,*
> *Y'odende den.*
>> Aso Ya-e!
> *Y'odende dende den,*
> *Y'odende den.*
>> Your eyes are red in vain!
> *Y'odende dende den,*
> *Y'odende den.*
>> You are bandy-armed!
> *Y'odende dende den,*
> *Y'odende den.*
>> Is that Aso Ya?
> *Y'odende dende den,*
> *Y'odende den.*
>> You are knock-kneed!
> *Y'odende dende den,*
> *Y'odende den.*
>> Your nose is a lump on your face!
> *Y'odende dende den,*
> *Y'odende den.*
>> Your feet are large as paddles,
>> like those of a slave!
> *Y'odende dende den,*
> *Y'odende den.*
>> Your head is like a cow!
> *Y'odende dende den,*
> *Y'odende den.*"

Ntikuma drummed and sang:

> "*Beautiful maiden,*
> *Beautiful maiden!*"

And Afudotwedotwe or Belly-Like-to-Burst and Nyiwankonfwea or Thin-Shanks, Ananse's children, danced. Anene, the crow, ran with speed and told the sky-god, "Ananse has a dance which is fitting for you but not for a spider."

Immediately the sky-god sent messengers there to Ananse to go and bring him this dance.

Ananse said, "This dance of mine, we perform it only in the harem, and if the sky-god agrees then I shall bring it along."

The messengers returned and told the sky-god. The sky-god said, "That is nothing, let him bring it to the harem." Ananse went with the drums to the harem, and the sky-god came and danced, and all his wives danced.

Now, there remained the one who had been sick. When she saw that Ananse had stretched a skin over the gourd in which were all her diseases, because of that she said she would not dance. And now the sky-god forced her, and she came; and when she was about to dance, Ananse lifted up the gourd and struck the woman with it, and the diseases scattered with a sound like *tese!*

That is how syphilis, stomach-ache, headache, leprosy, Guinea worm, smallpox, yaws, fits, diabetes, and madness came among the tribe. Once there was no sickness among mankind. It was the sky-god who was the cause of Ananse's bringing diseases among the tribe.

[ASHANTI]

15

How the Mason-Wasp Fetched Fire from God

VULTURE, Fish-Eagle, and Crow were without fire, for there was no fire on earth. So, needing fire, all the birds assembled and asked, "Whence shall we find fire?"

Some of the birds said, "Perhaps from God."

Thereupon Mason-Wasp volunteered, saying, "Who will go with me to God?"

Vulture answered and said, "We will go with you, I and Fish-Eagle and Crow."

So on the morrow they took leave of all the other birds, saying, "We are going to see whether we can get fire from God." Then they flew off. After they had spent ten days on the road, there fell to earth some small bones— that was Vulture; later, there also fell to earth some other small bones—that was Fish-Eagle. Mason-Wasp and Crow were left to go on alone. When the second ten days were ended, there fell other small bones to earth—that was Crow. Mason-Wasp was left to go on by himself. When the third ten days were over, he was going along, reposing upon the clouds. Nevertheless he never reached the summit of the sky.

As soon as God heard of it, He came to where Mason-Wasp was; and, answering God's question as to where he was going, Mason-Wasp said, "Chief, I am not going anywhere in particular. I have only come to beg some fire. All my companions have dropped by the way; but nevertheless, I have persevered in coming, for I had set my heart upon arriving where the Sky-God is."

Thereupon God answered him, saying, "Mason-Wasp, since you have reached Me, you shall be chief over all the birds and reptiles on earth. To you, now, I give a blessing. You shall not have to beget children. When you desire a child, go and look into a grainstalk and you will find an insect whose name is Ngongwa. When you have found him, take and carry him into a house. When you arrive in the house, look for the fireplace where men cook, and build there a building for your child Ngongwa. When you have finished building, put him in and let him remain there. When many days have

67

elapsed, just go and look at him. And one day you will find he has changed and become just as you yourself are."

So it is today: Mason-Wasp, before he builds a house, looks for the fireplace, just as he was commanded by God.

[B A I L A]

16

How Kintu Was Tested
before He Could Marry the Daughter
of the King of Heaven

WHEN KINTU CAME FIRST to Uganda he found there was no food at all in the country. He brought with him one cow and had only the food with which the animal supplied him. In the course of time a woman named Nambi came with her brother to the earth and saw Kintu. The woman fell in love with him and, wishing to be married to him, pointedly told him so. She had to return, however, with her brother to her people and her father, Gulu, who was king of the sky.

Nambi's relations objected to the marriage because they said that the man did not know of any food except that which the cow yielded, and they despised him. Gulu, the father, however, said that they had better test Kintu before he consented to the marriage, and he accordingly sent someone to rob Kintu of his cow. For a time Kintu was at a loss what to eat, but he managed to find different kinds of herbs and leaves which he cooked and ate. Nambi happened to see the cow grazing and recognized it, and complaining that her brothers wished to kill the man she loved, she went to the earth and told Kintu where his cow was, and invited him to return with her to take it away.

Kintu consented to go, and when he reached the sky he was greatly surprised to see how many people there were with houses and with cows, goats, sheep, and fowls running about. When Nambi's brothers saw Kintu sitting with their sister at her house, they went and told their father, who ordered them to build a house for Kintu and to give him a further testing to see whether he was worthy of their sister. An enormous meal was cooked, enough food for a hundred people, and brought to Kintu, who was told that unless he ate it all he would be killed as an impostor. Failure to eat it, they said, would be proof that he was not the great Kintu. He was then shut up in a house and left alone.

After he had eaten and drunk as much as he could, he was at a loss to know what to do with the rest of the food. Fortunately, he discovered a deep hole in the floor of the house, so he turned all the food and beer into it and covered it over so that no one could detect the place. He then called the people outside to come and take away the baskets. The sons of Gulu came in, but would not believe that he had eaten all the food. They, therefore, searched the house but failed to find it.

They went to their father and told him that Kintu had eaten all the food. He was incredulous, and said that Kintu must be further tested. A copper axe was sent to Kintu by Gulu, who said, "Go and cut me firewood from the rock, because I do not use ordinary firewood."

When Kintu went with the axe, he said to himself, "What am I to do? If I strike the rock, the axe will only turn its edge or rebound." However, after he had examined the rock, he found that there were cracks in it, so he broke off pieces of it, and returned with them to Gulu who was surprised to get them. Nevertheless, he said that Kintu must be further tried before they could give their consent to the marriage.

Kintu was next sent to fetch water and was told that he must bring only dew, because Gulu did not drink water from wells. Kintu took the waterpot and went off to a field, where he put the pot down and began to ponder what he must do to collect the dew. He was sorely puzzled, but upon returning to the pot, he found it full of water. So he carried it back to Gulu. Gulu was most surprised and said, "This man is a wonderful being; he shall have his cow back and marry my daughter."

Kintu was told to pick his cow from the herd and take it. This was a more difficult task than the others, because there were so many cows like his own that he feared he would mistake it and take the wrong one. While he was thus perplexed a large bee came and said, "Take the one upon whose horns I shall alight; it is yours."

The next morning Kintu went to the appointed place and stood and watched the bee, which was resting on a tree near him. A large herd of cows was brought before him, and he pretended to look for his cow, but in reality he was watching the bee which did not move. After a time, Kintu said, "My cow is not there." A second herd was brought and, again, he said, "My cow is not there." A third, much larger herd was brought, and the bee at once flew away and rested upon a cow which was a very large one, and Kintu said, "This is my cow." The bee then flew to another cow, and Kintu said, "This is one of the calves from my cow," and the bee went on to a second and a third cow which Kintu claimed as the calves which had been born during the cow's stay with Gulu.

Gulu was delighted with Kintu and said, "You are truly Kintu, take your cows. No one can deceive or rob you, you are too clever for that." He called Nambi and said to Kintu, "Take my daughter who loves you, marry her, and go back to your home." Gulu further said, "You must hurry and go back before Walumbe, or Death, comes, because he will want to go with you and you must not take him; he will only cause you trouble and unhappiness."

Nambi agreed to what her father said and went to pack up her things. Kintu and Nambi then took leave of Gulu, who said, "Be sure, if you have forgotten anything, not to come back, because Death will want to go with you and you must go without him."

They started off home, taking with them, besides Nambi's things and the cows, a goat, a sheep, a fowl, and a plantain tree. On the way Nambi remembered that she had forgotten the grain for the fowl, and she said to Kintu, "I must go back for the grain for the fowl, or it will die."

Kintu tried to dissuade her, but in vain. She said, "I will hurry back and get it without anyone seeing me."

He said, "Your brother Death will be on the watch and will see you."

She would not listen to her husband, but went back and said to her father, "I have forgotten the grain for the fowl, and I have come to take it from the doorway where I put it."

He replied, "Did I not tell you that you were not to return if you forgot anything, because your brother Walumbe would see you and want to go with you? Now he will accompany you."

Nambi tried to steal away without Walumbe, but he followed her. When she rejoined Kintu, he was angry at seeing Walumbe, and said, "Why have you brought your brother with you? Who can live with him?"

Nambi was sorry, so Kintu said, "Let us go on and see what will happen."

When they reached the earth Nambi planted her garden, and the plantains grew rapidly, and she soon had a large plantain grove in Manyagalya. They lived happily for some time and had a number of children, until one day Walumbe asked Kintu to send one of the children to be his cook.

Kintu replied, "If Gulu comes and asks me for one of my children, what am I to say to him? Shall I tell him that I have given her to be your cook?"

Walumbe was silent and went away, but he again asked for a child to be his cook, and again Kintu refused to send one of his daughters, so Walumbe said, "I will kill them."

Kintu, who did not know what he meant, asked, "What is it that you will do?" In a short time, however, one of the children fell ill and died, and from that time they began to die at intervals.

Kintu returned to Gulu and told him about the deaths of the children, and accused Walumbe of being the cause. Gulu replied, "Did I not tell you when you were going away to go at once with your wife and not to return if you had forgotten anything? But you allowed Nambi to return for grain. Now you have Walumbe living with you. Had you obeyed me you would have been free of him and would not have lost any of your children."

After some further entreaty, Gulu sent Kaikuzi, another brother, to assist Nambi, and to prevent Walumbe from killing the children. Kaikuzi went to the earth with Kintu and was met by Nambi, who told him her pitiful story. He said he would call Walumbe and try to dissuade him from killing the children. When Walumbe came to greet his brother they had quite a warm and affectionate meeting, and Kaikuzi told him he had come to take him back, because their father wanted him.

Walumbe said, "Let us take our sister too."

But Kaikuzi said he was not sent to take her, because she was married and had to stay with her husband. Walumbe refused to go without his sister, and Kaikuzi was angry with him and ordered him to do as he was told. Death, however, escaped from Kaikuzi's grip and fled away into the earth.

For a long time there was enmity between the two brothers. Kaikuzi tried in every possible way to catch his brother Walumbe, but he always escaped. At last Kaikuzi told the people to remain in their houses for several days and not to let any of the animals out, and he would have a final hunt for Walumbe. He further told them that if they saw Walumbe they must not call out or raise the usual cry of fear.

The instructions were followed for two or three days, and Kaikuzi got his brother to come out of the earth and was about to capture him, when some children took their goats to the pasture and saw Walumbe and called out. Kaikuzi rushed to the spot and asked why they called, and they said they had seen Death. Kaikuzi was angry, because Walumbe had again gone into the earth. So he went to Kintu and told him he was tired of hunting Death and wanted to return home. He also complained that the children had frightened Walumbe into the earth again. Kintu thanked Kaikuzi for his help and said he feared nothing more could be done, and he hoped Walumbe would not kill all the people.

From that time Death has lived upon the earth and killed people whenever he can, and then he escapes into the earth at Tanda in Singo.

[BAGANDA]

17

The Son of Kimanaueze and the Daughter
of Sun and Moon

I OFTEN TELL of Kimanaueze, who begat a male child. The child grew up, and he came to the age of marrying. His father said, "Marry."

He said, "I will not marry a woman of the earth."

His father asked, "Then whom will you marry?"

He answered, "*I!* If it must be, I shall marry the daughter of Lord Sun and Lady Moon."

But the people asked, "Who can go to the sky where the daughter of Lord Sun and Lady Moon lives?"

He simply said, "I, indeed; I want her. If it is anyone on earth, I will not marry her."

Thereupon he wrote a letter of marriage and gave it to Deer. But Deer said, "I cannot go to the sky."

Then he gave it to Antelope. Antelope also said, "I cannot go to the sky."

He gave the letter to Hawk. Hawk, too, said, "I cannot go to the sky."

He gave it to Vulture, but Vulture also said, "I can go half way to the sky; however, all the way I cannot go."

Finally the young man said, "How shall I do it?" He put his letter in his box and was quiet.

The people of Lord Sun and Lady Moon used to come to get water on earth, and one day Frog came and sought out the son of Kimanaueze and spoke to him.

"Young master," he said, "give me the letter that I may take it."

The young master, however, said, "Begone! If people of life, who have wings, gave it up, how can you say, 'I will go there?' How can you get there?"

Frog said, "Young master, I am equal to it."

So Kimanaueze gave Frog the letter, saying, "If you cannot get there and you return with it, I shall give you a thrashing."

Frog started out and went to the well where the people of Lord Sun and Lady Moon were wont to come to get water. He put the letter in his mouth and got into the well and kept very still. In a little while, the people of Lord Sun and Lady Moon came to get water. They put a jug into the well, and

Frog got into the jug. After they got the water, they lifted it up, not knowing that Frog had entered the jug. They arrived in the sky, set down the jug in its place and departed.

Then Frog got out of the jug. In the room where they kept the jugs of water, there was also a table. Frog spat out the letter and placed it on top of the table. Then he hid in the corner of the room.

After a while, Lord Sun himself came into the room where the water was; he looked at the table and saw the letter on it. He took it and asked his people, "Whence comes this letter?"

They answered, "Lord, we do not know." He opened it and read it. It ran thus: "I, the son of Na Kimanaueze Kia-Tumb'a Ndala, a man of earth, want to marry the daughter of Lord Sun and Lady Moon." Lord Sun thought to himself in his heart: "Na Kimanaueze lives on earth; I am a man who lives in the sky. He who came with the letter, who is he?" He put the letter away into his box and said nothing.

When Lord Sun finished reading the letter, Frog got into the jug again. After the water had been emptied out of the jugs, the water girls lifted them and went down to earth. They again arrived at the well and put the jugs in the water. Frog then got out and went under the water and hid himself. After the girls had finished the filling of the jugs they left.

The Frog came out of the water and went to his village. There he kept quiet and said nothing. When many days had passed, the son of Kimanaueze asked Frog, "O fellow, where did you take the letter, and how?"

Frog answered, "Master, I delivered the letter, but they have not yet returned an answer."

The son of Kimanaueze said, "O man, you are telling a lie; you did not go there."

Frog said, "Master, that same place where I went, that you shall see."

After six days, the son of Kimanaueze again wrote a letter to ask about the former letter, saying: "I wrote to you, Lord Sun and Lady Moon. My letter was delivered but you returned no answer whatsoever to me, saying neither 'We accept you' nor 'We refuse you.' " Having finished his letter, he sealed it. Then he called Frog and gave it to him. Frog started and soon arrived at the well. He took the letter into his mouth, got into the water, and squatted on the bottom of the well.

After a while, the water carriers came down and arrived at the well. They put the jugs into the water, and Frog got into a jug. When they had finished filling them, they lifted them up. They went up to the sky by means of a cobweb which Spider had woven. Soon they arrived there, and entered a house. There they set down the jugs and departed. Frog came out of a jug, spat out the letter, and laid it on the table. Then he hid in the corner.

After a while, Lord Sun passed through the room where the water was. He looked at the table and saw the letter on it. He opened it and read it. The letter said: "I, son of Na Kimanaueze Kia-Tumb'a Ndala, I ask you, Lord

Sun, about my letter that went before. You did not return me an answer at all."

Lord Sun said, "Girls, you who always go to fetch water, are you carrying letters?"

The girls said, "We, master? No."

Then doubt possessed Lord Sun. He laid the letter in the box and wrote to the son of Kimanaueze, saying: "You who are sending me letters about marrying my daughter: I agree, on condition that you in person, the man, come with your first-present, so that I may know you." When he finished writing, he folded the letter and laid it on the table and went away. Frog now came out of the corner and took the letter. He put it in his mouth and entered the jug. Then he remained very quiet.

After a while, the water was emptied from the jugs, and the girls came and lifted them up. Then they went to the cord of Spider and descended to earth. They arrived at the well and put the jugs into the water. Frog got out of the jug and went to the bottom of the well. When the girls had completed the filling of the jugs, they returned to the sky. Frog then left the well and soon arrived in his village. He kept very quiet.

When evening came, he said, "Now I will take the letter." He spat it out and arrived at the house of the son of Kimanaueze. He knocked at the door, and the son of Kimanaueze asked, "Who is it?"

Frog answered, "I, Mainu, the frog."

The son of Kimanaueze got up from his bed where he was reclining and said, "Come in."

So Frog went in and delivered the letter. Then he departed. The son of Kimanaueze opened the letter and read it. What Lord Sun announced pleased him. He said to himself: "Why, it was the truth Frog told me when he said 'you shall see where I went.'" Then he went to sleep.

The next morning, he took forty *macutas* and wrote a letter, saying: "You, Lord Sun and Moon, here is the first-present; I remain on earth to seek for the wooing-present. You up there, you tell me the amount of the wooing-present." He finished the letter and called Frog. When he came, he gave him the letter and the money, saying, "Take this."

So Frog started. Soon he arrived at the well. He went to the bottom of the well and remained very quiet. After a while, the girls came down and put the jugs in the water, and Frog entered one of them. When the girls had finished filling them, they took them up. Again they went up to the sky by means of a cobweb. Soon they arrived in the room for the water. They set down the jugs and went away.

Then Frog got out of the jug and put the letter on the table, together with the money. Then he hid in the corner. Some time later, Lord Sun came into the room and found the letter on the table. He took it with the money and read the letter. Then he told his wife the news that had come from the prospective son-in-law. His wife assented.

Lord Sun said, "Who is coming with these letters? I do not know. How shall his food be cooked?"

His wife, however, answered, "No matter, we shall cook it anyhow and put it on the table where the letters have been found."

Lord Sun replied, "Very well."

So they killed a mother hen and cooked it. When evening came, they cooked mush. They set these eatables on the table and shut the door. Frog came to the table and ate the victuals. Then he went to the corner and kept quiet.

Lord Sun now wrote another letter, saying: "You, son-in-law of mine, the first-present, which you have sent me, I have received. For the amount of the wooing-present, you shall give me a sack of money." When he had finished the letter, he laid it on the table and left the room. Then Frog came out of the corner and took the letter. Shortly afterward, he entered the jug and went to sleep.

In the morning the girls took the jugs and went down to the earth. They arrived at the well and put the jugs into the water. Frog then got out of the jug. When the girls had finished filling the jugs, they again went up to the sky.

Frog now got out of the water and soon arrived at his village. He entered his own house but waited quietly until sundown. When evening had come, he said, "Now I will take the letter." He started out and soon arrived at the house of the son of Kimanaueze. He knocked at the door and the son of Kimanaueze asked, "Who is it?"

Then Frog answered, "I, Mainu, the frog."

"Come in," he replied.

Frog went in; he gave him the letter and departed. The son of Kimanaueze opened the letter, read it, and then put it aside.

Six days passed; then he was ready with the sack of money. He called Frog, and when Frog had come, the son of Kimanaueze wrote the following letter: "You, my parents-in-law, the wooing-present is enclosed. Soon I myself, I shall find a day to bring my wife home." He gave the letter to Frog, together with the money.

Frog then started and soon arrived at the well. Again he went in under the water and hid. After a while, the water carriers came down and arrived at the well. They put the jugs, as usual, in the water; Frog, as usual, entered a jug. When they had finished filling the jugs, they took them up, going up by means of Spider's cobweb. Soon they arrived in the sky. There they set down the jugs in the regular room and departed. Frog then got out of the jug and laid the letter down on the table, together with the money. Then he went into a corner and hid.

Soon Lord Sun came into the room and found the letter and the money. He took both and showed the money to his wife, Lady Moon.

Lady Moon thereupon said, "It is good."

Then they took a young hog and killed it. When they had cooked the food, they set it down on the table and shut the door. Frog came in then and ate it. When he had finished, he entered the jug and went to sleep.

The next morning the water carriers took the jugs and again went down to earth. They soon arrived at the well and dipped the jugs in the water. Frog then got out of the jug and hid. When they had finished filling the jugs, they again returned to the sky. Then Frog left the well and soon arrived at his village. He entered his house and went to sleep.

The next morning, he said to the son of Kimanaueze, "Young master, I gave them the wooing-present, and they accepted it. They cooked me a young hog, and I ate it. Now, you, yourself, shall choose the day to fetch the bride home."

The son of Kimanaueze said, "Very well." Then twelve days elapsed.

Now the son of Kimanaueze spoke to Frog: "I need people to fetch the bride for me, but I cannot find them. All those to whom I speak say, 'We cannot go to the sky.' Now, what shall I do, Frog?"

Frog said, "My young master, be at ease; I shall find a way to go and bring her home for you."

But the son of Kimanaueze said, "You cannot do that. You could indeed carry the letters, but bring the bride home—that you are unable to do."

But Frog again said, "Young master, be at ease; be not troubled for naught. I indeed will be able to go and bring her home. Do not despise me."

The son of Kimanaueze said, "Well, I will try you."

Then he took some victuals and gave them to Frog.

Frog thereupon started. Soon he arrived at the well. Again he got into the well and hid. After a while, the water carriers came down and arrived at the well. They dipped the jugs in the water. Frog entered one of them. When they had filled them, they went back. Arriving at the proper room, they set down the jugs and departed. Then Frog got out of the jug and hid in a corner. When the sun had set and it was evening, Frog left the room of the water jugs and went to seek the room where the daughter of Lord Sun slept. He found it and saw her asleep there. First, he took out one of her eyes and, then, the other. These he tied up in a handkerchief and went back to the room where the jugs were. He hid in a corner and slept.

In the morning, all the people got up, but not the daughter of Lord Sun. So they asked her, "Why do you not get up?"

And she answered, "My eyes are closed; I cannot see."

Her father and mother said, "What may be the cause of this? Yesterday she did not complain."

So Lord Sun called for two messengers and said to them, "Go to Ngombo to divine about my child who is sick, whose eyes are sick."

They started immediately and soon arrived at the Ngombo-man's. They gave him presents and Ngombo took out his paraphernalia. Now the people who came did not let him know anything about the disease; they simply said, "We have come to be divined."

Ngombo looked into his paraphernalia and said, "Disease has brought you. The one who is sick is a woman. The sickness that ails her concerns her eyes. You have come, being sent; you have not come of your own will. I have spoken."

The people said, "True. Now tell us what caused the ailment."

Ngombo looked again, and said, "She, the woman who is sick, is not yet married. She is only chosen. Her master, who bespake her, has sent a spell, saying, 'My wife, let her come; if she does not come, she shall die.' You, who came to divine, go, bring her to her husband, that she may escape death. I have spoken."

The messengers agreed and got up. They went to Lord Sun and reported to him the words of Ngombo.

Lord Sun said, "All right. Let us sleep. Tomorrow they shall take her down to the earth."

Frog, being in his corner, heard all that they were saying. Then all slept.

The next morning, Frog got into the jug. Again the water carriers came. Again they took up the jugs. Then they descended to the earth and soon arrived at the well. They put the jugs in the water, and Frog came out of one of them. He hid under the well. When the jugs were filled, the water carriers went up to the sky.

Then Lord Sun told Spider, "Weave a large cobweb, down to earth, for this is the day when my daughter will be taken down to the earth." Spider wove and finished the web. Thus time passed.

Frog now got out of the well and went to his village. He found the son of Kimanaueze and said to him, "O young master! Thy bride, today she comes."

The son of Kimanaueze said, "Begone, man, you are a liar."

Frog answered, "Master, this is the truth itself. This evening I will bring her to you."

Frog then returned to the well and got into the water and was silent.

Now the sun had set, and the daughter of Lord Sun was taken down to the earth. They left her at the well and then went back.

Frog now got out of the well and spoke to the young woman, saying, "I myself will be your guide. Let us go immediately so that I can bring you to your master." Then Frog returned her eyes to her and they started. Soon they entered the house of the son of Kimanaueze. Frog exclaimed:

"O young master! Your bride is here."

The son of Kimanaueze said, "Welcome, Mainu, the frog."

And so the son of Kimanaueze married the daughter of Lord Sun and Lady Moon, and they lived on.

[AMBUNDU]

18

The Blue-Jay Who Married the Daughter of God

LONG AGO Blue-Jay had a wife but after a time he went to God; he went to seek the Daughter of God also as his wife. God replied, "Since you ask for her, you must not take her to the earth, you must stay just here in the sky. Because, if you take her to the earth, she may not eat meat of zebra or gnu or kudu; of any large animal she may not eat. If you desire to carry her to earth, let her eat only of smaller animals." Blue-Jay answered, "It is well, Chief."

So Blue-Jay was allowed to bring the Daughter of God to earth. Upon his arrival on earth he told these things to his earthly wife, saying, "I was told by God that his child may not eat of zebra or gnu or kudu; she may not eat of any large animal." These things he told his wife and mother; when they heard them, his mother said, "It is well, my child." Nevertheless, his first wife was terribly jealous.

One day Blue-Jay went off hunting. He went and killed a zebra and a young duiker. When he returned to his first wife, he ordered her, saying, "You must on no account give my wife the meat of the zebra. Let her eat only of the young duiker." His wife replied, "It is well."

Another day while Blue-Jay was out walking, the old wife deceived her fellow, the Daughter of God, giving her zebra meat and saying, "Eat, it is young duiker." But she was simply deceiving her. As soon as the Daughter of God ate it, she died. Then Blue-Jay returned; on his arrival he asked, "My wife! What has she died of?" The old wife replied, "I don't know."

Nevertheless God had seen her from the sky. Said he, "It is that one yonder who killed my child."

Thereupon Blue-Jay returned to the sky; on arrival he went to tell the news, saying, "My wife is dead, Chief." God answered, saying, "You forgot the orders I gave you that my child must not eat of zebra or gnu or kudu; nevertheless, there on earth she was given some. She ate and died." Then Blue-Jay replied, "It may be so, Chief." God answered, "Return."

When thirty days had passed, God gathered together a small cloud. Then he opened wide his mouth and thundered. After a time he descended and swept open the grave in which his child was buried; he took her out and carried her to the sky. Nevertheless, Blue-Jay did not survive; he took him away also. When he arrived midway he thrust him down to earth; but he never arrived: only some small bones reached the ground. He died just there midway. To this very day this is what Blue-Jay does: when he flies he goes up into the air with a loud cry; on the point of descending he dies.

[BAILA]

19

Mantis Creates an Eland

MANTIS ONCE DID as follows: Kwammang-a had taken off a part of his shoe and thrown it away, and Mantis picked it up and went and soaked it in the water, at a place where some reeds grew. Mantis went away, then he came back again, went up to the water, and looked. He turned away again, for he saw that the Eland was still small.

Again he came, and found the Eland's spoor where it had come out of the water to graze. Then Mantis went up to the water, while Eland went seeking the grass which it eats. He waited, sitting by the water; he was upon the water's bank, opposite Eland's assegai, and soon Eland came to drink there. He saw Eland as it came to drink. He said, "Kwammang-a's shoe's piece!" And young Eland walked up as when its father trilled to him. Mantis called, making his tongue quiver, as Bushmen still do in springbok hunting.

Then Mantis went to find some honey; he went to cut some honey. He came back and put the bag of honey down near the water and returned home. Then, before the sun was up, he came back to pick up the bag. He approached while Eland was in the reeds. He called to it, "Kwammang-a's shoe's piece!" And Eland got up from the reeds and walked up to its father. Mantis put down the bag of honey. He took out the honeycomb and laid it down. He kept picking up pieces of it, he kept rubbing it on Eland's ribs while he splashed them, making them very nice.

Then he went away and took the bag to seek for more honey to cut. When he came back he again laid the bag of honey down near the water and returned home. Once more he returned and picked up the bag, once more he went to the place and called Eland out of the water, saying, "Kwammang-a's shoe's piece."

Then Eland stood shyly in the water and walked up to its father, for he had grown. His father wept, fondling him. He again rubbed Eland's ribs making nice with honeycomb. Then he went away, while Eland walked back into the water, went to bask in the water.

Mantis did not come back for a time, and for three nights Eland grew, becoming like an ox. Then Mantis went out early. The sun rose, as he walked up to the water. He called Eland, and Eland rose up and came forth, and the ground resounded as it came. And Mantis sang for joy about Eland; he sang:

"Ah, a person is here!
Kwammang-a's shoe's piece!
My eldest son's shoe's piece!
Kwammang-a's shoe's piece!
My eldest son's shoe's piece!"

Meanwhile he rubbed Eland down nicely, rubbed down the male Eland. Then he went away and returned home.

The next morning he called young Ichneumon, saying that young Ichneumon should go with him and that they would be only two. Thus he deceived young Ichneumon. And they went out and reached the water while Eland was grazing. They sat down in the shade of the bush by which Eland's assegai stood, where he kept coming to take it.

Mantis spoke: "Young Ichneumon, go to sleep!" for he meant to deceive him. So young Ichneumon lay down, as Eland came to drink, because the sun stood at noon and was getting hot. Meanwhile young Ichneumon had covered up his head, because Mantis wished him to do so. But young Ichneumon did not sleep; he lay awake.

Then Eland walked away, and young Ichneumon said, "Hi, stand! Hi, stand, stand!"

And Mantis said, "What does my brother think he has seen yonder?"

And young Ichneumon said, "A person is yonder, standing yonder."

And Mantis said, "You think it is magic; but it is a very small thing, it is a bit of father's shoe, which he dropped. Magic it is not." And they went home.

Then young Ichneumon told his father Kwammang-a about it. And Kwammang-a said that young Ichneumon must guide him and show him Eland; he would see whether Eland was so very handsome after Mantis had rubbed it down. Then young Ichneumon guided his father, while Mantis was at another place, for he meant to go to the water later on. Meanwhile they went up to Eland at the water, and Kwammang-a looked at it and he knocked it down while Mantis was not there. He knocked Eland down and was cutting it up before Mantis came. So when Mantis arrived, he saw Kwammang-a and the others standing there cutting up his Eland.

And Mantis said, "Why could you not first let me come?" And he wept for Eland; he scolded Kwammang-a's people, because Kwammang-a had not let him come first, and let him be the one to tell them to kill Eland.

And Kwammang-a said, "Tell Grandfather to leave off. He must come and gather wood for us, that we may eat, for this is meat."

When Mantis came, he said he had wanted Kwammang-a to let him come while Eland was still alive, and not to have killed it when he was not looking. They might have waited to kill Eland until he was looking on. Then he himself would have told them to kill it. Then his heart would have been comfortable. Now his heart did not feel satisfied about Eland whom he alone had made.

Then, as he went to gather wood, he caught sight of a gall there; it was Eland's gall. And he said to himself that he would pierce the gall open and that he would jump upon it. And the gall spoke: "I will burst, covering you over."

Just then young Ichneumon said, "What are you looking at there, that you do not gather wood at that place?"

So Mantis left the gall, brought wood, and put it down. Then he again looked for wood at the place where the gall had been. He went up to the gall and again said he would pierce the gall open and that he would jump upon it. The gall again said it would burst, covering him all over. He said he would jump, and that the gall must burst when he trod on it and as he jumped.

Young Ichneumon scolded him again and asked, "What can be yonder, that you keep going to that place? You do not gather wood, you just keep going to that bush. You are going to play tricks and not gather wood."

And Kwammang-a said, "You must make haste and let us go when you have called Grandfather, for the gall lies there; Grandfather has seen it. So you must make haste. When Grandfather behaves like this about anything, he is not acting honourably; he is playing tricks with this thing. So you must manage that we start, when you have called Grandfather, that we may leave the place where the gall is."

Then they packed the meat into the net, while Mantis untied his shoe and put the shoe into the bag. It was an arrow-bag which he had slung on next the quiver. And so they carried the things and went along homeward. On the way Mantis said, "This shoestring has broken."

Then young Ichneumon said, "You must have put the shoe away."

And Mantis said, "No, no, the shoe must really be lying there where we cut up Eland. So I must turn back and go fetch the shoe."

But young Ichneumon said, "You must have put the shoe in the bag. You must feel inside the bag, feel in the middle of it and see whether you cannot find the shoe."

So Mantis felt in the bag, but he kept feeling above the shoe. He said, "See, the shoe is really not in it. I must go back and pick it up, for the shoe is truly yonder."

But young Ichneumon replied, "We must go home, we really must go home."

Then Mantis said, "You can go home, but I must really go and get the shoe."

Thereupon Kwammang-a said, "Let Grandfather be! Let him turn back and do as he wants."

And young Ichneumon said, "O you person! I do wish Mantis would for once listen when we speak."

Mantis only said, "You always go on like this! I must really go and get the shoe."

Then Mantis turned back. He ran up to the gall, reached it, pierced it, and made the gall burst. And the gall broke, covering his head; his eyes became big and he could not see. He groped about, feeling his way. And he went groping along, groping along, groping, until he found an ostrich feather. This he picked up, sucked it, and brushed off the gall from his eyes with it.

Then he threw the feather up and spoke: "You must now lie up in the sky; you must henceforth be the moon. You shall shine at night. By your shining you shall lighten the darkness for men, until the sun rises to light up all things for men. It is the sun under whom men hunt. You must just glow for men, while the sun shines for men. Under him men walk about; they go hunting; they return home. But you are the moon; you give light for men, then you fall away, but you return to life after you have fallen away. Thus you give light to all people."

That is what the moon does: the moon falls away and returns to life, and he lights up all the flat places of the world.

[BUSHMEN]

20

Why the Chief of the Smiths Was Unable
to Create Human Beings

A VERY LONG TIME AGO there was a king who called Walukaga, chief of the smiths, and gave him a great quantity of iron and said, "I want you to make a real man for me, one who can walk and talk, and who has blood in his body, and who has brains."

Walukaga took the iron and went home, but he was at a loss what to do, and no one could advise him how to set about making the real man. He went about among his friends telling them what the king had said, and asked what he had better do. No one was able to give him any advice. They all knew that the king would not accept anything short of an honest trial, and would punish the man for not carrying out his commands.

On the way home one day Walukaga met a former friend who had gone mad, and who lived alone on some wasteland. Walukaga did not know that he was mad until he met him. When they approached each other, Walukaga greeted his old friend, and the madman asked him where he had come from. Walukaga reasoned for a moment and then said to himself, "Why should I not tell him my story? Even though he is mad, he used to be my friend." So he answered, "I have come from some friends where I have been trying to get advice."

The madman asked what advice he wanted, and Walukaga told him all the king had said, and about the work he had given him to do, and how he had given him the iron, and then added, "What am I to do?"

The madman answered, "If the king has told you to do this work, go to him and say that, if he really wishes to have a nice man forged, he is to order all the people to shave their heads and burn the hair until they have made up a thousand loads of charcoal, and he is to get one hundred large pots of water from the tears of the people with which to slake the fire and keep it from burning too fiercely."

Walukaga returned to the king and said to him, "My lord, if you wish me to make this man quickly and well, order the people to shave their heads and burn their hair, and make a thousand loads of charcoal out of it for me to work the iron into the man. Further, make them collect a hundred pots full of tears to act as water for the work, because the charcoal from wood and the ordinary water from wells are of no use for forging a man."

The king agreed to the request and gave the order to all the people to shave their heads and burn their hair into charcoal, and to collect all the tears. When they had all shaved their heads and burnt their hair, there was scarcely one load of charcoal, and when they had collected all the tears there were not two pots full of water.

When the king saw the results of his endeavours, he sent for the smith Walukaga and said to him, "Don't trouble to make the man, because I am unable to get the charcoal or the tears for the water."

Walukaga knelt down and thanked the king. He then added, "My lord, it was because I knew you would be unable to get the hair for charcoal and the tears for the water that I asked for them; you had asked me to do an impossible thing."

All the people present laughed and said, "Walukaga speaks the truth."

[BAGANDA]

21

How Spider Read the Sky-God's Thoughts

THE SKY-GOD BEGAT three children, who were Esum (Darkness), Osrane (Moon), and Owia (Sun). When his three children grew up, the sky-god made them go to separate villages. The first one built his village, the second one also built his village, and the third one, he, too, built his village. And there they lived.

Now their father loved Sun most. And while the sky-god was reigning there, he blackened a stool and said to his attendants, "Who knows what my thoughts are?" Ananse, the spider, said, "As for me, I know them." At the time when he said, "As for me, I know them," the sky-god made all the attendants rise up. There and then the spider also rose up, saying he was going to the villages of the sky-god's children.

When Ananse reached the path, he said to himself, "I do not know his thoughts and yet I said, 'I know them.'" And he plucked some feathers out of every bird, stuck them on himself and flew off, alighting on a *gyedua* tree in the sky-god's village. And when the people saw the bird, they all made a great commotion which sounded like "*Ye-e-e-e!*" And the sky-god came out of the house and came under the *gyedua* tree and said, "Were Ananse here, he would have known the name of this bird. I had decided that Owia, Sun, is the one I wanted to make a chief, so I asked who knew what was in my head and Ananse said that he did. Now I have gone and pulled up the yam known as 'Kintinkyi,' and he who knows its name and utters it, to him I shall give it, my blackened stool. That is why Ananse has gone off to bring my children. Had he been here, he would have known the name of this bird."

Then the bird flew off, and Ananse pulled out the feathers and threw them away, and set out till he reached the village of Night. To Night he said, "Your father said that you must come with me." And Night replied, "It is well, I and you will go." Then Ananse said, "I am going on to fetch Moon and Sun." But Night said to him, "Let me first seek for something to give you to eat." Spider replied, "Ho!" Night thereupon went out and brought some roasted corn and gave it to Ananse. When he had finished chewing it, he set out for Moon's village. When he reached it, he said, "Your father says you must come along with me." And Moon replied, "It is well, I shall go."

Then Ananse said, "I shall go on to Sun's village in order to bring him." But Moon said, "Let me first get you something to eat." And Ananse replied, "Ho!" So Moon mashed up some yam for him to eat. Then Spider set out for Sun's village. When he reached Sun's village, he said to him, "Your father says you must come along with me." And Sun said, "It is well, I and you shall go, but let me get you something to eat first." Ananse replied, "Ho!" So Sun went and caught a sheep. When he came back, he said to Ananse, "I would have wished, had my father come here, that he should have seen what I was doing; if it were good, or if it were bad, in either case he would have seen. Since, however, he has not come and you have come, it is as if father had come. Therefore here is this, my sheep, that I shall kill so you may eat."

And he killed the sheep and prepared it beautifully for Spider to eat. After the meal Ananse said, "Let us go on a fallen tree." When they got there, Ananse said to Sun, "Your father has blackened a stool at his home. He wishes you to succeed to that stool, so he has pulled up a yam and if you know its name, he will take the stool and give it to you. Now this yam is called 'Kintinkyi.' And in order that you may not forget its name, I shall cut a short drum for you, and make a *mpintini* drum to go with it, so that when they beat the short drum and the *mpintini* drum then you will never forget this word, for the short drum will speak out and say:

> 'Firi bomo!
> Firi bomo!'

Then the *mpintini* drum will say:

> 'Kintinkyi bomo!
> Kintinkyi bomo!' "

So they set off to go to the sky-god's town. First they reached Moon's village and took him along; then they reached Night's village and took him along. All the way they played the *mpintini* drum. When they reached the outskirts of the town Ananse saw a man, and he sent him off to tell the sky-god that they were coming. Thereupon the sky-god called an assembly together, and soon Ananse and the others arrived and saluted every one. Ananse now gave the spokesman the news, saying, "The chief's errand on which I was sent I have performed; I have brought them." And the sky-god said, "My children, the reason I caused you to be sent for is this: I have blackened the stool standing there and I have also pulled up the yam over there. I shall now take this stool and give it to him who sees and names the yam. Because my eldest child is Night, let him try first." Then Night said, "It is called 'Pona.'" And all the people shouted, "Ye-e-e-e." Again the sky-god spoke, "My second child is Moon, therefore let him give its name." And Moon said, "It is the yam called 'Asante.'" The people shouted, "Ye-e-e-e." Again the sky-god spoke, "My child, the third one, is Sun, therefore let him name it."

Now, I forgot to say that the dance music was going on:

"*Kintinkyi bomo!*
Kintinkyi bomo!"

and Ananse was turning cart-wheels.

Then Sun rose up and stood there, and took hold of the yam, and he said, "Oh, as for this, since ever I began to walk beside my father and was very small, he used to tell me its name, and I have not forgotten; it is called 'Kintinkyi.'" And the tribe shouted applause three times, "*E!-E!-E!*"

Then his father rose up and stood there and said, "You, Night, you are the eldest, but the words which I told you you have allowed yourself to forget, because you did not pay attention to my words. Because of this, it is now decreed that wicked things only will be done during your time. And you, Moon, the words with which you and I walked and I told you, you too, did not follow. It is decreed therefore that only children will play during your reign. As for you, Sun, when I said words to you, you did not forget; you listened to my advice, so you are to be the chief. Should any one have any matter to settle, let it be heard in your time. Household cases, however, may be heard in the evening.

"So take the path which I have set you and if Moon wishes to trespass upon it, may Kontonkurowie, the circular rainbow seen at times around the sun, throw itself around you, so that Moon may not be able to come and touch you. Again, if the rainclouds gather, the sky-god's bow will be cast on the sky that your children who are under you may see when I have cast it so that the waters will not overflow and carry them away.

"One more thing. These words which were formerly known as the 'Sayings of the Sky-God,' now since Ananse, the spider, has been able to read these words in my head, let them be known henceforth as 'The Sayings of Spider.'"

[ASHANTI]

II

The Animal and His World

22

Mantis and the All-Devourer

MANTIS WAS SPEAKING: "Now I want you, Ichneumon, to catch some fat sheep for my father to cut up for us and hang up to dry near the house. I do not feel like cutting any up, as I am still writhing with pain. The swelling must first disappear, then I, too, can cut them up, then I, too, shall hang meat to dry at my house, because I, too, want the sheep's fat to be dry, that the women may render it, so that we may moisten the dry meat which we have been crunching. For the quagga's meat was white with age and not tender. Now I want you to cut up the old sheep, and let the young ones wait a little, for we shall not finish all these sheep; they are too many. I, furthermore, want Porcupine to go out tomorrow, when she has cooked and put aside the meat which she has dried. The Man yonder shall come and eat with me of these sheep, because I have counted them and I see that they are plentiful."

But Porcupine said, "Do you really want me to go to the Man yonder, who eats bushes? He will come and swallow all the sheep, as they stand in the kraal. You need not think that even these bushes will be left, for we shall be swallowed with the sheep. A Man who devours things as he does—walks along eating the very bushes among which he walks!"

Mantis replied to her, "You must go to your other father, the All-Devourer, that he may help me to eat up these sheep, and drink this soup. I have already poured away some of the soup, because I feel that my heart is upset. Fat has taken hold of my heart; I do not want to drink more soup. I want the Old Man yonder to come to drink it up. Then I can talk, for I do not talk now. Do you, therefore, fill the sack with cooked meat and take it. Then he will come; otherwise he might refuse."

Porcupine protested again: "People do not live with that Man. He is alone. People cannot hand him food, for his tongue is like fire. He burns people's hands with it. You need not think that we can hand food to him, for we shall have to dodge away to the sheep opposite. The pots will be swallowed with the soup in them. Those sheep will be swallowed up in the same way, for yonder Man always does so. He does not often travel, because he feels the weight of his stomach which is heavy. See, I, Porcupine, live with you, although he is my real father, because I think he might devour me, and you

93

will not devour me. Nevertheless, I will fetch him tomorrow, that he may come. Then you will see him yourself with your own eyes."

Porcupine went on the morrow, carrying cooked meat. She arrived at her real father's, the All-Devourer. There she stopped and set down the sack of meat. She said to her father, "Go! Cousin yonder invites you to come and help eat the sheep yonder, for his heart is troubling him. It is he who wants you to come. I have told you. Now I will go on in front, for I do not walk fast."

She shook the meat out of the bag upon the bushes. The All-Devourer licked up the meat and the bushes with it; he just gulped down the bushes too. Porcupine slung on her empty bag, and went forward quickly. While she walked she gave directions: "You must climb up to that place from which I came; you will see the sheep standing there." She went ahead in great fear of the All-Devourer, and was the first to reach the hut.

Mantis asked her, "Where is your father?"

Porcupine answered him, "He is still on his way. Look at that bush standing up there, and see if a shadow comes gliding from above. Watch for the bush to break off, then look for the shadow; when you see that, the bushes up there will have disappeared, for his tongue will take away the bushes beforehand, while he is still approaching from behind the hill. Then his body will come up and when he arrives the bushes will be gone all along the way to us. We shall no longer be hidden. Now I want Ichneumon to eat plenty, for of that meat he will never eat again and when the Man yonder comes, the bushes will be finished and the sheep likewise be swallowed up."

The All-Devourer followed Porcupine's spoor. As he went he ate up the bushes. He climbed up, finishing off the bushes, while his shadow glided up to Mantis's hut. The shadow fell upon Mantis. Mantis looked at the sun. He asked where the clouds were, for the sun seemed to be in clouds.

Porcupine said to him, "There are no clouds there, but I want Ichneumon to go and hide this pot away for me, for he truly feels the shadow of the Man coming yonder. It altogether shuts us in. The sun will seem to have set when he reaches us. His mouth sits black along there; it is not shadow, it is what the trees go into."

Then Mantis saw the All-Devourer's tongue. He asked Porcupine, "Is your father holding fire in his hand, for a fire is waxing red yonder?"

Porcupine answered, "It is the Man coming there, whose tongue is red. He is nigh, therefore you see his tongue. We will get out of the way here. We will not hand him anything ourselves, but put down something for him, for his tongue would singe our hands if we held anything out to him. Therefore I want Dasse to hide the other pot that she may still have soup. For now she herself sees the stomach, it truly extends to either side of us. We do not hear the wind, because he comes; the wind does not blow, for he always makes a shelter when he stands. He does not sit down, he stands; he will first eat up the things around him for they are still plentiful. He has put a layer of bushes in the bottom of his stomach and he has partly filled it, but he has not filled it up yet. Therefore he is still seeking food. He is a Man who fills himself to his trunk. If he looks round and finds no food, he will swallow these people, for they invited him to come to food which was not sufficient to his hunger.

The All-Devourer arrived, and Mantis placed food for him. The All-Devourer gulped it quickly down. Then Mantis took soup and poured it into a bucket. The All-Devourer swallowed the bucket. A pot was still keeping warm. Now Mantis took meat which had been put away in a bag, he put it into a bucket, and pushed the bucket toward the All-Devourer. The All-Devourer put out his tongue and licked and scorched Mantis's hands. Mantis pulled his arms quickly away and sprang aside, knocking against Dasse.

Dasse said, "Why does Mantis spring aside from the Man whom he invited to come? Porcupine told him not to give anything with his hands, but to put meat for the All-Devourer on the bushes."

Mantis took meat and put it in the pot. He said to young Mantis, "O Child, make a good fire for the pot. My hands are burning and keep me sitting where Grandfather scorched me. You can feel his breath which is hot. His tongue feels like that, too."

Then Dasse said to him, "You ought to ladle out sheep's meat and put it on the bushes." But Mantis did not hear, he sat spitting on his hands to cool them. He ladled out another bucketful. He again pushed the bucket to the All-Devourer. The All-Devourer licked his hands again. Mantis sprang aside, losing his balance, and tumbled into the hut. He got up, and sat licking, cooling his hands. He spoke to Ichneumon: "O Ichneumon, give me meat to cook, for you see it is as Porcupine told us, the buckets seem to have vanished."

But Ichneumon said to Mantis, "Mother told you that it would be like this. You would not listen; you invited the big cousin whom people know, whom no one invites, because his tongue is like fire."

Now Mantis called to young Mantis, "Go and fetch me the meat which Porcupine hid, for you see this bucket of meat has been devoured. You must look at the stomach."

Mantis brought two buckets and ladled out the meat. Dasse nudged him, and he winked at her. He slung a bucket forward with meat in it, then he slung another bucket forward alongside of it. The All-Devourer's tongue licked his ear, and he tumbled into the hut.

Dasse spoke to him and he winked at her. She said, "O Mantis, leave off winking at me! You must feed cousin, whom you invited. You must give him plenty to eat; Porcupine told you that she did not want to fetch him, because his tongue is always like this."

The All-Devourer gobbled up both buckets, he licked up the meat which was on the bushes of the hut and devoured it, together with the bushes.

Mantis then said to Ichneumon, "O Ichneumon, you must cook at that other place, and bring the meat which is on the bushes, for the buckets here are all swallowed. I will give the Old Man a pot which is hot to swallow, for you see the bushes are all gone. I shall no longer sit and cook in the bushes, when the wind blows."

The All-Devourer stepped backward, he licked up Kwammang-a's home bushes, he devoured them quickly with the meat on them.

Mantis spoke to Ichneumon: "O Ichneumon, quickly bring another sheep, you must cut it up quickly, for you see that the bushes have all been swallowed with all the meat."

The All-Devourer asked for water. Mantis lifted up a whole waterbag and set it before him. The All-Devourer's tongue took up the waterbag; he swallowed it with the water in it. He licked up a thorn bush.

Mantis then spoke to young Mantis: "You see, we shall not eat, for that thorn bush has been devoured, even though it has thorns." Again Mantis said to Ichneumon, "O Ichneumon, fetch that water there which is in the waterbag, for you see the other waterbag has been swallowed. Grandfather turns his head seeking for more water. He himself has devoured all the other things, he still seems likely to gobble up our beds. I shall truly sit upon the ground, if Grandfather eats up all the things in my hut."

The All-Devourer licked up Porcupine's things; he swallowed them quickly. Then Mantis said to his son, young Mantis, "See, sister's things there have been devoured; sister sits there on a bare place. All the sheep will soon be devoured."

The All-Devourer looked toward the sheep, his tongue took up all the sheep, he swallowed them quickly, while they were still alive.

Mantis exclaimed, "Have not the sheep been quickly swallowed, even before I had cut them up as I meant to do? Alas, the bushes have vanished, swallowed up! We are sitting on a bare place. Alas! Now I lack my things which I brought, that I might possess them."

Porcupine winked at Ichneumon. "O Ichneumon, I tell you, your younger brother must spring away. Father will be swallowed, if he goes on acting bravely like this; and Grandfather Mantis, the one who is talking, he will certainly be swallowed."

The All-Devourer called out his name, He-Who-Is-a-Devourer-of-Things, whom Mantis had called to come to him. He said to Mantis, "O Mantis, bring out the things to which you invited me, the real things which I, a devourer of things, should eat." He advanced and burned Mantis with his tongue.

But Mantis said, "I who am Mantis who invited You-Who-Devour-Things to my home. You came and finished off my things. You should not ask, seeking the real food to which I invited you, for those sheep which you have devoured were the food. There is no other food."

Thereupon the All-Devourer quickly devoured Mantis and Mantis was quiet. Young Mantis sprang away and took up the bow. The All-Devourer looked toward Kwammang-a. Young Kwammang-a sprang aside and ran away. Mantis was quite silent, because he was in the stomach of the All-Devourer. The All-Devourer stood opposite Kwammang-a and said that he was really going to swallow his daughter Porcupine's husband, even though he was handsome, yet he would swallow him, for he felt inclined to do so. He advanced and quickly swallowed his daughter's husband with the bed on which he was sitting. All-Devourer's stomach now hung almost down to the earth.

Porcupine wept; she stood sighing. The children came from afar. Then Porcupine asked young Mantis, "Are you a fierce man?" He was silent. She asked him, "Are you angry?" Young Mantis was silent, because he felt angry. She also questioned her son, young Kwammang-a. She turned as she sat, heated a spear, and asked her son, "Are you angry? You must remember that Grandfather's tongue resembles fire. I do not want you to flinch, if your heart is like father's heart." Young Kwammang-a sat still; they agreed to cut his grandfather open.

She took the spear out of the fire and drew it, burning hot, along her younger brother's temple. The fire burnt his ear; he sat still. She reheated the spear, it became red hot. She put the spear burning hot into her younger brother's nose. Tears slowly gathered and stood in his eyes. She said to him, "A mild person is this, whose tears slowly gather."

She reheated the spear and laid it, burning hot, on her son's ear-root. Her son sat still. She heated the spear again, and said to her son, "Grandfather's tongue is like this; I don't want you to flinch from him, if your heart is like your father's heart." She took out the spear when it was red, and put it into her son's nose. Then she looked at his eyes. They were dry. She said to herself, "Yes, a fierce man is this; that one is a mild man. This one is fierce; he resembles his father. That other one is mild; he resembles his father Mantis. He is a runaway." She said to her son, "Remember, Grandfather's tongue is like this. You must sit firmly when you go to Grandfather."

The children went in wrath to their Grandfather; they approached him as he lay in the sun. He arose, stood up, and waited. Young Kwammang-a said to the other, "Mother wished me to sit on one side of Grandfather, and you to sit on his other side. Because you cut with the left hand like your father, you must sit with your left arm, in which you hold the spear, outward. I will sit opposite on this side, so that I may have my right arm, in which I hold the spear, outside."

The All-Devourer scorched young Mantis's temple with his tongue. He walked forward, he scorched with his tongue the ear-root of his grandson, young Kwammang-a. He said that this little child really seemed very angry. He walked forward, and scorched the root of young Mantis's ear with his tongue. Young Mantis sat still. All-Devourer went forward, and scorched young Mantis's other ear with his tongue. Young Kwammang-a looked hard at the other and signed to him to hold his spear fast, and he held his own well. The other also held his spear well, because he had said beforehand, "You must cut one side, while I cut the other side. Then we must run away, while the people pour out."

He sprang forward and cut the All-Devourer; and the other cut him too. Then they ran away, while their fathers poured forth. The sheep also poured forth, the buckets poured forth; his father sat on his bed; the pots poured forth; all the things poured down. His grandfather doubled up and died.

Then the children said, "O bushes, we have cut you out. You shall truly become bushes; you shall again grow in your place; you shall be what you were before. The place shall be right again and these sheep shall wander over it. They shall graze over it, and again return to the kraal, which shall be as it was before. For that Man who now lies here, who ate up the bushes, shall utterly perish and disappear, so that the people may get dry bushes and be able to warm themselves." Thus young Mantis spoke. He felt that he truly resembled his father, that his speech resembled his father's speech. And it all came true.

Now Dasse gave Mantis water but said to him, "O Mantis, you must drink only a little!"

Mantis replied, "I am dying of thirst, I must drink up the eggshellful." He gulped all the water down and sank to the ground. Kwammang-a waited.

Porcupine said to Dasse, "Take that long stick lying there; you must beat your husband on the shinbone with it until he gets up, you must hold his face fast and rub it." So Dasse took up the long stick and hit Mantis on the shin. He started up quickly and sat shivering.

Dasse reproved him: "I told you to drink only a little, because you would be like this, if you gulped down all the water; but you would drink nearly all, thus killing yourself, so that you fell down."

Now Porcupine gave Kwammang-a some water and said to him, "O Kwammang-a! You must drink only a little. You must put the water down soon—when you have just wet your mouth. You must sit down then and wash yourself a little, for you have just come out of the stomach in which you were. Then presently you can drink plentifully, when you feel that your body is warm."

Kwammang-a drank a little, he put down the water quickly, and did not gulp it all down. He washed himself, drank again, and then he drank plentifully.

His wife cooked the meat for him which she had kept hidden away. She had told Ichneumon to hide some for her, so that they could eat it after the children had dealt with the Man who was devouring them, and he lay dead. "We must eat here, for he lies yonder, where the children have slain him. Then we will travel away, leaving him lying outside the hut. We will move away and seek a new home, because the Man lies in front of this home. We will live in a different hut which we will make our home."

Then they travelled away to a new home, and left the hut at which the Man who had devoured the people was lying. In this new home they always lived in peace.

[BUSHMEN]

23

The Fox and the Wolf

ONCE UPON A TIME there was a wolf and a fox. The wolf was the master and the fox the servant.

One day both were grazing their flock in the pasture and, as they were thus grazing, the wolf and the fox wandered off into the plains to dig up some wild onions. The sheep scattered in pasturing and then lay down. Wolf and Fox were in the plains eating wild onions; in this way they lost sight of the sheep. After a while, the wolf said to the fox, "Companion, go and bring back the sheep!"

The fox found the wild onions very much to his taste, but he got up and bound two sheep together, a ram and a ewe, and then returned. Again the wolf and the fox wandered over the plain to dig up wild onions. After a while the wolf again said to the fox, "Go and bring back the sheep once more!"

The fox, however, said, "Companion, look, the sheep are pasturing quietly." Thereupon the wolf himself got up and looked after the sheep, and there he found the two sheep which had been bound to the tree by the fox, a male one and a female one. He grew very angry when he saw what roguish trick the fox had played on him, and when he returned he asked the fox, "Rascal, where are the other sheep?" and he broke off some branches and struck the fox hard. The fox, thereupon, went to look for the sheep, but, as he was crying, he held his arms up to his head.

Then he looked into the distance and saw two cattle, a white one and a black one, and said, "Those cattle there are mine." And the wolf questioned him, saying, "Where are they?" And the fox said, "Was it not you who just beat me so severely?" And the wolf said, "Well, come and beat me now!" Thereupon the fox looked around for branches from a thorny bush, braided them together, and said to the wolf, "Lie down!"

Then he beat him hard, and the wolf's blood began to trickle down. And the wolf said, "By the blood of my mother! Did I beat you that hard?" So the fox said, "Come, just look at my back; it is all torn up." So the wolf said, "Go ahead then, beat me!" When he stopped beating him, he looked out into the distance and saw the two cattle. And the fox said, "The black one is mine." Then they raced toward the two cattle. The wolf seized the white one and the fox seized the black one. The wolf pierced his cow first, the fox pierced his last. The fox's cow showed fat in the wound, and the wolf's nothing but foam. Then the wolf grew angry and said, "The cow that you have given me is emaciated." And the fox said, "All right then; take mine." Then both pierced their cows again, the wolf that belonging to the fox, and the fox that belonging to the wolf. And when the wolf pierced the cow, foam once more appeared in the wound, whereas the wound that the fox made showed fat. So the wolf said, "Let us slaughter them together so that we may eat in common."

As they were slaughtering them, the wolf said to the fox, "Now that we have slaughtered a thing of this kind, why, in truth, are we eating? Let us therefore kill our mothers, so that we can grieve for them." Thereupon the fox said, "Yes," merely out of roguishness. So they went and came to their village and stowed away the meat. Shortly after they arrived, the wolf led his mother into the field and killed her. But the fox led his mother away and seated her in a cave by the road to the spring and then returned. Thereupon they fetched the meat. The wolf sent the fox out and said, "Get out the cooking-pot and go fetch some water." So the fox took the vessel and went.

On the road he rubbed some meat around his mouth and then went into the cave where his mother was and said, "Mother!," calling her. And the mother said, "*Uooo!*," answering him. Then he gave her the meat and went to draw water.

Upon his return he went to the village of the wolf, and the wolf was full of grief because he had really killed his mother. But the fox was joyful, because he had not really killed his mother. And so they put the meat on to cook. Then the wolf said, "Fox, go fetch me some water. Take some meat and go; you can eat on your way." And since his mother was hidden near the road, he eagerly hurried on.

One day the wolf said, "Today I shall go to fetch water." The fox said, "I beg you, I have an aunt there, and the road is bad, let me fetch water." But the wolf said, "It is my turn to go and fetch water." The fox was disturbed because the wolf would not yield. Now the wolf took the waterpail and went and fetched water, and he had not taken any meat along. On his way he came close to the cave, and the fox's mother called, saying, "Fox, my child, have you abandoned me?" So the wolf stayed still and listened to determine where the voice came from.

Then the fox's mother called again, saying, "My child, have you abandoned me?" So the wolf realized that the fox had deceived him and had not killed his mother. Then he went to the cave and stabbed the mother with the spear and laid her down in the opening. Then he went to fetch water and came back to the village.

The next morning the wolf sent the fox, saying, "Go, fetch me some water." Thereupon the fox took some meat and his pail and started out. When he came close to the cave, he called and looked in, thinking she was asleep. And he said, "Mother, mother!" Then he touched her foot. "The poor creature is not sleeping, she only sleeps on one eye, the other is open." But the mother did not stir, so he got an ant and placed it on her eye, so that it could bite her and wake her up. But she did not wake up; no, she was dead. Then he went into the cave and looked around. And then he saw the wound; and he sat down and cried very hard.

Thereupon he fetched some water and went home and did not want to return to the water any more. The wolf noticed that the fox had become angry. In the evening, when they set the meat to cook and sat by the fire to warm themselves, the fox was crying very hard. Thereupon the wolf questioned him, saying, "What are you crying about?" And the fox said, "I am bleary-eyed, that is all, perhaps it is the smoke." And the other said, "Get up, come here to my side where there is no smoke." Yet, when he had taken his seat there, he continued crying. Then the wolf said, "Yonder is your aunt, your mother, whom I have killed and for whom you are weeping. Is that not so? Now I am bewailing both my mother and your mother, my friend."

The next day dawned. The wolf went to graze his flock, but the fox stayed in the village. The wolf said to him, "Stay here and cook me a good meal!" Thus it was. The wolf went to graze his flock, and the fox stayed in the village and put meat in the pot to cook. As the meat was cooking, the fox took all of it out, scooped up the fat, gathered together some dung of dogs, cattle, and human beings and some pieces of leather for the pot and departed.

When the wolf came back in the evening from driving his flock, he found that the fox had disappeared. Under the fur blanket the fox had placed an insect and told it, "If the wolf calls, answer!" And the wolf came in and called saying, "There is the aunt." Thereupon the insect said "*Uooo!*" and the wolf was very pleased and said, "There is that aunt of yours; just put her in, she is boiling." He was very pleased.

He stepped up to the pot and took a stick and stirred with it, saying, "The fox has played a roguish trick again, he has eaten all the meat, the fat as well and then he has disappeared." Then he grew very wroth and took the fur and beat it thinking that the fox was inside. But the fox had gone long ago. He was far away. This the wolf discovered, so he pursued him and stayed on the spoor, till he found him on a rock. At this he was very well pleased, for now he would be able to kill him. He tried to climb up. He climbed part way but then slid back. Then he climbed again but again slid back and said, "Fox, how did you climb up?" But the fox had smeared the rock with tallow, and he said, "Yonder is the aunt; take this pebble, and I shall tell you where I climbed up. Take it and let me see!" Then he continued: "Do show me your teeth that I can see whether they are good or bad, whether they are filed out or whether they are not filed out yet." So the wolf opened his mouth and the fox threw the rock into the wolf's mouth and broke all his teeth.

Then the fox ran away. The wolf cried out but did not turn back; indeed, he did not. He continued his pursuit of him. Now the fox was at a woman's house in the village, so when the wolf arrived, he said, "Grab that fox." He went closer and closer and shouted, "Do not let him get away!" But the fox said, "People, you hear what he is saying: 'Let him get away!'" So the people went away.

Thereupon the wolf went to the lion and said, "Have pity on me and do seize that fox; do not let him get away!" And the fox said again, "Do you hear? There he says it again: 'Let him get away!'"

Finally the fox went into a cave and plucked out all his hair. The wolf caught up with him and said, "How this one resembles the fox with his thick tail and his long muzzle!" But the fox said, "How the man talks! Have I not plucked myself bare as a Hill Damara, and now he says, you resemble the fox!" And so the wolf went away.

[HERERO]

24

The Elephant and the Tortoise

Two beings, Elephant and Rain, had a dispute. Elephant said, "If you say that you nourish me, in what way is it that you do so?" Rain answered, "If you say that I do not nourish you, when I go away, will you not die?" And Rain then departed.

Elephant said, "Vulture! Cast lots to make rain for me!" Vulture said, "I will not cast lots."

Then Elephant said to Crow, "Cast lots!" and Crow answered, "Give the things with which I may cast lots." Crow cast lots and rain fell. It rained at the lagoons, but then they dried up, and only one lagoon remained.

Elephant went hunting. There was, however, Tortoise, to whom Elephant said, "Tortoise, remain at the water!" Thus Tortoise was left behind when Elephant went hunting.

There came Giraffe, and said to Tortoise, "Give me water!" Tortoise answered, "The water belongs to Elephant."

There came Zebra, who said to Tortoise, "Give me water!" Tortoise answered, "The water belongs to Elephant."

There came Gemsbok, and said to Tortoise, "Give me water!" Tortoise answered, "The water belongs to Elephant."

There came Wildebeest, and said, "Give me water!" Tortoise said, "The water belongs to Elephant."

There came Roodebok, and said to Tortoise, "Give me water!" Tortoise answered, "The water belongs to Elephant."

There came Springbok, and said to Tortoise, "Give me water!" Tortoise said, "The water belongs to Elephant."

There came Jackal, and said to Tortoise, "Give me water!" Tortoise said, "The water belongs to Elephant."

There came Lion, and said, "Little Tortoise, give me water!" When little Tortoise was about to say something, Lion got hold of it and beat it. Lion drank of the water, and since then all the animals drink water.

When Elephant came back from the hunting, he said, "Little Tortoise, where is the water?" Tortoise answered, "The animals have drunk the water." Elephant asked, "Little Tortoise, shall I chew you or swallow you down?" Little Tortoise said, "Swallow me, if you please," and Elephant swallowed it whole.

After Elephant had swallowed little Tortoise, and it had entered his body, it tore off his liver, heart, and kidneys. Elephant said, "Little Tortoise, you kill me."

So Elephant died. But little Tortoise came out of his dead body and went wherever it liked.

[HOTTENTOT]

25

The Frog and Umdhlubu

O<small>NCE ON A TIME</small>, a king married the daughter of another king; he loved her very much. His other wives were troubled on account of his love for her. She became pregnant, and gave birth to a girl: the father loved her exceedingly. The child grew, and when she was a fine handsome little child, the other wives formed a plot against her; they said, "Since her father is not at home, let us go and cut fibre." They told the children not to agree to carry the child. The mother called the little girl who nursed her child. She refused to carry her. The mother put her on her back, and went with her.

They cut fibre, and went on continually. It came to pass in one of the valleys they sat down and took snuff. The mother made a bundle of fibre, and gave it to the child: the child played with it. They set out again and cut fibre. They went on continually. The mother forgot the child. They went on continually cutting fibre; they tied it up in bundles, and carried it home.

When they came home, they called the children's nurses: they all came. But hers came without the child. She asked, "Where is my child?" They said, "You took her with you." She was troubled, and cried, and ran to find her. She did not find her, and came back.

There was a great lamentation. The other wives said, "How is it now? We have destroyed the father's darling. The pet wife is confounded."

A messenger was sent to tell the father; it was said, "King, your child has been lost, while we were cutting fibre." The father was greatly troubled.

In the morning an old woman of the royal household of another nation went to fetch water: she heard the child playing; she heard something saying, "*Ta, ta, ta.*" She wondered and said, "Ah! what is this?" She went stealthily along, and found the child, sitting and playing. She went home, and left both her and the waterpot. She called the king's chief wife, and said, "Come here." The queen went out of the house. She said, "Let us go; there is something by the river which you will see." She went with the old woman. They arrived. She said, "Behold a child." The queen said, "Take her." She said so with joy. The old woman took her. They came to the river. The queen said, "Wash her." She washed her. The queen took her, and placed her on her back, and went home.

She suckled her, for she had given birth to a boy. The queen brought her up. She grew. Both she and the queen's own child walked. She grew and be-

106

came a great girl. She was appointed chief of the girls, when a great feast was made. Many cattle were slaughtered, and all the people rejoiced.

After that the chief men said to the boy, "Marry this girl." The boy wondered, and said, "O! what is the meaning of this? Is she not my sister? Did we not suck together at my mother's breast?" They said, "No, she was found in a valley." He denied, and said, "No, she is my sister." The next morning they said, "It is proper you should take her to be your wife." He refused, and was greatly troubled.

On another occasion an old woman said to the girl, "Do you know?" She answered, "What?" She said, "You are going to be married." She inquired, "To whom?" She said, "The young man of your own house." She said, "O! what is the meaning of this? Is he not my brother?" The old woman said, "No, you were taken from a valley, and brought up by the queen." She cried, being much troubled.

The girl took a waterpot, and went to the river, and sat down and wept. She filled the waterpot, and went home. She sat down in the house. Her mother gave her food; she did not like it, and refused. The mother asked, "What is it?" She said, "Nothing. There is a pain in my head." So it was evening, and she went to lie down.

In the morning she awoke and took the waterpot, and went to the river; she sat down and wept. As she was crying, there came out a great frog, and said, "Why are you crying?" She said, "I am in trouble." The frog said, "What is troubling you?" She replied, "It is said that I am to become the wife of my brother." The frog said, "Go and take your beautiful things, which you love, and bring them here."

She rose and took the waterpot, and went home. She took another pot, and fetched her things, and put them in the pot; she took her brass rod, and her *ubenthle* kilt, and a petticoat with a border of brass balls, and her fillet, and her brass, and her beads. She took these things, and went to the river, and threw them on the ground.

The frog inquired, saying, "Do you wish me to take you to your own people?" The child said, "Yes." The frog took her things and swallowed them; he took her and swallowed her; and set out with her.

On the way he met with a string of young men: they saw the frog. The one in front said, "Just come and see: here is a very great frog." The others said, "Let us kill him, and throw stones at him." The frog said:

> "*I am but a frog; I will not be killed.*
> *I am taking Umdhlubu to her own country.*"

They left him. They said, "*Hau!* How is it that the frog speaks, making a prodigy? Let us leave him." They passed on, and went their way.

And so the frog too went on his way. Again he met with a string of men. The one in front said, "O, come and see a huge frog." They said, "Let us kill it." The frog replied:

"I am but a frog; I will not be killed.
I am taking Umdhlubu to her own country."

They passed on, and the frog went on his way.

He fell in with some boys herding cattle: they saw him, and he was seen by a boy of the damsel's father. He said, "*Wau!* By Umdhlubu the king's child! Come and kill a great frog. Run and cut sharp sticks, that we may pierce him with them." The frog said:

"I am but a frog; I will not be killed.
I am taking Umdhlubu to her own country."

The boy wondered, and said, "O, sirs, do not let us kill him. He calls up painful emotions. Leave him alone, that we may pass on." They left him.

The frog went on his way and came to others. He was seen by the girl's own brother: he said, "By Umdhlubu the king's child! There is a very great frog. Let us beat it with stones and kill it." The frog said:

"I am but a frog; I will not be killed.
I am taking Umdhlubu to her own country."

He said, "O, leave him alone. He speaks a fearful thing."

He went on and came near her home: he entered a bush below the kraal: he placed her on the ground with her things. He put her in order: he cleansed her with *udonqa:* he anointed her, and put on her ornaments.

So she set out. She took her brass rod, and went and entered at the gateway, and she passed across the cattle enclosure: she went in the middle of it: she came to the opening, she went out, and entered the house of her mother. Her mother followed her into the house and said, "Where do you come from, damsel?" She said, "I am merely on a journey." The mother said, "Tell me." She said, "There is nothing, I am merely on a journey." The mother said, "Women are satisfied who have such fine children as you. For my part, I am in trouble: my child was lost: I left her in the valley: she died there." The child answered, saying, "Why did you leave her? Did you do it because you did not love her?" She said, "No; the queens made me forget her; they would not allow the nurse to carry her." The girl said in answer, "No! there is no woman who can forget her own child." She said, "No; it happened through my not being accustomed to carry a child; for she used to remain with the nurse." Umdhlubu said, "Yes; you did it because you did not love me." She began to look very earnestly at her; she saw that it was her child.

When she saw her she rejoiced. She praised with the praise-giving names of her child. The mother took her robe, and girded her herself; she took her head-ornament, and put it on her head; she took her petticoat, and put it on; she took her staff, and went out; she leaped for joy, and *halala'*d; she went into the cattle-pen; she played leaping about with joy. The people wondered and said, "What has happened to Untombinde today? Why does she rejoice so much? Since the time her first-born died, she has never rejoiced, but has constantly been in sorrow."

One from her side went out, and said, "Just let me go and see what is in the house? Why do I hear the queen praising with the praise-giving names of her dead child?" So she went, and entered the house, and saw the girl. She went out, and shouted aloud, and gave thanks.

All the people went out. They ran to the house, hurrying to get there first. They crowded each other together at the doorway. They saw the child. All the people on her side rejoiced. All the others were troubled, and the queens of the other side said, "Ah! What does it mean? For we thought we had already killed this child. She has come to life again. We shall be confounded together with our children. The supremacy of our children is coming to an end."

A messenger set out and went to her father; he arrived and said, "O king, your child that was dead is come to life again." The king said, *"Hau!* Are you mad? Which is that child?" The messenger said, "Umdhlubu." The father said, "Whence comes she?" He said, "I do not know, O king." The father said, "If it is not she, I will kill you. If it is she, run, raise a cry in all places, that the people may bring together all the large oxen, and come with them."

He went and raised a cry, and said, "The princess has come. Make haste with the oxen." The men asked, "Which princess?" He replied, "Umdhlubu, the child of the king, who was dead."

They rejoiced; they took their shields; they took the oxen, and drove them; they took also their presents to gladden the princess; for she had risen from death; they found her when they no longer expected it. They came; they slaughtered many cattle, even in the paths, in order that the old men and the old women and the sick might eat, who were not able to reach the home where the princess was.

The father came and said, "Come out, my child, that I may see you." She did not answer. He slaughtered twenty oxen. She made her appearance at the doorway, and stood still. He slaughtered thirty; she came out. The father said, "Go into the cattle-kraal; let us go to dance for you, for our great joy; for I used to say, you are already dead, but in fact you are still alive." She stood still. Again he slaughtered forty oxen. Then she went, and entered into the kraal.

They danced for her very much. But the other side of the kraal did not rejoice; it did not dance together with the children and queens of that side. They left off dancing.

The father went with her into the house, and sat down with her. He said, "Let a fat young ox be taken, that we may eat and rejoice, for she was dead, and has risen from death."

So all the people rejoiced. The child returned to her royal position. Her father did right, royally; he returned to his former habits, and lived at that kraal, for he had ceased to be there much, because he remembered his child which had died. Her mother and the children of her house rejoiced together.

Her father asked her, "How did you come here?" The child said, "I was brought by a frog." The father said, "Where is he?" The child replied, "He is yonder in the bush." The father said, "Let oxen be taken, that he may be danced for, and come up to our home." So they went and danced for him.

They brought him home. They brought him into the house and gave him meat, and he ate. The king inquired, "What do you wish that I should give you as a reward?" He said, "I wish some black hornless cattle." He took many cattle and people, and said, "Go with him." So they went and came to his country.

The frog built a great town, and became a great chief. He slaughtered cattle continually; and men came to ask for meat. They inquired, "What is your chief who built this town?" They said, "Uselesele." They inquired, "Whence did he obtain so large a town as this?" They said, "He got it because he brought our princess to the king; so he gave him cattle and men." They answered, saying, "Are you then the people of Uselesele?" They said, "Yes. Do not speak disrespectfully of him; he will kill you, for he is a great chief."

Uselesele took many people under his protection. They revolted from their chiefs through seeing the abundance of food at Uselesele's. So Uselesele reigned and became a king.

Unkosi-yasenthla heard it said, "Unkosi-yasenzansi has a beautiful daughter, named Umdhlubu." He said to his people, "Go and see what kind of damsel it is." They went, and came to Unkosi-yasenzansi, and said, "King, we have been sent by Unkosi-yasenthla, that we might select a beautiful damsel from among your children."

He summoned them, and they came. At length they saw only one damsel which excelled all the others in beauty. For they remembered, that if a king has sent people to go and choose a beautiful damsel, it is proper that they should look very earnestly; for those people are the king's eyes, because he trusts them. They look earnestly, that they may not be reproved when the damsel is brought home. When they see she is ugly, not like a damsel which has been chosen for a king, they find great fault, saying, "Why have you disgraced the king by choosing an ugly thing for him?" The honour of those men is ended; they are removed from their honourable office, because they are not trustworthy. Therefore they chose Umdhlubu for her beauty's sake, saying, "It is she only who is fit to be the king's queen above all the others."

Therefore those who were left were ashamed; and their mothers were ashamed; and their brothers were ashamed. There was rejoicing in the house of Umdhlubu. The joy began with Umdhlubu, who was conspicuous for beauty among many other damsels and in the eyes of them all, for it was said, "There is a beautiful woman indeed!" Her mother rejoiced in her heart, saying, "I did well when I gave birth to my child!" And the children of her house were exalted, although their mother had been long ago exalted by the king, through being loved. There, then, was the hatred which increased towards that house of Umdhlubu, as her mother also was loved very much by the father of Umdhlubu. There was a very great hatred in the hearts of the other queens, on account of the beauty of Umdhlubu, which was admired by the king of another people above all their own children. They were ashamed for ever.

So they looked, and chose Umdhlubu. They departed to tell the king. They arrived home, and said, "King, we have seen the beautiful damsel; her name is Umdhlubu." The king said, "Aye; it is well. We must set out and go thither, and take a thousand head of cattle." So they set out.

Unkosi-yasenzansi, as he was sitting in the shade within the cattle-pen with his people, said, "What is that yonder? There is a great dust which rises to the heaven." They were afraid. He said to his soldiers, "Get ready to fight, for we do not know what is coming." After that the cattle appeared coming with the king and his people. Unkosi-yasenzansi went to meet them.

But the chief said, "I am Unkosi-yasenthla; I come to see Umdhlubu. Then they all went to her house. When they arrived, they asked to have Umdhlubu given them. Her father rejoiced when he heard that.

They had cattle slaughtered for them. They spoke with the father. Unkosi-yasenthla said, "I come to you, Unkosi-yasenzansi, I being desirous of taking your daughter; if you assent, it is well. I come with a thousand cattle." The father assented, saying, "It is well."

He assembled all the girls, and all the men, the young men with head-rings, and the youth; he set apart men for the purpose of working for Umdhlubu. He took out brass and beads for her marriage, and five hundred oxen, and said, "Now it is right. Set out with her. There is an officer for the purpose of conducting the wedding ceremonies."

So they all went with him, and reached the king's home. As they were coming into sight, a great cry was raised, and the people appeared in all directions, shouting, "The queen of Unkosi-yasenthla has come." They rejoiced.

They retired to rest. In the morning, when the sun had risen, and it was hot, the damsels went out with the young men and youths, and went into the bush; they sat down there. When the time for dancing arrived, they danced; they fetched the damsel from the bush; she went to the kraal to dance.

So they ended the dance. She took brass, and placed it before her father, and prayed, saying, "Sire, take care of me for ever, for now I am in thy hand, preserve me."

The whole marriage party sat down. They danced for them. They ended the dance. In the morning the damsel had ten bullocks killed and they ate and rejoiced.

The officer of the ceremony said, "Sire, we now wish to set out to return home, for the work is done."

The king took five hundred head of cattle, and sent them as a present to his mother. The men returned home.

And the damsels remained. Umdhlubu's father had said that they were not to return, but stay with her, and work for her; and many people, both male and female, remained there to build her town.

The king said, "Now build the town of the queen, where she may live with her people."

So the town was built and completed. The king visited it; many cattle were killed, that the soldiers might eat, and complete the queen's town. The king also went to live there at the new town. Thus he took Umdhlubu to be his wife.

The people of Umdhlubu's father reached their home, and said, "O king, we have done all things very well. There are cattle for Umdhlubu's mother; they are given to her by her son. He told us to give his respects to both his father and mother."

So all lived together in peace.

[ZULU]

26

The Caterpillar and the Wild Animals

ONCE UPON A TIME a caterpillar entered the house of a hare when the owner was absent. On his return the hare noticed the marks on the ground, and cried out, "Who is in my house?"

The caterpillar replied in a loud voice, "I am the warrior son of the long one whose anklets have become unfastened in the fight in the Kurtiale country. I crush the rhinoceros to the earth and make cow's dung of the elephant! I am invincible!"

The hare went away, saying, "What can a small animal like myself do with a person who tramples an elephant under foot like cow's dung?"

On the road he met the jackal and asked him to return with him and talk with the big man who had taken possession of his house. The jackal agreed, and when they reached the place he barked loudly and said, "Who is in the house of my friend, the hare?"

The caterpillar replied, "I am the warrior son of the long one whose anklets have become unfastened in the fight in the Kurtiale country. I crush the rhinoceros to the earth and make cow's dung of the elephant! I am invincible!"

On hearing this the jackal said, "I can do nothing against such a man," and left.

The hare then fetched the leopard, whom he begged to go and talk with the person in his house. The leopard, on reaching the spot, grunted out, "Who is in the house of my friend, the hare?"

The caterpillar replied in the same manner as he had to the jackal, and the leopard said, "If he crushes the elephant and the rhinoceros, he will do the same to me."

They went away again, and the hare sought out the rhinoceros. The latter, on arriving at the hare's house, asked who was inside, but when he heard the caterpillar's reply, he said, "What! He can crush me to the earth! I had better go away then."

The hare next tried the elephant and asked him to come to his assistance, but on hearing what the caterpillar had said, the elephant remarked that he had no wish to be trampled under foot like cow's dung, and he departed.

A frog was passing at the time, and the hare asked him if he could make the man who had conquered all the animals leave his house. The frog went to the door and asked who was inside. He received the same reply as had been given to the others, but, instead of leaving, he went nearer and said, "I, who am strong and a leaper, have come. My buttocks are like the post and God has made me vile."

When the caterpillar heard this, he trembled, and as he saw the frog coming nearer, he said, "I am only the caterpillar."

The animals who had collected nearby seized him and dragged him out; and they all laughed at the trouble he had given.

[MASAI]

27

The Gazelle and the Leopard

THE GAZELLE SAID to the leopard, "It is now the dry season, and we should be cutting down the bush, so our women may plant as soon as the first rains come."

"Well," said the leopard, "I cannot go today, but you may as well go."

The gazelle went; and all that day he cut the bush, and cleared the ground for planting, and the next day he also went alone.

On the third day the leopard called on the gazelle and asked him to go to the plantation with him. But the gazelle said he was sick and could not go, so the leopard went by himself.

The next day the leopard again called for the gazelle, but he was not in.

"Where's he gone?" inquired the leopard.

"Oh, he has gone to another part."

And each day the leopard called upon the gazelle he was either sick or out of town; so that the leopard had nearly all the hard work himself.

When the women had planted, and the harvest was ripe, the gazelle went to look at the plantation. He was greatly pleased to find so much planted, and thought how pleased his friends would be if he invited them to a feast; so he called in all the antelopes and other beasts of the field, and they had a splendid feast.

By and by the leopard thought he would go and see how his plantation was getting on, and no sooner had he arrived there than he exclaimed, "Hullo, who has been feeding on my plantation and eaten up my corn? Surely I will set a trap for them and catch the thieves."

The next day the animals, led by the little gazelle, came again; and he warned them, saying, "Be careful, for the leopard will surely set a trap for us." But the antelope became careless, and finally fell into the leopard's trap. "There," said the gazelle, "I told you to be careful. What shall we do? They have all run away and left us, and I am not strong enough to release you."

Then the leopard came, and rejoiced greatly at having caught the thief. He took the antelope to his town. "Please, sire, the gazelle told me to go," cried the antelope. "Don't kill me! Don't kill me!"

"How am I to catch the gazelle?" the leopard replied. "No, I must kill you." And so he killed the antelope and ate him.

When the gazelle heard what the leopard had done, he was greatly annoyed, and declared that as the leopard was their chief, the animals were quite right in eating the food he had provided for them. Was it not the duty of the father to provide for his children? "Well, well, never mind, he will pay us for this."

Then the gazelle made a drum, and beat it until all the animals came as if to a dance. When they were assembled, he told them that they must be revenged upon the leopard.

The leopard heard the drum, and said to his wife, "Let us go to the dance." But his wife said she would rather stay at home, and did not go. The leopard went; but no sooner had he arrived than they all set upon him and killed him. And when the dance was over, the leopard's wife wondered why he did not return. The gazelle sent her the head of her husband, skinned, as her part of the feast; and not knowing that it was her husband's head, she ate it.

"Oh, for shame," said the gazelle, "you have eaten your husband's head."

"Nay, sir, the shame rests with you; for you gave it to me to eat, after having murdered him." And she wept and cursed the gazelle.

[BAKONGO]

28

The Leopard, the Squirrel, and the Tortoise

MANY YEARS AGO there was a great famine throughout the land and all the people were starving. The yam crop had failed entirely, the plantains did not bear any fruit, and the corn never came to a head; even the palm-oil nuts did not ripen, and the peppers and okras also failed.

The leopard, who lived entirely on meat, did not care for any of these things, and although some of the animals who lived on corn and the growing crops began to get rather skinny, he did not really mind very much.

However, in order to save himself trouble, since everybody was complaining of the famine, the leopard called a meeting of all the animals. He told them that, as they all knew, he was very powerful and must have food, that the famine did not affect him, as he lived only on flesh, and that as there were plenty of animals about, he did not intend to starve. He then told all the animals present at the meeting that, if they themselves did not wish to be killed, they must bring their grandmothers to him for food, and that when the grandmothers were finished, he would feed off their mothers. The animals might bring their grandmothers in succession, and he would take them in turn, so that, as there were many different animals, it would probably be some time before their mothers were eaten. By that time it was possible that the famine would be over. But, in any case, the leopard warned them that he was determined to have sufficient food for himself and that, if the grandmothers or mothers were not forthcoming, he would turn upon the young people themselves and kill and eat them. For this, of course, the young generation, who had attended the meeting, had little liking, and in order to save their own skins they agreed to supply the leopard with his daily meal.

The first to appear with his aged grandmother was the squirrel. The grandmother was a poor decrepit old thing with a mangy tail, and the leopard swallowed her at one gulp and then looked round for more. In an angry voice he growled out, "This is not the proper food for me; I must have more at once."

Then a bush cat pushed his old grandmother in front of the leopard, but he snarled at her and said, "Take the nasty old thing away; I want some sweet food."

It was then the turn of a bush buck and, after a great deal of hesitation, a wretchedly poor and thin old doe tottered and fell in front of the leopard, who immediately dispatched her and, although the meal was very unsatisfactory, declared that his appetite was appeased for that day.

The next day a few more animals brought their old grandmothers, until at last it became the turn of the tortoise; but, being very cunning, he produced witnesses to prove that his grandmother was dead, and so the leopard excused him.

After a few days all the animals' grandmothers were exhausted, and it was necessary that the mothers be sacrificed to supply food for the ravenous leopard. Now, although most of the young animals did not mind getting rid of their grandmothers, whom they had scarcely even known, many of them had very strong objections to providing their mothers, of whom they were very fond, as food for the leopard. Among the strongest objectors were the squirrel and the tortoise. The tortoise had thought the whole thing out. As everyone knew that his mother was alive, she being rather an amiable old person and friendly with all, he was aware that the same excuse would not avail him a second time. He therefore told his mother to climb up a palm tree, and he would provide her with food until the famine was over. He instructed her to let down a basket every day and said that he would place food in it for her. The tortoise made the basket for his mother and attached it to a long string of tie-tie. The string was so strong that she could haul her son up whenever he wished to visit her.

All went well for some days, as the tortoise used to go at daybreak to the bottom of the tree where his mother lived and place her food in the basket. Then the old lady would pull the basket up and have her food, and the tortoise would depart on his daily round in his usual leisurely manner.

In the meantime, the leopard had to have his daily food. The squirrel's turn came first, after the grandmothers had been finished, and as he was a poor, weak thing and not possessed of any cunning, he was forced to produce his mother for the leopard to eat. The squirrel was, however, very fond of his mother, and after she had been eaten he remembered that the tortoise had not produced his grandmother or his mother for the leopard's food. He therefore determined to set a watch on the movements of the tortoise.

The very next morning, while he was gathering nuts, the squirrel saw the tortoise walking very slowly through the bush and, being high up in the trees and able to travel very fast, he had no difficulty in keeping the tortoise in sight without being noticed. When the tortoise arrived at the foot of the tree where his mother lived, he placed the food in the basket which his mother had already let down by the tie-tie and, having got into the basket and given a pull at the string to signify that everything was right, was hauled up and after a time was let down again in the basket. The squirrel was watching all the time and, as soon as the tortoise had gone, he jumped from branch to branch of the trees and very soon arrived at the place where the leopard was napping.

When the leopard woke up, the squirrel said, "You have eaten my grandmother and my mother, but the tortoise has not provided any food for you. It is now his turn, and he has hidden his mother away in a tree."

Hearing this, the leopard was very angry and told the squirrel to lead him at once to the tree where the tortoise's mother lived.

But the squirrel said, "The tortoise only goes at daybreak when his mother lets down a basket; so if you go early in the morning, she will pull you up, and you can then kill her."

To this the leopard agreed, and the next morning the squirrel came at cockcrow and led the leopard to the tree where the tortoise's mother was hidden. The old lady had already let down the basket for her daily supply of food. The leopard got into it and gave the line a pull, but except for a few small jerks nothing happened, as the old mother tortoise was not strong enough to pull a heavy leopard off the ground. When the leopard saw that he was not going to be pulled up, being an expert climber, he scrambled up the tree. When he got to the top he found the poor old tortoise whose shell was so tough that he thought she was not worth eating, so in a violent temper he threw her down on the ground and then came down himself and went home.

Shortly after this, the tortoise arrived at the tree and, finding the basket on the ground, gave his usual tug at it but there was no answer. He then looked about and after a little while came upon the broken shell of his poor old mother who by this time was quite dead. The tortoise knew at once that the leopard had killed his mother and made up his mind that for the future he would live alone and have nothing to do with the other animals.

[EFIK-IBIBIO]

29

The Hare, the Hyena, and the Lioness's Cave

THE HARE ONCE MET the hyena and proposed that they should go for a walk. They went for a walk together and then separated, after which the hare went to the lioness's cave and found it closed. She cried out, "Stone, open," and the stone rolled away from the mouth of the cave. She entered and said, "Stone, close," and the stone returned to its place. She then proceeded to the room where the lioness stored her fat, after which she went to the room where the meat was kept, and having had enough to eat, she returned to the entrance, told the stone to open, and when she had passed out, to close once more.

Feeling hungry again later she returned to the cave. On the road she met the hyena, who asked her where she came from and why her mouth was oily. The hare denied that her mouth was oily, but as the hyena persisted in his statement, she told him to rub ashes on his mouth and it would become as beautiful as hers. The hyena did as he was recommended, but no change took place in his appearance. The hare next suggested washing it with water and afterwards with urine; but although the hyena tried both, his mouth remained as dry as before. The hyena then said, "Please tell me where you go and feed." At first the hare refused to comply with his request and said, "You are so foolish whenever you go anywhere and are sure to be caught." But as the hyena would take no refusal, she consented to allow him to accompany her and told him about the lioness's cave. "There are," she said, "five rooms. In the first the ashes are kept; in the next, the bones; in the third, the tough meat; in the fourth, the tender meat; and in the last, the fat." The hyena cried, "Get out of the way, take me there," and off they started.

When they arrived at the cave, the hare told the hyena that when he wanted the cave to open he must say, "Stone, open," and when he wanted it to shut, "Stone, close." The hyena cried out, "Stone, open," and the stone rolled aside. When they were inside, the hare said, "Stone, close," and it closed again.

The hyena at once started on the ashes, while the hare went to the room where the fat was kept. When the latter had had enough to eat, she returned to the entrance and said she was going away. The hyena remonstrated with her as he was not nearly satisfied. After telling him how to get out of the cave, the hare went up to the stone and said, "Stone, open," and again, when she was outside, "Stone, close."

When the hyena was alone, he went to the place where the bones were kept, after which he proceeded to the next room, where the tough meat was stored, and ate until he was satisfied. He then returned to the entrance and said to the stone, "Stone, close," instead of "Stone, open." He repeated the words "Stone, close," several times and could not understand why nothing happened.

At this point the lioness, the owner of the cave, returned and said, "Stone, open." When the hyena heard her, he cried, "Ah! Woe is me! That is what I wanted to say. Poor fellow that I am! Stone, open! Stone, open!"

The lioness entered and said, "Shall I eat you, or shall I make you my servant?"

The hyena asked to be made her servant and was told to look after the lioness's cub. He was also given a bone and instructed to break it when the lioness had crossed four rivers. The hyena counted the lioness's footsteps and, when he calculated that she had crossed the four rivers, broke the bone. A chip flew, fracturing the cub's skull. Fearing that the lioness would kill him on her return, he searched for some hornets and stuffed one up each of the cub's nostrils so that it might be supposed that it had been stung to death.

The lioness returned to her cave a short while afterwards and called to the hyena to bring her cub. The hyena told lies for some time and invented several excuses for not doing as he was told; but the lioness was firm, and the hyena had to pick up the cub and bring it to its mother. The lioness at once saw that it was dead and told the hyena to take it outside. While he was doing this, he ate one of the cub's legs.

A little later he was again ordered to bring the cub to its mother and then to take it away once more. He devoured another leg while carrying it away, and when the lioness called out to him a third time to bring the cub to her, he said the birds had eaten two of its legs. He then ate up the cub.

The lioness intended to punish the hyena for his misdeeds, and after tying him to a tree, went to get some sticks with which to beat him. As he was standing there, bound to the tree, some other hyenas bent on a raiding expedition passed close by, and one of them, seeing him, asked him why he had been tied up in this manner. He replied that he was being punished for having refused to drink some oil which had flies in it. The other hyena suggested that they should exchange places and, after untying the knots, he allowed himself to be bound to the tree instead, while the first hyena followed in the wake of the raiding party.

After a time the lioness returned, and commenced to flog the hyena, who cried out, "Stop! I will drink it now."

"Drink what?" said the lioness, and she commenced to flog him again.

"Oh! Oh!" the hyena cried, "I will drink the oil with the flies in it."

The lioness then saw that this was not the hyena that had killed her cub.

The next morning the hyenas on their way back from their raid passed the cave, and the one who had killed the cub saw on the ground some strips of bark, which the lioness had spread out in the sun to resemble meat. "I will go to my mistress's kraal," quoth he, "For I see there has been a kill." On reaching the spot, however, he was seized by the lioness, who bound him to the tree once more and then beat him to death.

After this the lioness returned to her cave and said, "Stone, open." When the stone had rolled aside and she had entered, she said, "Stone, close," and it closed again.

[M A S A I]

30

Nwashisisana, the Hare

HARE, THAT WILY TRICKSTER, went to live with Grey Antelope. One day he said to her, "Suppose we go and till our fields and plant some beans!" So off they went and set to work. Antelope stole Hare's beans, and Hare stole Antelope's beans, but Hare did most of the stealing.

Hare set a trap in his field, and Antelope was caught by the leg. In the early morning the cunning rascal went out and found Antelope caught in the trap. "Don't you think you deserve to be killed," said he, "now that I have found you out?"

"No! No!" she cried. "Let me go, and we will go back to my house where I will give you a hoe." So he let her go, and she gave him the hoe.

Hare then packed his beans, harvested all his fields, and made ready to be off. Good-bye," he said to Antelope, "I won't stay with you any longer. You are a thief!"

Hare soon came across the great lizard, Varan, lying at the edge of a water-hole. It was the chief's waterhole, where they drew their water, and he had been placed there on guard to find out who it was that was continually disturbing it and making it muddy. "What are you doing here?" said Hare.

"I am watching this hole to see who it is that muddies the chief's water."

"I'll tell you what," said Hare, "we had much better go and till a field together."

"How can I dig?" said Varan. "I can't stand on my hind legs and hold the hoe in my forepaws."

"That doesn't matter! Just come along. I will tie the hoe to your tail and you will be able to dig beautifully."

So the hoe was tied on, but when this was done Varan could not move. Then Hare ran back to the hole, drank his fill of water, and finished by stirring it up well, making it as muddy as possible. After this he walked all over Varan's fields and regaled himself on his groundnuts. In the heat of the day he came back and said, "Ho! An army has passed through the country. I hear that the warriors have dirtied the water in the hole. I hear, too, that they have ravaged all your crop of groundnuts!"

"Untie me!" said Varan. "I can't budge."

"All right, but only on condition that you don't go and accuse me, Hare, of having stirred up the water."

"But who told you this story about those soldiers who did all the mischief?"

"Don't ask me so many questions. If you do, I won't untie you!"

"Very well! I'll be quiet, but take away this hoe. It hurts me!"

"Listen! First of all, I'll go and draw some water for you. You must be thirsty."

"No, I'm not thirsty. Only let me go!"

"If you are not thirsty, all right! I won't untie the hoe."

"Oh, very well, I am thirsty. Hurry up, and come back as fast as you can."

Hare went to Varan's village, took the wooden goblet from which he always drank, drew some water, and once again stirred up the hole. He took a drink to Varan, and said to him, "If anyone asks you whether I have disturbed the water, you must say that you did it. If you don't promise me this, I won't untie you."

"All right. Very well."

Then Hare ran to call the chiefs—Lord Elephant, Lord Lion, and the rest. They all came and asked Varan, "Who has been drawing our water and making it all muddy?"

"It is I," said Varan.

And Hare, the rascal, added, "Yes, I found him committing this crime and I tied him up to a hoe, so that he couldn't run away."

The chiefs congratulated Hare. "Ah! you have been very clever! You have discovered the villain who has been muddying our pool!" And they immediately killed Varan.

The wily trickster, Hare, took the hoe and then went to look for Grey Antelope. She was on sentry duty, on the edge of a pool, for guards were placed at all the pools to prevent anyone from approaching, as the water still continued to be muddied during the night. Hare, not being able to get anything to drink, said to Antelope, "What are you doing there so close to the water?"

"I am guarding the chief's pool."

"You will get thin and die of hunger, if you stay like that at the edge of the pools. Listen! You would do much better to come with me and till a field. Then, in time of famine, you would have something to eat."

"Let us go!" said Antelope.

Hare set to work in grand style. He gave Antelope a hoe and told her to dig. "I can't get on my hind legs," said she, "and hold the hoe with my forelegs."

"Let me have a look at your forelegs. I'll tie the hoe to them, and you will be able to dig all right."

Antelope tried, but she couldn't do it.

"Never mind," said Hare. "Wait a minute." He ran back to the pool, quenched his thirst, and muddied the water. Then he filled a calabash and hid it in the bush. On returning to Antelope, he said, "Hello! Haven't you done any hoeing yet?"

"No, I can't manage it."

"Would you believe it! An army has passed by, and they have stirred up the pool."

"No! Truly? Untie me, Hare!"

"I won't untie you unless you swear that what I said is true."

"Very well! Untie me."

Off Hare went to get the calabash to give her a drink, and he made her promise to confess that it was she who had disturbed the water. Then he called the chiefs, who killed Antelope.

But there was one creature that outdid Hare in cunning and that was Tortoise. She mounted guard at the pond. Hare arrived there. "You will die of hunger, if you stay at the edge of the pool with nothing to do. We had much better go and till a field together."

"How can I hoe with such short legs?" asked Tortoise.

"Oh! That will be all right. I'll show you how to do it."

"Eh! No thank you! I think not!"

"Well then! Let's go and help ourselves to some of the wild boar's sweet potatoes."

"No," said Tortoise uncompromisingly, "no pilfering!"

However, before very long Tortoise began to feel hungry, so much so that, when Hare again proposed a marauding expedition, she overcame her scruples and they went off together to root up the sweet potatoes. Then they lighted a fire of grass in the bush and roasted them.

"Tortoise," said Hare, "just go and see if the owners of these fields are anywhere about, as we must not let them catch us."

"Yes, but let us both go. You go one way and I'll go the other."

Off went Hare, but Tortoise, instead of following his example, stayed behind and crawled into Hare's sack. Hare soon came back, filled up his bag with sweet potatoes, threw it over his back, and ran away to escape the proprietors, shouting at the top of his voice, "Hi, Tortoise! Look out! They will catch you! I'm off! Fly!"

He ran as hard as he could to escape capture. Tortoise, inside the sack, ate the sweet potatoes. She picked out all the best ones and finished the lot. She said, being satisfied, "*Kutlu.*" After a while Hare was tired out and lay down quite exhausted. He felt the pangs of hunger.

"Aha!" said he to himself. "I will have a good feed!" He sat down in a shady spot, opened his sack, put his hand inside, and pulled out one very small sweet potato. "This is much too small for me," said he, and putting his hand in again, felt a nice big one. "Oho! here's a beauty!" When he had pulled it out of his bag, what was his surprise to find that his potato turned out to be Mistress Tortoise!

"Hello! Why! It's you!" he cried in disgust and threw her on the ground. She scuttled away as fast and as far as she could. Then Hare began to wail, "When I think that I have been carrying her all this time!" He felt very crestfallen.

Continuing his travels, Hare next met King Lion, surrounded by his courtiers. He at once asked permission to swear allegiance to the king and to settle in that country. But every day he went out to steal other folk's groundnuts. When the owners of the fields came to look at their crops, they exclaimed, "Who can it be that digs up our groundnuts?"

Hare went off to find King Lion, and said to him, "Sire, your subjects are not what they should be, for they are in the habit of stealing."

"Indeed!" said Lion. "Go and keep watch, and if you discover anyone stealing, catch him."

Hare went off to take up his position in the fields, but Lion followed him and surprised him in the very act of feasting on groundnuts. "Ha! Ha! You tell me that my subjects are not honest folk, while it is you who do the thieving!"

"Not at all! I was only keeping a look out! Come here, and I will show you the footprints of your subjects, for I know them well!"

So they went to a large shady banyan tree. Hare made a strong string of one of the long tendrils and said to Lion, "As you think I don't speak the truth, just sit down here and you will soon see the thieves passing by. I shall while away the time by making you a crown of wax."

"All right," said Lion, "make me a crown."

Hare began by parting Lion's mane down the middle and arranging the hairs carefully, one by one, on either side of his neck, as if he were preparing a spot on the top of his head for a crown. Then he made holes through the bark of the tree, on both sides of the trunk, and passed the hairs of the mane right through them, some on one side, some on the other. This done, he tied all the hairs securely together at the back of the tree with the string he had made, and he said to Lion, "I've finished the job. Jump up quickly and you will see one of your subjects stealing in the fields!"

Lion tried to jump up. He couldn't! He half killed himself struggling to get on his feet!

Hare ran to the village. "Come," he shouted, "and see who it is who ravages your fields!" He had previously torn up a lot of groundnut leaves and thrown them down close to the Lion. The villagers hurried to the spot.

"There! Don't you see him? Haven't I found him out, eh?" Lion didn't dare to say a single word.

Then his subjects cut great staves and beat him to death. "Ah! Hare, you are very clever, and we are grateful!" they said.

Hare cut Lion up into pieces. Then he took the skin and wrapped himself in it. Thus disguised, he went to Lion's village and entered the queen's hut. He said, "I am not well," and shut himself up, refusing to see anyone. He gave orders to the servants to kill an ox because he was ill. Then he had a second one slaughtered, then a third.

The women said to him, "Are you going to move to another place, since you are killing all your oxen?"

"No," said Hare, "I have no intention of moving any more. I am killing them because I know very well that I shall never get over this illness." So he had a general slaughtering of all Lion's oxen, goats, and sheep, to the very last head of cattle. When all were killed, he said to the queen, "Haven't you got my money in your keeping?"

"Yes," she replied.

"Well, bring it all out and put it together with my royal mat and all my valuables on the village square."

The lion's skin had now acquired a rather loathsome odour, the flies were settling upon it in swarms, and Hare was by no means comfortable inside of it.

"What sort of complaint have you got?" asked the queen. "It is something that smells very nasty."

"Oh! I have only got some sores. I must go and find a doctor. Good-bye, I shall start at once."

Lion's wife replied, "Then I will go with you, my husband."

"No," said he, "No occasion for that, for I know exactly where I must go."

He went out to the square, picked up the mat in which all the money and valuables had been packed, and then, throwing off the lion's skin, he tore away as fast as his legs could carry him with all the village in pursuit.

Hare came to a burrow, and in he ran. The pursuers got a hooked stick to pull him out. They tried to hook him and managed to get hold of his leg. "Oh, pull away!" cried he. "Pull away! You've only got hold of the root of a tree!"

So they left off pulling. They tried again, and this time they really hooked a root.

"Hi! hi!" he yelled. "Hi! hi! Take care! You're hurting me! You're killing me! Ow! Ow!"

They all pulled as hard as they could, and they pulled and pulled until the hook broke and they all fell over backward. They said, "*Qaa.*" Finally they were tired out and said, "Oh! Let us give it up and leave him where he is!" So they stopped up the burrow with a bunch of grass and went away.

The south wind now sprang up and blew the grass deeper into the burrow. "I am done for," said Hare to himself, as he fancied they were succeeding in getting nearer to him. He was suffering the pangs of hunger and was terribly thirsty, but did not dare to leave the burrow, supposing his enemies to be close at hand. At length he cried out, "Have pity on me and let me go, my good fathers, I beseech you!" He crept cautiously toward the entrance of the burrow, and found only a bunch of grass. Then he made off at once, leaving all his treasures behind him, not even giving them a single thought.

He ran on and on. He became thin and ill. He ate grass, but it did not remain in his insides; it passed through him immediately. He came to the home of Grey Antelope. "Say, Antelope, suppose we sew one another up! You stitch me up, but not completely, you know! It will keep the grass much longer in our insides when we browse, and we shall get much more nourishment out of it." Antelope consented, and partially stitched up Hare. Hare sewed her up entirely. Antelope swelled and died. Fortunately for her, however, she fell in a field belonging to a woman who picked her up, put her in her basket on the top of her head, and carried her to the village to be eaten. She gave her to her husband to cut up. He set to work and began by cutting the stitches that Hare had sewn. All that was in Antelope's interior at once came out, she jumped to her legs, and galloped away.

She met Hare, and she said to him, "All right! I've found you out now! Never again do I call you my friend!"

Hare, being thirsty, was looking for a pool but could not find one. At last he came to one where no one was on guard. Tortoise was really in charge, but she was in the water. Hare walked in. "What luck! How nice and cool it is!" said he, quenching his thirst and swimming about. Tortoise snapped at one of his legs, then at another.

"Hello! Let me go! I'll promise you a goat if you will let go!"

They came out of the pool together, and Hare said to her, "Come along to my house, and get your goat." They reached his home, but no goat! Nothing! Hare did not give her anything. Then he remembered the money that he had left in the burrow and said, "Let us go and see Chameleon. He has my valuables, for he borrowed a lot of money from me. I'll just run round and fetch my brother; he knows all about the business and will be my witness." Having said this, Hare ran off. Tortoise arrived at Chameleon's abode and said, "Give me Hare's money which he says you have!"

"What! I haven't anything belonging to Hare!" Whereupon Chameleon blew into Tortoise's eyes. She swelled, and swelled, and died.

That's the end.

[THONGA]

31

Master Rabbit and the Berries

THIS IS WHAT MASTER RABBIT DID:
The beasts were dying of thirst. They dug a well, but Master Rabbit refused to dig, saying, "I have enough juicy food."

He went and met the crane. They resolved to gather certain berries called *mfulimuninga* or *nkoroondo,* and soon they found them. Then they ate some and put the others aside. This done, they went and walked each his own way in the forest.

While they were on their walk, Master Rabbit bethought himself of going back, and he went and ate all the berries.

He then called to the crane and asked, "Who has eaten my berries? It must be you, Crane, since you were here."

"Friend," said the crane, "I have not seen them."

"Now," said the rabbit, "what will you pay me for the berries, *my* berries which you have eaten?" And he went on singing:

> *"My berries!*
> *I am dead, I am eaten up."*

Mother! There is the crane shaking off and shaking off some of his feathers. . . . "Which is the biggest?" he said. He threw a big one to Master Rabbit, who picked it up and went on his way home.

There he goes. . . . He happened to meet on the road some people who were dancing the war dance and throwing the assegai at one another. "Here is a feather," he said, "for one of you to put on." So one of them stuck the feather on his head, but a gust of wind came and blew it off. . . .

"Hello, *munsanje!*" said the man. "There is your feather going away."

"Let it go," said the rabbit, "let it go. What is it worth?"

"Well, Rabbit," asked some of the people, "does it not look as if we were men?"

The sun was going down. Someone said, "Have they given you back your feather?"

"They have not."

So he sang:

"Alas! My big feather,
That I got from my brother the crane,
The crane that ate my berries,
My berries that I found on a dry tree.
My berries! I am dead, I am eaten up."

They gave the rabbit a fish-spear. He picked it up and went and met some people who were fishing. "Here is a spear," he said, "for one of you to spear the fishes."

One man took it and went on killing fish after fish until he hit a big one. There was the spear disappearing into the water. Dear! Dear! It was going to stop only at the bottom.

"O *munsanje*, your spear is gone."

"Let it go. What is it worth?"

When the rabbit saw the sun go down, he said, "It looks as if the sun were going while we rabbits are still here."

"Let them give you your spear first."

"Yes," he sang,

"My spear that I got from playing at war,
The people playing at war that lost my big feather,
The big feather that I got from my brother the crane,
The crane that ate my berries,
My berries that I found on a dry tree.
My berries! I am dead, I am eaten up."

They made for the rabbit a parcel of fish, and he picked it up.

He went on and met some people who were eating porridge without relish. He asked them, "Do you really eat without relish? Here is some fish."

They put the pot on the fire, then ate, and finished the fish while Rabbit slept. He then awoke. "Have you finished them?" he asked.

"Alas! My fishes which you have eaten,
The fishes that I got from people
fishing with kafir-corn stalks,
The fishermen that lost my fish-spears,
The fish-spear that I got from people playing at war,
The people playing at war that lost my big feather,
The big feather that I got from my brother the crane,
The crane that ate my berries,
The berries that I found on a dry tree.
My berries! I am dead, I am eaten up."

They gave him kafir corn. He took it and went and met some people who were eating sour milk. "Here is some grain," he said. "Grind it and cook some light porridge."

They cooked it and ate it all up. . . .Then he remembered: "Have they given you back your kafir corn, Rabbit?"

The sun was going down. So he said, "Give me back my kafir corn."

"What?" they replied. "Did you not give it to us?"

"And I, did I tell you to eat it? O mother!

> *"Alas! my kafir corn that you have eaten,*
> *The kafir corn that I got from people*
> *who were eating porridge without relish,*
> *The people eating without relish that ate my fishes,*
> *The fishes that I got from people*
> *fishing with kafir-corn stalks,*
> *The fishermen that lost my fish-spears,*
> *The fish-spear that I got from people playing at war,*
> *The people playing at war that lost my big feather,*
> *The big feather that I got from my brother the crane,*
> *The crane that ate my berries,*
> *My berries that I found on a dry tree.*
> *My berries! I am dead, I am eaten up."*

They gave him sour milk. So he went on and on, walking carefully. He then saw clouds: "Now," he said, "it looks as if this little cloud were going to drench me. Somebody will have to pay for it."

So he went to the top of an ant-hill. And there the little cloud burst upon him. He began to slip and fell over there. There was the sour milk spilt on the ground. . . ."To think," he said, "that my sour milk should be spilt like that!

> *"My sour milk that I got from people eating thick milk,*
> *The people eating thick milk, that ate my kafir corn!*
> *Ant-hill!*
> *Give me my sour milk.*
> *Ant-hill!*
> *Give me my sour milk."*

O mother! Did not the ant-hill actually send out winged ants for him!

He picked them up and went to meet the lion, who was guarding the animals' well. "Give me some water," he said, "I am thirsty."

"This is no water for the rabbit," said the lion. "Did you not refuse to dig?"

The rabbit said, "Do you know what I have here?"

"What is it that you have?" asked the lion.

"They are winged ants," answered the rabbit.

"Well!" said the lion. "Tie me up while I eat, but let me have the winged ants."

The rabbit tied him up properly, then gave him the winged ants. After that he went and drank his fill, and, when he had had enough, he took a bath in the well. Then he said, "Your water is all dirtied, as we are rabbits." He went away.

Soon after that the beasts came to drink from their well. They found the water all dirty and asked, "Who is it that has made our water so dirty?"

The lion said, "It is the rabbit. Do you not see how he has tied me up?"

"What! The little rabbit has tied up such a big person! How did that happen?"

"He deceived me by giving me winged ants."

The beasts, hearing that, got up and, coming up to the rabbit, fired a cannon at him, *boom!* and he came to an end.

So does my little story.

[TONGA]

32

How It Came About That We Shall Always See Okra the Cat Lying on a Velvet Cushion, While Okraman the Dog Sleeps Among the Ashes of the Kitchen Fire

THEY SAY that there once was a certain woman who was so unfortunate that whenever she gave birth to a child it died. So she set out to consult one of the lesser-gods about it and to tell him that she desired a child. The lesser-god said, "I shall give you one, but as for the child, all the work he will ever do will be to get you into debt, but nevertheless, some day he will repay you."

It was not two days, it was not three days after consulting the lesser-god, when the woman conceived. She gave birth to a child—a spider-story child it was, for it was not long in growing up. The infant grew into a comely youth. One day he was with his mother and he said, "Mother, give me gold dust that I may go to the Edge-of-the-Sea-Country and buy salt."

The mother said, "How much do you want?"

He said, "An *asuanu*." And the mother took it and gave to him, and he set out on the journey.

Now, as he was going, he met a certain man and his spotted dog. He said, "Bring it that I may buy it."

The dog's master said, "You cannot buy it."

The youth said, "How much is it?"

The dog's master replied, "An *asuanu*'s weight of gold dust."

The youth said, "What's that to me! Take this *asuanu*." He received the dog and brought it back home.

When he returned, his mother said, "Why did you not reach your destination?"

He replied, "I used the gold dust to buy a dog."

His mother said, "Ho!"

Now they were living there, it would be for about one moon, when the youth said, "Mother, give me gold dust that I may go trading."

She said, "As for you, as is your wont, you will only take the gold dust and throw it away again, but how much do you want?"

He replied, "An *asuanu*-and-*suru*'s worth of gold dust."

She said, "Take it, then." So he set out along the trade road.

As he was going along, he met a certain man carrying a cat. He said, "Man, bring that animal that always falls on its feet, that I may buy it."

The man said, "When I lie down in my room, the mice gnaw my feet; for that reason I bought it."

He said, "I beseech you, let me have it."

The man said, "You cannot buy it."

The youth asked, "How much will you take for it?"

The man then replied, "An *asuanu*-and-*suru*'s worth of gold dust."

The boy said, "So that's why you say I cannot buy it! Here, take it." The boy received the cat and went off home with it.

When he reached home, he said, "Mother, look here at what I have brought."

She replied, "Ah, that is just what they said would happen." The child remained there at home.

It would be about forty days later when the son again addressed his mother, saying, "Give me gold dust that I may go trading."

The mother said, "All the money I have about me is finished with the exception of an *asuasa*'s weight of gold dust. If I give you this, and you go, and you do not buy goods with it, that's the end of this business."

The boy said, "I have heard."

The next morning, when things became visible, the youth took up his bag and was off, *pa!* As he was going, he met a certain Ashanti fellow who was carrying a pigeon. He said, "Friend, bring that creature of yours that I may buy it."

The Ashanti replied, "I am not selling it, for I amuse myself with it."

The youth said, "I shall buy it."

The bird's master said, "I will not sell it, for I know what it may do for me."

The boy said, "Oh, give it to me."

He said, "Will you be able to buy it?"

The boy said, "How much?"

He replied, "An *asuasa*'s weight of gold dust."

He said, "Do you suppose because of that I would not buy it? Here is the sum."

The boy brought the bird home. His mother said, "This has turned out no better than before. So this is what you have brought?" He replied, "Nevertheless, this is what I have brought."

Now one day the boy was living there at home, when the pigeon called to him, saying, "Come." When he went up to it, the pigeon informed him, saying, "In my own village I am a chief, and I was about to go on a journey when a certain fellow came and seized hold of me. Then you, out of your kindness, bought me, and now I beseech you, if you will only take me back to my town, the people will thank you greatly."

The boy said, "You are telling me lies. You will run away."

The pigeon said, "If you can't see your way to do as I ask, then take a string and tie it to my leg, and take me along."

The boy took a string and fastened it to the pigeon's leg, and it followed slowly behind him until they arrived at the pigeon's town. When they reached the outskirts of the town, the children were playing *nte* marbles. As soon as they saw the bird they said, "Here is the chief! Here is the chief!" One of the children ran to tell the Korenti chief, but they seized him and cut his throat, saying, "You are causing us to call to mind our late sorrow." But another one went again with the same tidings.

And now the Akwamu chief said, "You, Gyase chief, do you yourself go and see what this is all about."

He went and looked, and returned. He said, "Oh, it is true!" Then they got a hammock and the regalia and went to bring the chief to his house. The whole tribe was told the news—how he was setting out on a journey, and how a certain fellow had caught him, and how this youth by his kindness had bought him, and how today he had brought him home.

Elders and young people all rose up and thanked the youth. The queen mother brought a waterpot full of gold dust, and all of the elders also each gave a waterpot full of gold dust. The chief himself looked on his hand and slipped off a ring and gave it to the youth. And he said, "Take this ring, and whatever you desire this ring will give to you."

He said, "I have heard." And he went off with the ring to his village, and he showed the gold dust and the ring to his mother.

Then the mother said, "Welcome Aku, welcome Aku!"

Formerly, when the boy, having burned up his gold dust and returned from his journeys, would salute his mother, she used not to answer him. And he gave his mother the news, saying, "You have seen this gold dust and this ring; I shall go and build a great village for us to live in."

The mother said, "Press your eyes hard; try your best to do so."

The youth set out and went and stood in the bush. He slipped off the ring and placed it on the ground and said, "Ring, clear all this land of forest and of bush for me." And the whole of the place became cleared. He said, "Collect all which you have cleared into heaps for burning." And it did so. He said, "Set up houses." And it set up many houses. He said, "Ring, let people come and inhabit these houses." And people came.

The youth made his mother the queen mother and he became chief.

Now, Ananse, the spider, was his best friend. One day, when he was living there in his new home, Kwaku Ananse set out to come to this youth's village. When he reached it, he said, "Oh, little mother's child, little father's child, you have been fortunate and successful and you don't care any more about me or to look after me. But what has happened to bring all this about?"

Then the youth told him all the news. The spider replied, "I shall go to my village to get something and return."

Ananse went off to his village. He said to his niece, "I shall send you to my friend yonder, and when you go you will take this white wine for him, and pay attention and do whatever he orders, and you must try secretly to lay your hands on that ring."

The girl set out and went to the youth's village. The youth said to her, "As for this, I shall see to it that you do not go back again, for you must stay with me three days before you return."

The girl said, "I have heard."

Now he and the girl were there together, and the youth went to bathe. He slipped off the ring and placed it on a table, and the girl took it and went off with it to her uncle, Kwaku Ananse. As soon as Ananse laid his hands upon it, he made use of the ring to build a big town.

Now, the youth, when he came to look for his ring, could not find it. He came to hear that the spider had built a big town which was greater than his own. Then he went off to consult one of the lesser-gods yonder. The lesser-god told him, "Ananse's niece who came there to you has taken your ring and gone and given it to her uncle." The spider also went to consult the lesser-god, and it was revealed to him that Okra, the cat, and Okraman, the dog, would be sent to recover the ring. Therefore he went and got medicine with which to treat the meat he was going to place on the path, so that when the animals who were walking there took some to eat, they would be unable again to go anywhere at all.

The youth who had lost his ring came home and told the cat and the dog: "The time has now come for me to tell you the reason I bought you, and it is this: something belonging to me has been lost, and they say it is in the possession of the spider, but that it lies in a box which is in the middle of all the rest of his boxes. They say he has taken medicine and mixed it with the flesh of the sheep and placed it on the path. So when you reach there, don't eat it but jump over it."

The dog said, "Cat, have you heard? You are the one who will chew it."

The cat said, "Oh, go along, you who every little while take your nose to sniff and sniff!"

Then they began to talk a lot, and their master said, "That's all right, be off."

The two animals set out and were going along the path. Now there remained only a short time for them to reach the place where the meat was, when the dog detected the smell of it. He said, "Cat, I have a pain in my stomach and I cannot go on."

The cat said, "Come, come! Let us go on, the business in hand is important."

The dog said, "Cat, I am unable."

The cat went on alone. The dog then went to where the meat was, and he chewed up the whole of the meat. There he lay! He was unable to go on any more. And the cat reached Ananse's village, and lay down in Ananse's sleeping-room, on the ceiling above the room. As he lay there, he saw a mouse passing. *Squeak!* as he landed on its head. The mouse said, "Don't catch me, what is the matter?"

The cat replied, "My master's ring has been lost and they say it lies in Ananse's box, which stands in the middle of all the rest of his boxes. If you are able to go and bring it to me, then I shall let you go."

The mouse said, "I am able."

The cat said, "Suppose I let you go, and you go off and don't bring it but run away?"

The mouse said, "If you wish, fasten a string around my waist."

The cat took a string and tied it around the mouse's waist. Then the mouse went off into the spider's room and gnawed a hole in the box which stood in the middle of all the rest. Little by little he made an opening, and soon it became large. He passed through it to go and get the ring to take to the cat. No sooner did the cat lay his hands upon it, than he ran off and came across the dog. He was lying just where the cat had left him. The cat said, "You are still lying here! And where is that meat?"

The dog said, "Oh, I did not see what became of it. Perhaps the people to whom it belonged came and removed it. But where is the ring?" The cat said, "Here it is." The dog said, "They say that the river which lies in the path is in flood, and as you, Cat, walk on the bottom when you cross water, it might be that the ring would fall down, so give it to me, for as for me, you know, I pass on the surface of the water."

The cat said, "That's so; you take it."

They reached the river, and the dog jumped in—so did the cat. At once the cat crossed over. The dog reached the centre of the stream and became tired and, as he was about to take a deep breath, the ring fell out of his mouth into the water. He crossed over and came to where the cat was.

The cat said, "Where is that ring?" He said, "It fell out of my mouth into the water." The cat ran and entered the water; he saw a great fish passing. The cat caught it. The fish said, "What is it?"

He said, "My ring has just fallen into this river, so unless you want trouble, give me what belongs to me at once. If you don't give it to me I shall kill you immediately."

The fish said, "Let us go to the river bank that I may give you what belongs to you."

When they both reached the bank, the fish vomited and the ring came out.

The cat took it and came and showed it to the dog. The dog said, "Father, I beg of you, when you go, don't speak about what has happened." The cat remained silent. They reached home and the cat told his master all that had happened, saying, "Because of the meat which the dog chewed as we were going along, he became unable to go farther. And again, when I had gone and got the ring and brought it back, the dog said to me, as he crossed a river on its surface, that I must hand over the ring to him. I gave it to him, and he threw it away in the river. It was only after a little while that I laid my hands on it again."

All the people who were present said, "Praise be to the cat!" And they shouted "*E!*"

Then the chief said, "You, Cat, whatever kind of food I am eating, I will see to it that I break some and place in your little dish. Whatever mat I sleep upon, I shall only lie upon it provided you lie on some of it. As for you, Dog, you will only lie on the smouldering embers of the dead fire when the chilly night comes. Only with floggings, the folk will flog you."

That is why you will always see the cat sleeping nowhere but on the best mat; also, if you cast some food down on the ground for him, he will not eat it unless it is on a plate. But as for the dog—we shall always see him sleeping in the courtyard on the dead ashes of the day's fire; also you will see him there being beaten, he will yelp "*Kao!*"

It is all because of the time when the cat and the dog were sent on this business of the ring.

[ASHANTI]

33

How It Came About That the Hinder Part of
Kwaku Ananse the Spider Became Big,
at the Expense of His Head,
Which Is Small

THEY SAY that once a great hunger came, and that Kwaku Ananse, the spider, said he would go and search for meat and vegetable food and bring it that he and his wife Aso might eat. He went into a certain stream and there he met certain people. Now these people whom he met, excuse my saying so, were spirits. When Ananse met the spirits, they were standing in the water and splashing the stream-bed dry to catch the fish. Kwaku Ananse said, "Brothers, may I come and splash a little too?"

The spirits said, "Come."

Ananse went, and he saw that they were using their skulls to splash the stream dry. The spirits said to Ananse, "You have seen that which we take to splash the stream dry. Will you allow us to remove your skull in order that you may splash too?" Ananse said, "I will permit you, take it off for me."

Of a truth, the spirits removed it and gave it to him. Kwaku Ananse and the spirits joined together in splashing the bed of the stream dry. As they splashed, the spirits raised a song:

> "We, the spirits, when we splash the river-bed
>   dry to catch fish, we use our heads to splash the water.
> O the spirits, we are splashing the water."

The spider said, "This song is sweet, may I sing some of it?" The spirits said, "Sing some." And he lifted up his voice:

> "The spirits, we are splashing the water,
>   we take our heads to splash the water.
> O the spirits, we are splashing the water.
> Since the Creator made things,
>   do we take our heads to splash the water?
> O the spirits, we are splashing the water.

139

I take my head to splash the water dry today O,
O the spirits, we are splashing the water."

Ananse finished singing, and the spirits told him, saying, "We have splashed, we have got fish, your share is a basketful. Take it and go and eat. Take your skull, join it on your body, and go off. But what we have to say most particularly is this—the very day you sing any of that song, your skull will open and fall off."

The spider said, "Fish in abundance, which you have given to me, is all that I desire, and as for a song—for what reason should I sing it?"

The spirits said, "That is well, go off."

So the spider set off. The spirits, too, got everything together and they, also, went away. When the spirits had reached yonder, as it were, then they raised their song:

"We, the spirits, when we splash the river-bed dry
to catch fish, we use our heads to splash the water.
O the spirits, we are splashing the water."

And the spider heard the song and he, too, took it up:

"Since the Creator made things
have we taken our heads to splash the water?
O the spirits, we are splashing the water."

No sooner had he finished than his skull opened and dropped off. Ananse lifted it up and held it against his chest. He said, "Spirits, spirits, my head has fallen off."

The spirits heard, and they said, "That's the spider. He hasn't listened to what we told him, and he is calling us. Let us all go back and hear him."

Almost immediately, Spider came hastening along. He said, *"Puo!* Children of my father! My head has opened and fallen off, so I beg of you, if I have done you any harm, forgive it. You are in the right, but take my head and put it back in its place for me."

The spirits took it, and replaced it. They said to him, "Now, if you sing this song again and your head falls off again, we shall not answer when you call us. So get along with you!" The spirits set off again.

As they were going they sang their song. Then Ananse began to sing again, and his head became detached and fell off, *kutukum!* And he lifted it and, excuse my vulgarity, clapped it against his anus, and leaped to the side of the path. *Sora!* was the sound of the grass parting as he entered it. He said, "Path, save me! When the day dawns that I am rich, I shall give you some."

That is why you will see Ananse with a small head and a very big bottom. It all comes from the hardness of his ears.

[ASHANTI]

34

Why There Are Cracks in Tortoise's Shell

M R. TORTOISE, who was married to Mrs. Tortoise, had in Vulture a friend who was constant in visiting him. But, having no wings, Tortoise was unable to return the visits, and this upset him. One day he bethought himself of his cunning and said to his wife, "Wife!"

Mrs. Tortoise answered, "Hello, husband! What is it?"

Said he, "Don't you see, wife, that we are becoming despicable in Vulture's eyes?"

"How despicable?"

"Despicable, because it is despicable for me not to visit Vulture. He is always coming here and I have never yet been to his house—and he is my friend."

Mrs. Tortoise replied, "I don't see how Vulture should think us despicable unless we could fly as he does and then did not pay him a visit."

But Mr. Tortoise persisted: "Nevertheless, wife, it is despicable."

Said his wife, "Very well, then, sprout some wings and fly and visit your friend Vulture."

Mr. Tortoise answered, "No, I shan't sprout any wings because I was not born that way."

"Well," said Mrs. Tortoise, "what will you do?"

"I shall find a way," he replied.

"Find it then," said Mrs. Tortoise, "and let us see what you will do."

Later Tortoise said to his wife, "Come and tie me up in a parcel with a lump of tobacco and, when Vulture arrives, give it to him and say that it is tobacco to buy grain for us." So Mrs. Tortoise took some palm leaf and made him into a parcel and put him down in the corner.

At his usual time, Vulture came to pay his visit and said, "Where's your husband gone, Mrs. Tortoise?"

"My husband has gone some distance to visit some people, and he left hunger here. We have not a bit of grain in the house."

Vulture said, "You are in trouble indeed, not having any grain."

Mrs. Tortoise replied, "We are in such trouble as human beings never knew." And she went on: "Vulture, at your place is there no grain to be bought?"

"Yes," said he, "any amount, Mrs. Tortoise."

She brought the bundle and said, "My husband left this lump of tobacco thinking you would buy some grain with it for us and bring it here."

Vulture willingly took it and returned to his home in the heights. As he was nearing his native town he was surprised to hear a voice saying, "Untie me, I am your friend Tortoise. I said I would pay a visit to you."

But Vulture, in his surprise, let go his hold of the bundle and down crashed Tortoise to the earth, *pididi-pididi*, his shell smashed to bits, and he died. And so the friendship between Tortoise and Vulture was broken: and you can still see the cracks in Tortoise's shell.

[BAILA]

35

Why Some Animals Became Domesticated

IN THE OLDEN DAYS all cattle, sheep, and goats lived in the forests. Then, one day, Tororut called all the animals before him at a place in the jungle, and he lighted a large fire there. And when the animals saw the fire they were frightened and fled away back into the forests. There remained only the cattle, sheep, and goats who were not frightened. And Tororut was pleased with these animals and blessed them, and he decreed that henceforth they should always live with man who would eat their flesh and drink their milk.

[SUK]

36

How Honey-Guide Came to Have
Authority over Honey

HONEY-GUIDE and Capped Wheatear lived together in one place at first and ate out of one dish. Honey-Guide was the elder, Wheatear the younger. They set their minds on going to hunt for honey, and it happened when they arrived in the vicinity of the honey that Honey-Guide said, "Smile, Wheatear, when you see where the honey is." Wheatear smiled, but he did not see the honey. When Honey-Guide smiled he had really seen it. That is what they did, and then they returned home leaving the honey behind, but Wheatear quietly disappeared and went off to steal the honey.

Next morning Honey-Guide said, "Let us go to our honey." There they found a bit of bare honeycomb mangled and thrown about, so he asked Wheatear about it, and Wheatear replied, "My brother, I have seen neither it nor him who has stolen the honey. Since we came out yesterday nobody has come back here to demolish the honey in this way." And once again Wheatear said to Honey-Guide, "As for me, I could not eat any of this honey unless you had given it to me."

So then Honey-Guide said no more, and they went out again looking for honey. Once more they found some honey. Honey-Guide saw it before Wheatear did, and he tested Wheatear by saying, "Smile." Wheatear said, "I cannot see the honey, smile yourself, my brother." Honey-Guide: "No, child, smile." So Wheatear smiled and he saw the honey; then Honey-Guide asked him, "What do you see?"

Wheatear said, "It looks as if it might be flies fluttering before the eyes."

Honey-Guide said, "Haven't you seen it?"

But Wheatear was deceiving him, for he saw the honey all the time. When Honey-Guide was about to smile, he saw the honey and said, "Let us cut down the tree to get it."

Wheatear refused, saying, "No, as you said yesterday that I stole the honey, well, I am Wheatear! Let us bring some bird-lime and set a trap beside the honey, then if it be I who steal the honey you will catch me."

"Good business," replied Honey-Guide.

They went off to get some bird-lime from the human beings. Then when they arrived at their village, Honey-Guide said, "We will come tomorrow to set the trap." But after a time Honey-Guide quietly disappeared and went off to set the bird-lime at the honey. Said Wheatear to himself, "Let me go quietly and eat the honey." But the bird-lime was set already, although he did not notice it. When he thought of sitting down beside the honey, he sat on the bird-lime. Said he, "I will strike it with my wing," but he stuck to it. And when he struck with his tail he stuck to it. When he wanted to draw back his right wing, it was stuck fast. He tried to strike it with his breast but he stuck. When he attempted to bite it with his beak, he bit the bird-lime. Then he simply died for lack of breath.

When Honey-Guide appeared on the scene, after he had looked for him at the village, he found him already dead. Then he mocked him, saying, "Wheatear, smile!" As he was dried up, he said that was the reward of thievery. "From today you will not steal any more. The chieftainship is mine over honey and to be extolled by people! As for you, from today your portion shall be bird-lime already spread, and thus will you be killed by people."

Now since they separated there on account of thievery, Wheatear belongs to bird-lime and Honey-Guide is still extolled. While he talked like this, Honey-Guide was standing upon the corpse of Wheatear. They became distinct in other directions, while their cry remained the same and, to this day, Wheatear's portion is bird-lime and to be entrapped by men.

[BAILA]

37

The Bird That Made Milk

I T I S S A I D that there was once a great town in a certain place which had many people living in it. They lived only upon grain. One year there was a great famine.

Now in that town there was a poor man, by name Masilo, and his wife. One day they went to dig in their garden, and they continued digging the whole day long. In the evening, when the digging gangs returned home, they returned also. Then there came a bird which stood upon the house which was beside the garden, and it began to whistle and said:

"Masilo's cultivated ground, mix together."

The ground did as the bird said. After that was done, the bird went away.

In the morning, when Masilo and his wife went to the garden, they were in doubt, and said, "Is this really the place we were digging yesterday?"

They saw that it was the place by the people who were working on each side of them. The people began to laugh at them, and mocked them, and said, "It is because you are very lazy."

They continued to dig again that day, and in the evening they went home with the others.

Then the bird came and did the same thing.

When they went back next morning, they found their ground altogether undug. Then they believed that they were bewitched by some of the others.

They continued digging that day again. But in the evening when the digging gangs returned, Masilo said to his wife, "Go home; I will stay behind to watch and find the thing which undoes our work."

Then he went and laid himself down by the head of the garden, under the same house on which the bird always perched. While he was thinking, the bird came. It was a very beautiful bird. He was looking at it and admiring it, when it began to speak.

It said, "Masilo's cultivated ground, mix together."

Then he caught it, and said, "Ah! it is you who eats the work of our hands!"

He took out his knife from the sheath and was going to cut off the head of the bird.

Then the bird said, "Please don't kill me and I will make some milk for you to drink."

Masilo answered, "You must bring back the work of my hands first."

The bird said, "Masilo's cultivated ground, appear," and it appeared.

Then Masilo said, "Make the milk now," and, behold, it immediately made thick milk, which Masilo began to drink. When he was satisfied, he took the bird home. As he approached his house, he put the bird in his bag.

After he entered his house, he said to his wife, "Wash all the largest beer pots which are in the house."

But his wife was angry on account of her hunger and she answered, "What have you to put in such large pots?"

Masilo said to her, "Just listen to me, and do as I command you, then you will see."

When she was ready with the pots, Masilo took his bird out of his bag, and said, "Make milk * for my children to drink."

Then the bird filled all the beer pots with milk.

They commenced to drink, and when they were finished, Masilo charged his children, saying, "Beware that you do not tell anybody of this, not even one of your companions."

They swore to him that they would not tell anybody.

Masilo and his family then lived upon this bird. The people were surprised when they saw him and his family. They said, "Why are the people at Masilo's house so fat? He is poor, but now since his garden has appeared he and his children are so fat!"

They tried to watch and to see what he was eating, but they never could find out at all.

One morning Masilo and his wife went to work in their garden. About the middle of the same day the children of that town met together to play. They met just before Masilo's house. While they were playing the others said to Masilo's children, "Why are you so fat while we remain so thin?"

They answered, "Are we then fat? We thought we were thin just as you are."

They would not tell them the cause. The others continued to press them, and said, "We won't tell anybody."

Then the children of Masilo said, "There is a bird in our father's house which makes milk."

The others said, "Please show us the bird."

They went into the house and took it out of the secret place where their father had placed it. They ordered it as their father did, to make milk, and it made milk, which their companions drank, for they were very hungry.

After drinking they said, "Let it dance for us," and they loosened it from the place where it was tied.

The bird began to dance in the house, but one said, "This place is too confined," so they took it outside the house. While they were enjoying themselves and laughing, the bird flew away, leaving them in great dismay.

* See glossary, s.v. "amasi."

Masilo's children said, "Our father will this day kill us, therefore we must go after the bird."

So they followed it and continued going after it the whole day long, for when they were at a distance it would sit still for a long while and, when they approached, it would fly away.

When the digging gangs returned from digging, the people of the town cried for their children, for they did not know what had become of them. But when Masilo went into the house and could not find his bird, he knew where the children were, but he did not tell any of the other parents. He was very sorry about the bird, for he knew that he had lost his food.

When evening set in, the children wanted to return to their homes, but there came a storm of rain with heavy thunder, and they were very much afraid. Among them was a brave boy, named Mosemanyanamatong, who encouraged them and said, "Do not be afraid. I can command a house to build itself."

They said, "Please command it."

He said, "House appear!" and it appeared, and also wood for a fire. Then the children entered the house and made a large fire, and began to roast some wild roots which they dug out of the ground.

While they were roasting the roots and were merry, there came a big cannibal, and they heard his voice saying, "Mosemanyanamatong, give me some of the wild roots you have."

They were afraid, and the brave boy said to the girls and to the other boys, "Give me some of yours."

They gave some to him, and he threw the roots outside. While the cannibal was still eating, they went out and fled. He finished eating the roots, and then pursued them. When he approached, the children scattered more roots upon the ground, and while the cannibal was picking them up and eating, they again fled.

At length they came among mountains, where trees were growing. The girls were already very tired, so they all climbed up into a tall tree. The cannibal came there and tried to cut the tree down with his long sharp fingernail.

Then the brave boy said to the girls, "While I am singing you must continue saying, 'Tree be strong, Tree be strong!'"

He sang this song:

> *"It is foolish,*
> *It is foolish to be a traveller,*
> *And to go on a journey*
> *With the blood of girls upon one!*
> *While we were roasting wild roots*
> *A great darkness fell upon us.*
> *It was not darkness,*
> *It was awful gloom!"*

While he was singing, there came a great bird which hovered over them, and said, "Hold fast to me."

The children held fast to the bird and it flew away with them, and took them to their own town.

It was midnight when it arrived there, and it sat down at the gate of Mosemanyanamatong's mother's house.

In the morning, when that woman came out of her house, she took ashes and cast them upon the bird, for she said, "This bird knows where our children are."

At midday the bird sent word to the chief, saying, "Command all your people to spread mats in all the paths."

The chief commanded them to do so. Then the bird brought all the children out, and the people were greatly delighted.

[XOSA]

38

The Man and the Snake

A MAN ONCE FOUND some snakes fighting. As he came near and looked at them he saw that one snake had been killed. He reproved them. He said, "Go away."

One snake gave him a charm, saying, "By means of this charm you will hear all things. When the rat talks, you will hear it. When the cow talks, you will hear it. You will hear everything that is said." The man passed on. He came to the village.

At night the man's wife locked the house so that there was no open place. All was quite dark. She and her husband lay down to sleep. A mosquito came to the door. It examined the house and found no way in. The mosquito exclaimed, "They have locked the house very tightly. How can one get in?"

The man understood and laughed.

"What are you laughing about?" asked his wife.

"Nothing," said he.

Later, a rat came. He examined the door. He found it fast closed and left it. Then he tried the eaves of the house and got in. He searched everywhere. He wanted butter but he found none. He said, "Oh, where has that woman stored her butter?" The man laughed.

His wife asked him, "What are you laughing about?"

He answered, "Nothing."

In the morning the man went to his barn. He let the cattle out. When it was nearly milking time his wife came to milk. When she arrived the cow said, "Of course you come, but you will not milk me today. I shall withhold my milk. My calf will drink it afterward." The man laughed.

His wife asked him, "What are you laughing at?"

He answered, "Nothing."

The wife left the cow. She returned to the village. Then the calf sucked its mother.

The next day the wife again came to milk. The cow again withheld its milk. In the afternoon the woman's child was ill for want of milk. She brought it to the barn and she talked to her husband. She said, "That calf will kill my daughter."

The cow interrupted, "What! My daughter will kill your daughter?"

The man laughed.

His wife asked him, "What are you laughing about?"

He answered, "Nothing."

When it was nearly sunset his wife said, "I shall get a divorce."

She called all the people. They came to her husband's place. They seated themselves. They said to the wife:

"You and your husband talk. We will listen."

The wife talked. She said to the people, "When we lie down to sleep, my husband always laughs at me without any reason. When I ask him why he does it he hides the reason from me. That is why I object to him."

Then they asked the husband, "Why do you laugh at your wife? Tell us."

He answered, "Nothing."

They said again, "Tell us."

He answered, "Men, if I tell it, I will die."

They said, "Tell it, man! Do not hide it."

He replied, "Oh, men, I will not tell it. I will surely die if I do."

They urged him. When he was worn out he told them. He said to the people, "This is the reason why I laughed when we were lying down in the house. After a while at night the mosquito would talk. It would say, 'Who is this woman that has locked up her house so tightly? Where can one get in?' That is why I laughed."

The man died, as he had said. The people cried. Some of them dug a grave. As they were about to bury the body a certain snake hastened to the desolate spot. It wrapped itself around the body. It stuck its tail in the nose of the dead man. He sneezed. The people were amazed. Some of them said, "Is it his god?"

Others replied, "Why ask who it is?"

When the man stood up the snake left.

When the man had quite recovered he travelled through the desolate places. He found the snake under a tree. The snake said, "But why did you tell? Long ago when I gave you that charm I told you it would make you hear all things."

The man replied, "They urged me, so I told them."

The snake said, "Oh!"

Then the snake gave him another charm, saying, "You will hear the words of the birds which eat the kafir corn. When a bird eats the kafir corn in the field you will hear its words."

The snake went away.

The man returned to the village. He heard many things. When a bird was eating the kafir corn, if another bird came near, the first one would say, "Bird! Do not come. We shall be seen. I am eating quietly. This is my place. Let us separate. The field is large."

After a while another bird would reply, "What! I shall be found out?" A third would break in, "How will you get out? Perhaps they will find us."

"Let him go." cried one bird.

"I am not going," said the other. The man laughed there in the kafir corn. The man always held that snake sacred as his god.

[NUER]

39

How Elephant Married a Nama Woman
and Was Deceived by Her

IT IS SAID that Elephant fell madly in love with a Nama woman and married her. Her two brothers came to visit her secretly but, for fear of him, she told Elephant she wanted to fetch some wood and then went and hid the two in the firewood.

Then she said, "Since I have married into this kraal, I beg you to tell me, has the one-without-hair-at-the-knees been slaughtered for me?" (That would be a fully grown ram.) The blind mother-in-law answered her, "Things that were not spoken about of old, these she now speaks of and the smell of a Nama is present." Thereupon the woman answered her mother-in-law, "Should I not anoint myself in the old way and sprinkle myself with incense?" And the mother-in-law said, "Hum, things are being said by my son's sweetheart which she did not say of old."

Just then, Elephant, who had been in the field, came home and behaved as though he had found out that the woman's two brothers had come. He rubbed himself against the house. Then the wife said, "What I did not do of old, now I do. Which day did you slaughter for me the ram lying far back in the kraal, and when did I anoint myself and sprinkle myself with my incense?" Thus the woman spoke to him. Thereupon the mother-in-law said to him, "Things which were not spoken about of old are spoken now; therefore grant her her desire."

So the one-without-hair-at-the-knees was slaughtered. And the woman herself fried it. That night she asked her mother-in-law, "How do you breathe when you sleep the sleep of life, and how do you breathe when you sleep the sleep of death?" And the mother-in-law said, "Hum, this is an evening rich in conversation. When we sleep the sleep of death, we breathe *sui sui*, and when we sleep the sleep of life, we breathe *choo awaba, choo awaba.*"

Then the woman prepared all her things as well as herself, while the others just slept. When they snored heavily and slept the *sui sui* sleep, she rose and said to her brothers, "The people are sleeping the sleep of death, let us make ready!" So the two rose and went out, and she uncovered the mat-house and took all the necessary things and said, "Any noise that is made means that someone wants me to die." So all things were done in silence. Then with the two brothers, who stood ready to go, she went among the flock, leaving her husband just a cow, a sheep, and a goat. Then she instructed the cow, "Do not cry as though you were only one, if you do not desire my death." She spoke to the sheep and the goat in a like manner. Then they moved on with all the flock behind them. Now, the animals that had been left behind, cried out and cried out noisily in the night, as though all of them were still there, and Elephant thought all of them were really there. When he arose at daybreak, he saw his wife had left with everything, so he grabbed a stick and said to his mother, "If I fall, the earth will resound with a thud." And he pursued them.

When his wife and her brothers saw him coming close, they turned aside but could not penetrate a rock which barred the way. Thereupon the woman said, "We are people behind whom a big company of travellers is following, so, rock of my forefathers, spread out to both sides for us!" And the rock parted and then, when all had gone through, closed again.

Elephant, too, soon arrived and said to the rock, "Rock of my forefathers, cleave yourself for me too!" Then it spread itself and when he had entered, closed again. There Elephant died. The earth resounded with a thud. His mother at home said, "As it was predicted by my oldest son, so it has happened. The earth has just resounded with a thud."

[NAMA]

40

How Kwaku Ananse Got Aso in Marriage

THERE ONCE LIVED a certain man called Akwasi-the-Jealous-One, and his wife was Aso. He did not want anyone to see Aso or anyone to talk to her, so he went and built a small settlement for Aso to live in. No one ever went into that village.

Now he, Akwasi-the-Jealous-One, could not beget children. Because of that, if he and his wife lived in town, someone would take her away. Now the sky-god advised the young men, saying, "Akwasi-the-Jealous-One has been married to Aso for a very, very long time. She has not conceived by him and borne a child; therefore he who is able, let him go and take Aso and, should she conceive by him, let him take her as his wife." All the young men tried their best to lay hands on her, but not one was able.

Now Kwaku Ananse, the spider, was there watching these events and he said, "I can go to Akwasi-the-Jealous-One's village."

The sky-god said, "Can you really do so?"

Ananse said, "If you will give me what I require."

The sky-god said, "What kind of thing?" Ananse replied, "Medicine for gun and bullets." And the sky-god gave them to him.

Then Ananse took the powder and bullets to various small villages, saying, "The sky-god has bade me bring powder and bullets to you, and you are to go and kill meat, and on the day I shall return here I shall take it and depart." He distributed the powder and the bullets among very many small villages, until all were exhausted. All the villagers gave him some meat.

On a certain day Ananse wove a palm-leaf basket. Its length, as it were, was from here to over yonder. Ananse took it to the small villages where he had distributed the powder and bullets to receive all the meat which they had killed. Father Ananse took the meat and palm-leaf basket, set them on his head, and set out on the path leading to Akwasi-the-Jealous-One's settlement. When he reached the stream from which Akwasi and his wife drank, he picked out some meat and put it in the stream.

Ananse strode hard, carrying the palm-leaf basket full of meat, and passed through the main entrance leading into Akwasi-the-Jealous-One's compound. Aso saw him. She said, "Akwasi-e! Come and look at something which is coming to the house here. What can it be?"

Ananse said, "It is the sky-god who is sending me, and I am weary, and I am coming to sleep here."

Akwasi-the-Jealous-One said, "I have heard my lord's servant."

Aso said to Ananse, "Father man, some of your meat has fallen down at the main entrance to the compound."

The spider said, "Oh, if you happen to have a dog, let him go and take it and chew it." So Aso went and got it and gave it to her husband. Then Ananse said, "Mother, set some food on the fire for me." Aso put some on, and Ananse said, "Mother, is it *fufuo* that you are cooking or *eto?*"

Aso replied, "*Fufuo.*"

Ananse said, "Then it is too little; go and fetch a big pot."

Aso went and fetched a big one, and Ananse said, "Come and get meat." There were forty hindquarters of great beasts. He said, "Take only these and put them in the pot. If you had a pot big enough, I would give you enough meat to chew to make your teeth fall out."

Aso finished preparing the food, turned it out of the pot, and placed it on a table, splashed water, and put it beside the rest of the food. Then Aso took her portion and went and set it down near the fire, and the men went and sat down beside the table. They touched the backs of each other's hands and ate out of the same dish. All the time they were eating, Kwaku Ananse said, "There is no salt in this *fufuo.*"

Akwasi said to Aso, "Bring some."

But Ananse said, "Not at all. When the woman is eating, you tell her to get up to bring salt. Do you yourself go and bring it."

Akwasi arose from the table, and Ananse looked into his bag and took out a pinch of purgative medicine and put it in the *fufuo.* Then he called Akwasi, saying, "Come back for I have brought some with me."

When Akwasi came Ananse said, "Oh, I shall eat no more; I am full." Akwasi, who suspected nothing, continued eating.

When they had finished their meal, Akwasi said, "Friend, we and you are sitting here and yet we do not know your name."

Ananse replied, "I am called 'Rise-Up-and-Make-Love-to-Aso.'"

Akwasi said, "I have heard, and you, Aso, have you heard this man's name?"

Aso replied, "Yes, I have heard."

Akwasi rose up to go and prepare one of the spare bedrooms and to make everything comfortable. He said, "Rise-Up-and-Make-Love-to-Aso, this is your room, go and sleep there."

The spider said, "I am the soul-washer to the sky-god and I sleep in a open veranda-room. Since mother bore me and father begat me, I have never slept in a closed bedroom."

Akwasi said, "Where, then, will you sleep?"

He replied, "Were I to sleep in this open veranda-room here, to do so would be to make you equal to the sky-god, for it would mean that I was sleeping in the sky-god's open veranda room. Since I am never to sleep in anyone's open room except that of a sky-god, and since that is so, I shall just lie down in front of this closed sleeping-room where you repose."

The man took out a sleeping mat and laid it there for him. Akwasi and his wife went to rest, and Ananse, too, lay down there. Ananse lay there and he slipped in the crossbar of the bedroom door. Ananse lay there and took his musical bow and sang:

> "*Akuamoa Ananse, today we shall achieve something, today.*
> *Ananse, the child of Nsia, the mother of Nyame, the sky-god, today we shall achieve something, today.*
> *Ananse, the soul-washer to Nyame, the sky-god, today I shall see something.*"

Then he ceased playing his *sepirewa*, and he laid it aside and lay down. He had slept for some time when he heard Akwasi-the-Jealous-One calling, "Father man!" Not a sound in reply except the chirping of the cicada, *dinn!* "Father man!" Not a sound in reply except *dinn!* Akwasi-the-Jealous-One was dying. The medicine had taken effect on him, but he called, "Father man!" Not a sound in reply except *dinn!* At last he said, "Rise-Up-and-Make-Love-to-Aso!"

The spider said, "*M! M! M!*"

Akwasi said, "Open the door for me." Ananse opened the door, and Akwasi went out. And the spider rose up and went into the room there.

He said, "Aso, did you not hear what your husband said?"

She replied, "What did he say?"

Ananse replied, "He said I must rise up and make love to you."

Aso said, "You don't lie."

And he did it for her, and he went and lay down.

That night Akwasi rose up nine times. The spider also went nine times to where Aso was. When things became visible next morning, Ananse went off.

It would be about two moons later when Aso's belly became large. Akwasi questioned her, saying, "Why has your belly got like this? Perhaps you are ill, for you know that I who live with you here am unable to beget children." Aso replied, "You forget that man who came here whom you told to rise up and make love to Aso. Well, he took me and I have conceived by him."

Akwasi-the-Jealous-One said, "Rise up, and let me take you to go and give you to him." They went to the sky-god's town. On the way Aso gave birth. They reached the sky-god's town and Akwasi went and told the sky-god what had happened, saying, "A subject of yours whom you sent slept at my house and took Aso, and she has conceived by him."

The sky-god said, "All of my subjects are roofing the huts. Go and point out the one you mean." They went off, and the spider was sitting on a ridge-pole.

Aso said, "There he is!" Then Ananse ran farther on.

And again Aso said, "There he is!" Then Ananse fell down from up there where he was sitting.

Now that day was Friday. Ananse said, "I, who wash the sky-god's soul—you have taken your hand and pointed it at me, so that I have fallen down and got red earth on me." Immediately the attendants seized hold of Akwasi-the-Jealous-One and made him sacrifice a sheep. When Akwasi-the-Jealous-One had finished sacrificing the sheep, he said to the sky-god, "Here is the woman; let Ananse take her." So Ananse took Aso, but as for the infant, they killed it, cut it into pieces, and scattered them about.

That is how jealousy came among the tribe.

[ASHANTI]

III

The Realm of Man

41

The Young Man Who Was Carried Off by a Lion

A YOUNG MAN of the early race once ascended a hill in order to hunt. As he looked around for game, however, he became sleepy—so sleepy, in fact, that he decided to lie down. What had happened to him? he wondered, as he stretched himself out on the ground, near a waterhole. Never before had he been thus overcome by sleep.

As he slept, a lion, exhausted by the noonday heat, came to the pool to quench its thirst. The lion espied the man lying there asleep and seized him. Startled, the man awoke and, realizing that he had indeed been seized by a lion, he decided that it would be best not to stir, lest the lion bite and kill him. So he waited to see what the lion would do, for it was clear that the animal thought he was dead.

The lion carried him to a zwart-storm tree. There it laid him in the tree, in the lower branches however, and in such fashion that his legs protruded. Apparently the lion thought he would continue to be thirsty if he consumed the man's body immediately and that it would be better first to go down to the pool and drink some more water.

Before leaving, the lion pressed the man's head firmly between the branches of the zwart-storm tree.

No sooner had the lion left than the man moved his head ever so little. The lion noticed the movement, however, as he looked back, and was puzzled. How could the head move after it had been forced so firmly between the branches of the tree? Perhaps he had not fastened the man securely enough.

Just then the man fell over. So the lion returned and, once again, pushed the man's head into the middle of the branches of the zwart-storm tree. As he did so, tears came into the man's eyes and the lion licked them away.

The man lay there in pain, for a stick was pressing into the hollow at the back of his head. He faced the lion steadily with closed eyes and turned his head just a little. To the lion it seemed again as if the man had moved, and again he licked away the tears from the man's eyes. Puzzled, the lion trod once more upon the man's head and pressed it down in order to be certain that the head might have moved because the body had not been properly confined, and not from any other reason.

161

The man, now fearing that the lion suspected that he was not dead, remained absolutely motionless, in spite of the fact that the stick was cruelly piercing his head.

The lion, finally satisfied that the body was now firmly and properly secured, moved a few steps away. Then he looked back. The man opened his eyes ever so little and through his eyelashes watched what the lion was doing.

The lion then ascended the hill and was about to proceed down to the water on the other side.

The man, on his part, turned his head gently, in order to see if the lion had really departed. But, as he did so, he saw the lion peering from behind the top of the hill. He had come back to take one more look at the man, for he had suspected that the man might possibly be only feigning death. That is why he had reascended the hill to take one more look. Since, however, the man still lay there immobile, the lion thought he might quickly run to the waterhole, drink his fill, and return without delay to consume the body. The lion was hungry enough but also not a little thirsty.

All this time the man lay there quietly watching to see what the lion was going to do next. He saw its head and shoulders finally turn and disappear; but, before he made the slightest movement, he wanted to be absolutely certain that the lion had really gone and would not return to peer again over the hill. He knew that the lion is a thing of cunning and that the animal had been suspicious of the movement which his head had made.

The man lay there a long time without moving, and only when he was positive that the lion had truly gone did he arise and spring forward to a different place. But he did this circumspectly, running in a zigzag direction, so that the lion could not smell him out and know where he had gone. That is why he ran this way and that and did not run straight toward his own house. He knew that when the lion returned and missed him, he would immediately seek for him, following his spoor.

As soon as the man came to the top of the hill, he called out to his people that he had just been "lifted up"—while the sun had stood high, he had been "lifted up." More he would not say. They were therefore to gather together all the many hartebeest skins they possessed so that they might roll him in them, for he had just been "lifted up," while the sun had stood high. He wanted his people to do this, for he was certain that the lion, when it returned and missed him, would seek and track him out. It is the way of a lion, with anything it has killed, not to leave it until he has eaten it. So insistently the man besought his people to get the hartebeest skins and the mats and roll him up in them.

The people thereupon did this for the young man, for it was their hearts' young man who had made the request and they did not wish the lion to eat him. Accordingly, they hid him well, in such fashion as to prevent the lion from getting hold of him. Indeed, they loved this young man greatly and they announced that they would cover him over with the huts' sheltering bushes: all this they would do, to prevent the lion, when he arrived, from seizing their hearts' young man.

Everyone now went out to look for some *kuisse* and when they found some, they dug it up, took it home, and baked it.

At just about this time, an old Bushman, who had gone out to get some wood for his wife so that she might make a fire with which to cook the *kuisse*, espied the lion as he came over the top of the hill at the exact place where the young man had appeared. Immediately he told his house folk about it. Speaking, he said, "Do you see what it is that stands there yonder on the top of the hill, at the place where the young man came over?"

Thereupon the young man's mother, looking, exclaimed, "Not on any account must you permit that lion to come into our huts! You must shoot it and kill it before it ever comes that far!"

So the people slung on their quivers and went to meet the lion. Again and again they shot at him, but he would not die.

Then another woman addressed the people, saying, "In what manner are you shooting at this lion that you cannot manage to kill him?"

But one of the older men replied, "Can you not see that this lion must be a sorcerer? It will not die despite our shooting at it, for it insists upon having the young man that it carried off."

The people now threw children for the lion to eat, but the lion merely looked at them and left them alone.

Again and again the people shot at the lion but all to no avail. The lion remained unharmed and kept looking for the young man. After a while, some of the people said, "Bring us some *assegais*, so that we can spear it." So they began spearing it while others continued shooting. But, despite the shooting and the spearing, the lion remained unharmed and continued its search for the young man, for the young man whose tears it had licked. It wanted that man, none other.

Coming upon the huts, it tore them asunder and broke them to pieces, seeking for the young man. The people addressed one another in terror saying, "Do you not see that the lion will not eat the children we have thrown him? Can you not see that he must be a sorcerer?"

But some people answered, "Give the lion a girl. Perhaps it will eat her and then go away."

The lion, however, did not touch the girl. It wanted the young man it had carried off, none other.

Everyone was now completely bewildered, for no one knew in what manner to act toward the lion to persuade it to leave. It was late in the day and the people had been spearing and shooting at it since the morning; yet the lion remained unharmed and would not die. It kept walking about, searching for the young man.

"We no longer know what to do to induce it to leave," the people said.

"We have offered children and a young girl but the lion has always refused them. It desires only the young man it carried off."

Finally, in desperation, some of the people said, "Tell the young man's mother what is happening. Tell her that, despite her great love for the young man, she must take him and deliver him to the lion, even though he be the child of her heart. She herself must realize that the sun is about to set and that the lion is still threatening us, that it will not depart. It insists upon having the young man."

The mother heard and answered, "Be it so. Give my child to the lion. In no wise, however, must you allow the lion to eat him, in no wise must you allow the lion to continue walking about here. You must kill him and lay him upon my child. Let the lion die and lie upon my son."

When the young man's mother had thus spoken, the people unwrapped the young man from the hartebeest skins in which he had been rolled and gave him to the lion. The lion immediately seized him and bit him to death, but as he was thus biting him to death, the people shot and stabbed the lion.

Finally the lion spoke and said that he was ready to die, for now he had secured the man he had all the time been seeking; now he had got hold of him.

And so the lion died, and both the man and the lion lay there dead, next to each other.

[BUSHMEN]

42

How a Hunter Obtained Money from His Friends the Leopard, the Goat, the Bush Cat, and the Cock, and How He Got Out of Repaying Them

MANY YEARS AGO there was a Calabar hunter named Effiong who lived in the bush. He killed plenty of animals and made much money. Every one in the country knew him, and one of his best friends was a man called Okun, who lived near him.

Effiong was very extravagant and spent much money in eating and drinking with everyone until at last he became quite poor, and he had to go out hunting again. But now his good luck seemed to have deserted him, for although he worked hard and hunted day and night, he could not succeed in killing anything.

One day, as he was very hungry, he went to his friend Okun and borrowed two hundred rods from him. He told him to come to his house on a certain day to get his money, and he told him to bring his gun, loaded, with him.

Now sometime before this, Effiong had made friends with a leopard and a bush cat whom he had met in the forest while on one of his hunting expeditions; and he had also made friends with a goat and a cock at a farm where he had stayed for the night. But, though Effiong had borrowed the money from Okun, he could not think how he was to repay it on the day he had promised. At last, however, he thought of a plan. The next day he went to his friend the leopard and asked him to lend him two hundred rods, promising to return the amount to him on the same day as he had promised to pay Okun. He also told the leopard that, if he were absent when he came for his money, he could kill anything he saw in the house and eat it. The leopard was then to wait until the hunter arrived, when he would pay him the money. To this the leopard agreed.

The hunter then went to his friend the goat and borrowed two hundred rods from him in the same way. Effiong also went to his friends the bush cat and the cock and borrowed two hundred rods from each of them on the same conditions, and told each one of them that if he were absent when they arrived, they could kill and eat anything they found about the place.

When the appointed day arrived, the hunter spread some corn on the ground, and then went away and left the house deserted. Very early in the morning, soon after he had begun to crow, the cock remembered what the hunter had told him and he walked over to the hunter's house but found no one there. On looking around, however, he saw some corn on the ground and, being hungry, he commenced to eat.

About this time the bush cat also arrived, and not finding the hunter at home, he too looked about and very soon he espied the cock who was busy picking up the grains of corn. So the bush cat went up very softly behind and pounced on the cock and killed him at once, and began to eat him.

By this time the goat had come for his money; but not finding his friend, he walked about until he came upon the bush cat who was so intent upon his meal off the cock that he did not notice the goat approaching; and the goat, being in rather a bad temper at not getting his money, at once charged at the bush cat and knocked him over, butting him with his horns. This the bush cat did not like at all, so, as he was not big enough to fight the goat, he picked up the remains of the cock and ran off with it to the bush; and so he lost his money, as he did not await the arrival of the hunter. The goat was thus left master of the situation and started bleating. This noise attracted the attention of the leopard, who was on his way to receive payment from the hunter. As he got nearer, the smell of goat became very strong and, being hungry, for he had not eaten anything for some time, he approached the goat very carefully. Not seeing anyone about, he stalked the goat and got nearer and nearer until he was within springing distance.

The goat, in the meantime, was quietly grazing, quite unsuspicious of any danger, as he was in the compound of his friend the hunter. Now and then he would say "Ba!" But most of the time he was busy eating the young grass and picking up the leaves which had fallen from a tree of which he was very fond. Suddenly the leopard sprang at the goat and, with one crunch at the neck, brought him down. The goat was dead almost at once, and the leopard started on his meal.

It was now about eight o'clock in the morning, and Okun, the hunter's friend, having had his early morning meal, went out with his gun to receive payment of the two hundred rods he had lent to the hunter. When he got close to the house he heard a crunching sound. Being a hunter himself, he approached very cautiously and, looking over the fence, he saw the leopard only a few yards off busily engaged eating the goat. He took careful aim at the leopard and fired, whereupon the leopard rolled over dead.

The death of the leopard meant that four of the hunter's creditors were now disposed of, as the bush cat had killed the cock; the goat had driven the bush cat away, who thus forfeited his claim; and in his turn the goat had been killed by the leopard, who had just been slain by Okun. This meant a saving of eight hundred rods to Effiong, but he was not content with this. As soon as he heard the report of the gun he ran out from where he had been hiding all the time and found the leopard lying dead with Okun standing over it. Then in very strong language Effiong began to upbraid Okun and asked him why he had killed his old friend the leopard. He said that nothing would satisfy him and that he would report the whole matter to the king, who would no doubt deal with Okun as he thought fit. When Effiong said this, Okun was frightened and begged him not to say anything more about the matter, as the king would be angry; but the hunter was obdurate and refused to listen to him. At last Okun said, "If you will allow the whole thing to drop and will say no more about it, I will make you a present of the two hundred rods you borrowed from me." This was just what Effiong wanted; but still he did not give in at once. Eventually, however, he agreed and told Okun he might go and that he would bury the body of his friend the leopard.

Directly Okun had gone, instead of burying the body, Effiong dragged it inside the house and skinned it very carefully. The skin he put out to dry in the sun and covered it with wood ash, and the body he ate. When the skin was well cured, the hunter took it to a distant market where he sold it for much money.

And now, whenever a bush cat sees a cock he always kills it and does so by right, as he takes the cock in part payment of the two hundred rods which the hunter never paid him.

Moral: Never lend money to people, because if they cannot pay they will try to kill you or get rid of you in some way, either by poison or by setting bad *jujus* for you.

[EFIK-IBIBIO]

43

The Little Wise Woman

A GIRL, it is said, once went to seek for onions. As she arrived at the place where they grew, she met several men, one of whom was half-blind, having only one eye. As she dug, the men helped her, digging also. When her sack was full, the men said to her, "Go, tell the other girls, that many of you may come." So she went home and told her companions, and early the next morning they started. But a little girl followed them. The other girls said, "Let the little girl go back."

Her elder sister protested, saying, "She runs by herself; you need not put her into your *awa* skin."

So they all went on together and, having reached the onion field, began to dig. Now the little girl saw traces of feet, and she said to the one who had guided them thither, "Wonderful! Whence so many traces? Were you not alone here?"

The other replied, "I walked about and looked around; therefore there must be many of my footprints."

The child, however, did not believe that if the other girl had been alone the traces could be many, and she felt uneasy, for she was a wise little woman. From time to time she rose from her work and peeped about and once, while doing this, found by chance an anteater's hole.

Still further spying about, she perceived some men, but they did not see her. She then returned and continued digging with the other girls, without, however, saying anything; but in the midst of the work, she always rose and looked about her.

So the others asked her, "Why do you always spy about you and leave off digging? What a girl!" But she continued her work in silence. When she rose from it again, she saw the men approaching. As they drew near, the one-eyed man blew through a reed pipe the following:

"Today blood shall flow, blood flow, blood flow!"

The little girl understood what was blown on the reed. She said to the elder ones, while they were dancing, "Do you understand the tune that is blown on the reed?"

But they only said, "What a child she is!"

So she mixed in the dance with the others, but managed while so doing to tie her sister's *kaross* to her own. In this manner they danced until the merriment became very noisy. Then the two sisters found an opportunity to slip away.

On their way out the little sister asked, "Do you understand the reed—I mean what is blown on it?"

The elder one answered, "No, I do not understand it."

Then the little girl explained to her that the tune on the reed said, "Today blood shall flow!"

While they walked along, the little girl let her elder sister go first and she herself followed, walking backwards and carefully stepping in her sister's marks, so that thus they left only one set of footprints, and these going in a contrary direction. In this manner they arrived at the anteater's hole.

The men killed all those girls who had remained dancing with them. When the elder of the two who had escaped heard their wailing, she said, "Alas, my sisters!"

But the younger one answered her, "Do you think you would have lived if you had remained there?"

Now the one-eyed man was the first to miss the sisters, and he said to the other men, "Where may the two handsome girls be who danced with me?"

The others replied, "He lies. He has seen only with his single eye." But the one-eyed man insisted that two girls were truly missing.

Then they went to find their tracks, but the footmarks had been rendered indistinct enough to puzzle them.

However, the men finally arrived at the anteater's hole. They could not see that the footmarks went farther, and they peered into the hole but saw nothing. Then the one-eyed man looked also, and he saw the girls and cried, "There they sit!"

The others now looked again, but still saw nothing, for the girls had covered themselves with cobwebs.

One of the men then took an assegai and, piercing through the upper part of the hole, hit the heel of the older girl. The wise little woman took hold of the assegai, however, and wiped off the blood. The elder sister was about to cry, but the little one warned her not to make a sound.

When the one-eyed one spied again the little girl made big eyes at him. He said, "There she sits."

The others looked too, but as they could see nothing they said, "He has only seen with his one eye."

At last the men became thirsty and said to the one-eyed one, "Stay you here and let us go to drink, and when we have returned you may go also."

When the one-eyed man was left alone there, the little girl said, conjuring him:

> *"You dirty son of your father,*
> *Are you there? Are you alone not thirsty?*
> *Oh, you dirty child of your father!*
> *Dirty son of your father!"*

"I am indeed thirsty," said the one-eyed one and went away.

Then the two girls came out of the hole, and the younger one took her elder sister on her back and walked on. As they were going over the bare, treeless plain, the men saw them and said, "There they are, far off," and ran after them.

When they came near, the two girls turned themselves into thorn trees, called "Wait-a-bit," and the beads which they wore became gum on the trees. The men then ate of the gum and fell asleep. While they slept, the girls smeared gum over the men's eyes and went away, leaving them lying in the sun.

The girls were already near their kraal, when the one-eyed man awoke and said, "Oh, the disgrace! Fie on thee!"

"Our eyes are smeared over; fie on thee, my brother!" said the others.

Then they removed the gum from their eyes, and hunted for the girls, but the two sisters reached home in safety and told their parents what had happened.

Then all the people lamented greatly, but they remained quietly at home and did not search for the other girls.

[HOTTENTOT]

44

Zimwa-mbanje the Hemp Smoker

THERE ONCE LIVED a man named Zimwa-mbanje, the hemp smoker. One year there was a severe drought, and the hemp did not grow. He said to his children, "What am I to do? I have no hemp."

They answered, "If you wish it, send us that we may search for some."

Thereupon he sent his eight sons and three daughters, and said, "If you secure hemp, leave the girls with the man from whom you get it."

They walked for a long time, nearly two months, but they did not find hemp. They said to each other, "As we have not found that which we seek, it is best that we return."

On their return they met two men, wanderers, who asked them what they sought. "We seek hemp. We were sent by our father who is in great need of it, and we fear he will be dead by now."

The wanderers replied, "Very well. Come with us, and we will take you to a man who has lots of it."

Thus they travelled together, and when they arrived at one man's village they met his son, who asked, "What do you seek?"

They replied, "Hemp."

"Only hemp?" he asked.

"Yes, indeed," they replied.

"If it should be offered to you, what would you give for it?" he asked further.

They answered, "Father said to us if you find a man with hemp, leave all the girls with him."

The man who owned the hemp, and who was also named Zimwa-mbanje, rejoiced when he heard this and killed a goat for them. The next morning he filled eight bags with hemp and gave them to Zimwa-mbanje's sons. He also sent his four sons and two daughters, and said to his sons, "When you come to the man who desires the hemp and find that his village is a pleasant place, leave the two girls with him."

When Zimwa-mbanje's eight sons returned with the hemp, he rejoiced and praised them for what they had done and killed a goat for them. They said, "The man from whom we got the hemp has also sent his four sons and two daughters to see your abode and whether it is a pleasant place."

He replied, "It is well."

The next morning the four sons returned to their home and left their two sisters at Zimwa-mbanje's village.

The two families thereafter became friends and visited each other.

Some time later, Zimwa-mbanje said, "I am old. Take me to my friend that I may see him before I die." To this his children agreed. They went ahead, and he followed, until they arrived at Zimwa-mbanje's village.

When Zimwa-mbanje heard the greetings and the clapping of hands, he asked, "Whom is it you greet?"

One of his sons said, "It is the father of the girls who were left here—he who sought hemp."

He answered, "I am ashamed to meet him, as I married his daughters before I met him. Go and tell him that his friend Zimwa-mbanje is ill." The sons went and told the man as they were desired to do by their father.

Thereupon the eldest son of the other said, "My father is also ill. I brought him, as he wished to see his friend who supplied him with hemp. You say he is ill, therefore both are ill."

The son of the other replied, "It is as you say. Enter the hut. We shall see tomorrow."

They prepared food and, when they were about to take it to the visitors, there suddenly arose shouting and wailing, and the people of the village cried out, "Father is dead."

Thereupon the visitors also set up a wailing and shouting, crying, "Father is dead. He died at the village which was not his home."

Then all the people said, "We shall see tomorrow when we bury them."

The next morning the people of the village said to the visitors, "It is day-break. Go and choose a spot where you may bury your father; we shall do likewise for our father."

But the sons of him who came on the visit replied, "Speak not thus. Let them be buried together, because they had become friends."

Those of the village answered, "Have people ever been buried together?"

The visitors said, "You say people are not buried together. Have you known of a case where one man went to visit his friend and it was said 'He is dead,' and that the other also died, thus both dying at the same time? Where did you ever see this?"

Thereupon they agreed to bury the bodies together.

They dug a deep grave for the two and carried the bodies thither. First they lowered into the grave the body of the man of the village and then that of the visitor. They then called out, "Bring stones that we may fill up the grave."

When they were about to throw in the stones, the man who was lowered first called out, "I am not dead, take me out, and do not cover me with stones." Then the body of the visitor said, "I am on top, I want to get out first."

Thus both came out.

They went and killed a goat of which all ate. Then the old men called their sons together and said to them, "We wish to instruct you, our children. Do not do this: do not marry a girl before you ask her in marriage of her father."

Then the old man of the village, whose name was Zimwa-mbanje, said to his sons, "I thought I would be clever. I did not wish to see the man whose daughters I had married without telling him. Therefore I said I was sick, hoping he would go home."

Thus the custom arose that when a man desires to marry, he first informs the girl's father of what he desires to do, for at the beginning this was not done.

[MASHONA]

45

Konyek and His Father

A BIG DANCE was once held at which many warriors and girls were present. Toward evening the dancers dispersed, and each warrior selected one or more of the girls to accompany him home.

One of these men, a particularly handsome and well-built fellow, went away with three sisters. On leaving, he asked the girls where they would like to go, and they told him they wished to accompany him to his kraal. He said that it was a long way off, but they replied that that did not matter.

They started off, and after walking some distance, they approached the kraal. The girls noticed some white things scattered about on the ground and asked the warrior what they were. He said that they were his sheep and goats; but when they reached their destination, the girls saw that they were human bones. They entered the warrior's hut, and the girls were surprised to find that he lived quite alone.

It transpired later that this warrior was in reality a devil who ate people, but it was not known because he concealed his tail under his garment. He had even eaten his mother and had thrown her bones into a heap of grass which formed the bed.

Shortly after their arrival at the hut, the warrior went outside, leaving the girls alone. A voice, which came from the bed, startled them by asking them who had brought them there. They replied that the warrior had brought them, whereupon the voice told them to open the mattress. The girls threw off the top layer of grass, exposing the bones to view. The voice, which came from the bones, then related that she had been the warrior's mother and that he had become a demon and had eaten her. The girls asked the bones what they should do, and the voice answered, "The warrior will come presently and bring you a sheep. Accept it. He will then go outside again and, having shut the door, sit down there. Make a hole in the wall and pass out. If you are asked what the knocking is, say that you are killing the sheep."

Everything took place as the voice had predicted, and the girls made a hole in the wall of the hut through which they passed and escaped. When they reached the road, however, one of them suddenly remembered that she had left her beads behind. Her sisters told her to go and fetch them while they waited for her. She returned to the hut but met the warrior, who asked her if he should eat her or make her his wife. She thanked him for giving her the choice and said that she preferred the latter.

They lived together for a considerable period and, after a time, the woman presented the demon with a son, whom they named Konyek. From the day of his birth Konyek accompanied his father on his journeys to the forest in quest of people to devour; and, while the man and the boy ate human beings, they took home with them for the woman goats and sheep to eat and cows to milk.

One day one of the woman's sisters came to the kraal to visit her. As Konyek and his father were both absent when she arrived, the two women sat and talked until it was time for the visitor to depart. The weather looked threatening as she rose to take her leave, and Konyek's mother cried out to her not to go to the tree in the middle of the plain, should it rain, for it was the custom of her husband and son to rest there on their way home. But the woman hurried away without paying attention to her sister's warning, and when it came on to rain a little later, she ran to the tree in the middle of the plain, which was a baobab tree, and climbed up into it. She had not been there long when Konyek and his father arrived and stood beneath the tree to get shelter from the rain. Their appearance recalled to the woman her sister's words and she was greatly alarmed.

Konyek gazed up into the tree and remarked that there was something peculiar about it, but his father said it was only because it was raining hard. Shortly afterward, however, Konyek saw the woman and called out, "There is my meat." The woman was forced to descend, and she gave birth to twins.

Konyek picked up the children and said, "I will take these kidneys to mother to roast for me."

When it stopped raining, the two returned home and Konyek asked his mother to roast his kidneys for him. But the woman knew at once that her sister had been put to death, and she hid the children in a hole in the earth, roasting instead two rats. When they were ready, Konyek went to the fire, picked them up off the stones and ate them, grumbling at the same time because they were so small. His mother pretended to be very annoyed at this and, turning to her husband, complained of what their son had said. The old man told her not to mind the boy as he was a liar.

The woman fed and tended the children, who were both boys, and gradually they grew up. One day she asked her husband to bring her an ox which, she said, she wished to slaughter and eat. Konyek on hearing this request at once pricked up his ears and remarked, "It really amuses me to hear of a woman who wants to eat an ox all by herself. I think those kidneys of mine have something to do with this matter." However, the two men searched for an ox which they procured and brought back with them. They slaughtered the animal and left the meat with the woman, after which they went for a walk in the forest.

As soon as they had departed, the woman let the children out of their hole and gave them the ox to eat. They ate until sunset, when she sent them back again to their hiding place.

Konyek and his father returned shortly afterward, and the former, being very sharp, at once noticed the small footmarks on the ground. "I wonder," he said, "what those small and numerous footmarks are. They are certainly not mine." His mother, however, stoutly insisted that the marks had been made by herself or by the two men, and in this she received her husband's support. Being annoyed with Konyek on account of the way he treated his mother, the old man killed him and ate him. But he immediately came to life again and cried out, "There, I have come back again."

As time passed, the children grew up, and their aunt asked them one day if they knew that the people who lived in the same kraal with them were in reality demons and cannibals. She also inquired if, in the event of her being able to obtain weapons from her husband, they could put Konyek and his father to death. The boys replied that they could, but asked the woman what she would say if her husband wanted to know why she required the weapons. She told them that she would say she wanted them to protect herself against any enemies who might come.

When Konyek and his father next returned home, the woman asked her husband if he would procure two spears, two shields, and two swords for her. "For I am always here alone," she said, "and if enemies come, I wish to be able to fight with them." Konyek remarked that he had never before heard of a woman who wanted men's weapons and said he thought that those kidneys, which he had brought to his mother to roast for him, must have something to do with this request. Notwithstanding Konyek's protest, the old man obtained for his wife the weapons that she required. When he had given them to her, she fetched an oxhide, and asked the two men to lie down on the ground while she stretched the hide over them and pegged it down. She told them that when she was ready she would cry out and would see if the enemy came, in which case they could assist her. She pegged the oxhide down securely and asked them if they could get out. Konyek found a hole and began to crawl out, but his mother told him to get in again, and she pegged it down once more. She then raised her voice and called to the children, who came from their hiding place and killed Konyek and his father.

As Konyek was dying, he said to his parent, "Did I not tell you so, and you said I lied?"

The boys, after killing the two devils, took their aunt away to their father's kraal.

[M A S A I]

46

The Lost Sister

ONCE UPON A TIME there were a brother and sister who lived together. The mother had died leaving many goats, and the brother looked after the goats in the daytime, but in the evening he went away from home, for he was very handsome, and had many friends. The name of the girl was Wachera, the name of the brother Wam'wea.

Now one day when the brother returned Wachera said to him, "Two men were here yesterday, and if you go away and leave me they will carry me off." But he replied, "You talk nonsense." She insisted, "I am speaking the truth. Now when they take me I will bear with me a gourd full of sap which is like fat, and I will let it drop along the path so that you can follow my trail." That night when Wam'wea brought the goats home, Wachera made a great feast and gruel, but again he went away. When Wam'wea came back the next morning he found the homestead empty, for his sister had been carried away as she had said. However, he saw the track where drop by drop she had let fall the sap which was like fat. And Wam'wea followed over hill and down dale, and ever and again he heard her voice crying from the opposite hillside, "Follow after where you see the trail."

The following day the sap began to take root and to spring up into little plants, but he did not see his sister. At last, he returned to his home to herd the flock. He took them out to feed, but he had no one to prepare food for him when he returned home at night, and if he himself prepared the food there was no one to care for the flocks. So he slew a goat and ate it and, when it was finished, he slew yet another, and so on till all the goats were finished. Then he killed and ate the oxen one by one. They lasted him months and years for the flock was large but, at last they were all gone, and then he bethought him of his sister.

Now the plants which marked the way she had gone were, by this time, grown to trees, and so he journeyed on for one month and half a month and at the end of that time he came to a stream and by the stream were two children getting water. Then he said to the younger, "Give me some water in your gourd," but the child refused. The elder child spoke to the younger and said, "Give the stranger to drink, for our mother said if ever you see a stranger coming by the way of the trees he is my brother!" So he and the children went up to the homestead, and he waited outside, and Wachera came out, and he knew her at once. However, she did not know him, for he was not dressed as before with ochre and fat. He came into her hut and she gave him food, not in a good vessel, but in a potsherd. Then he slept in the hut, but on the floor, not in the bed.

Now the next day he went out with the children to drive away the birds from the crops and as he threw a stone he would say, "Fly away, little bird, as Wachera flew away and never came back any more." Soon another bird would come and he would throw another stone and say the same words again. This happened the next day and the next for a whole month.

The children heard this, and so did others, and they said, "Why does he utter the name Wachera?" So they went and told their mother. At last she came and waited among the grass and listened to his words, and said, "Surely this is my brother Wam'wea," and she went back to the house and sent for a young man and told him to go and fetch Wam'wea to come to her, for she said, "He is my brother." And the young man went and told Wam'wea the words of his sister. But he refused, for he said, "I have dwelt in the abode of my sister, and she has given me no cup for my food but a potsherd," and he would not go in. Then the young man returned to Wachera and told her the words of her brother, and she said, "Take ten goats and go again and bid him to come to me." So the young man took ten goats and said, "Your sister has sent these ten goats." But again Wam'wea refused, and the young man returned. So Wachera said, "Take ten oxen and give them to my brother." However, Wam'wea would not come. Wachera then sent him ten cows, and another ten cows, but still Wam'wea refused to come in. Wachera thereupon told her husband how she had found her brother and how he would not be reconciled to her, and her husband said, "Send him still more animals," so Wachera sent ten other cows and again ten more, till Wam'wea had received forty cows besides the goats and the oxen which Wachera had sent at the first. And the heart of Wam'wea relented, and he came into the house of his sister. And she killed a goat, and took the fat and dressed his hair and his shoulders, for she said, "I did not know you, for you were not adorned as before."

After Wam'wea had been reconciled to his sister, he asked that eight wives should be given him. So the husband of Wachera sent to all his relations round about, and they brought in goats, and Wam'wea bought eight girls, some for thirty goats, some for forty. Other relations all came and built eight huts for the wives near to the dwelling of Wachera, so Wam'wea and his wives dwelt near the homestead of his sister.

[AKIKUYU]

47

The Woman and the Children of the Sycamore Tree

THERE WAS ONCE a woman who had no husband, and she lived for many days in trouble. One day she said to herself, "Why do I always feel so troubled? It is because I have neither children nor husband. I shall go to the medicine-man and get some children."

She went to the medicine-man and told him she was unhappy owing to the fact that although she had now grown old, she had neither husband nor children. The medicine-man asked her which she wanted, husband or children, and she told him she wanted children.

She was instructed to take some cooking pots—three, or as many as she could carry—and to search for a fruit-bearing sycamore, to fill the pots with the fruit, to put them in her hut, and to go for a walk.

The woman followed these instructions carefully. She gathered the fruit, filled the pots, placed them in her hut, and went for a walk until the evening.

On arriving near the kraal, she heard the sound of voices and asked herself, "Why does one hear the voices of children in the kraal?" She went nearer, and found her hut filled with children, all her work finished, the boys herding the cattle, the hut swept clean by the girls, the warriors singing and dancing on the common, and the little children waiting to greet her. She thus became a rich woman, and lived happily with her children for many days.

One day, however, she scolded the children, and reproached them for being children of the tree. They remained silent and did not speak to her; then, while she went to visit her friends in the other kraals, the children returned to the sycamore tree, and became fruit again. On her return to her own kraal, the woman wept bitterly when she found it empty, and paid another visit to the medicine-man, whom she taxed with having spirited away her children.

The medicine-man told her that he did not know what she should do now, and when she proposed to go and look at the sycamore tree, he recommended her to try.

She took her cooking pots to the tree and climbed up into it. But when she reached the fruit they all put forth eyes and stared at her. This so startled her that she was unable to descend, and her friends had to come and help her down.

She did not go to the tree again to search for her children.

[MASAI]

48

The Girl Who Stayed in the Fork of a Tree

THIS IS WHAT A WOMAN DID. She was then living in the bush, never showing herself to anyone. She had living with her just one daughter, who used to pass the day in the fork of a tree making baskets.

One day there appeared a man just when the mother had gone to kill game. He found the girl making baskets as usual. "Here now!" he said. "There are people here in the bush! And that girl, what a beauty! Yet they leave her alone. If the king were to marry her, would not all the other queens leave the place?"

Going back to the town, he went straight to the king's house and said, "Sire, I have discovered a woman of such beauty that, if you call her to this place, all the queens you have here will make haste to go away."

The following morning people were called together and set to grind their axes. Then they started for the bush. As they came in view of the place, they found the mother had once more gone to hunt.

Before going, she had cooked porridge for her daughter and hung meat for her. Then only had she started on her expedition.

The people said, "Let us cut down the tree on which the girl is."

So they put the axes to it. The girl at once started this song:

> "Mother, come back!
> Mother, here is a man cutting our shade tree.
> Mother, come back!
> Mother, here is a man cutting our shade tree.
> Cut! Here is the tree falling in which I eat.
> Here it is falling."

The mother dropped there as if from the sky:

> "Many as you are, I shall stitch you
> with the big needle.
> Stitch! Stitch!"

They at once fell to the ground. . . . The woman left just one to go back and report.

"Go," she said, "and tell the news." He went. . . .

When he came to the town the people asked, "What has happened?"

"There," he said, "where we have been! Things are rather bad!"

Likewise, when he stood before the king, the king asked, "What has happened?"

"Sire," he said, "we are all undone. I alone have come back."

"*Bakoo!* You are all dead! If that is so, tomorrow go to the kraal over there and bring more people. Tomorrow morning let them go and bring me the woman."

They slept their fill.

The next morning early, the men ground their axes and went to the place.

They, too, found the mother gone, while the porridge was ready there, and the meat was hanging on the tree. . . .

"Bring the axes." Forthwith they went at the shade tree. But the song had already started:

> "*Mother, come back!*
> *Mother, here is a man cutting our shade tree.*
> *Mother, come back!*
> *Mother, here is a man cutting our shade tree.*
> *Cut! Here is the tree falling in which I eat.*
> *Here it is falling.*"

The mother dropped down among them, singing in her turn:

> "*Many as you are, I shall stitch you*
> *with the big needle.*
> *Stitch! Stitch!*"

They were dead. The woman and her daughter picked up the axes. . . .

"*Olo!*" said the king when he was told. "Today let all those that are pregnant give birth to their children."

So one woman after another straightway brought forth her child. Soon there was a whole row of them.

Then the whole band departed, making a confused noise.

When the girl saw that, she said, "There is no joke about it now. There comes a red army with the umbilical cords still hanging on."

They found her at her own place in the fork of the tree.

"Let us give them some porridge," thought the girl.

She just plastered the porridge on their heads, but the children did not eat it.

The last-born then climbed up the shade tree, picked up the baskets which the girl was stitching, and said, "Now bring me an axe."

The girl shouted once more:

> "*Mother, come back!*
> *Mother, here is a man cutting our shade tree.*

Mother, come back!
Mother, here is a man cutting our shade tree.
Cut! Here is the tree falling in which I eat.
Here it is falling."

The mother dropped down among the crowd:

> *"Many as you are, I shall stitch you*
> > *with the big needle.*
> *Stitch! Stitch!"*

But there was the troop already dragging the girl. They had tied her with their umbilical cords, yes, with their umbilical cords. The mother went on with her incantation:

> *"Many as you are, I shall stitch you*
> > *with the big needle.*
> *Stitch! Stitch!"*

In vain! The troop was already in the fields and the *ngururu* went up as far as God's abode, and soon the children were in the town.

As they reached it, the mother said, "Since you have carried away my child, I must tell you something. She is not to pound in the mortar, nor to go to fetch water at night. If you send her to do one of these things, mind you! I shall know where to find you."

Then the mother went back to her abode in the bush.

The following day the king said, "Let us go hunting." And to his mother he said, "My wife must not pound in the mortar. All that she can do is to stitch baskets."

While the husband was away there in the open flat, the other wives as well as the mother-in-law said, "Why should not she also pound in the mortar?"

When the girl was told to pound in the mortar, she said, "No."

A basket of kafir corn was brought to her.

The mother-in-law herself took away the meal from the mortar, and then the other women in their turn brought corn and put it all there.

So the girl pounded, singing at the same time:

> *"Pound! At home I do not pound,*
> *Here I pound to celebrate my wedding.*
> > *Yepu! Yepu!*
> *If I pound, I go to God's."*

She began to sink into the ground but she went on singing:

> *"Pound! At home I do not pound,*
> *Here I pound to celebrate my wedding.*
> > *Yepu! Yepu!*
> *If I pound, I go to God's."*

She was now in the ground as far as her hips, then as far as her chest.

> *"Pound! At home I do not pound,*
> *Here I pound to celebrate my wedding.*
> *Yepu! Yepu!*
> *If I pound, I go to God's."*

Soon she was down as far as her neck. Now the mortar went on by itself pounding the grain on the ground, pounding on the ground. Finally the girl disappeared altogether.

When nothing more was seen of her, the mortar still pounded as before on the ground.

The women then said, "Now what shall we do?"

They went and called a crane, and said, "Go and break the news to her mother. But, first, let us know, what will you say?"

The crane said, "*Wawani! Wawani!*"

They said, "That has no meaning, go back. Let us send for the crow."

The crow was called, "Now what will you say?"

The crow said, "*Kwa! Kwa! Kwa!*"

"The crow does not know how to call. Go, quail. How will you do?"

The quail said, "*Kwalulu! Kwalulu!*"

"The quail does not know how to do it either. Let us call the doves."

They said, "Let us hear, doves, what will you call to her mother?"

Then they heard:

> *"Kuku! Ku!*
> *She-who-nurses-the-sun is gone,*
> *She-who-nurses-the-sun.*
> *You who dig,*
> *She-who-nurses-the-sun is gone,*
> *She-who-nurses-the-sun."*

They said, "Go, you know how to do it, you."

The mother went when she heard the doves. There she was going toward the town. She carried medicines on a potsherd, also tails of animals with which she beat the air.

While she was on the road, she met a zebra:

> *"Zebra, what are you doing?*
>   —Nsenkenene.
> *The wife of my father is dead.*
>   —Nsenkenene.
> *O mother! You shall die.*
>   —Nsenkenene."*

The zebra died. The woman went on, went on, went on, and then found people digging:

"You who dig, what are you doing?
> —Nsenkenene.
The wife of my father is dead.
> —Nsenkenene.
O mother! You shall die.
> —Nsenkenene."*

They also died. The woman went on and went on, then she found a man beating a skin:

"You who beat, what are you doing?
> —Nsenkenene.
The wife of my father is dead.
> —Nsenkenene.
O mother! You shall die.
> —Nsenkenene."*

When she reached the town there:

> *"Let me gather, let me gather*
> *The herd of my mother.*
> *Mwinsa, get up.*
> *Let me gather the herd.*

> *"Let me gather, let me gather*
> *The herd of my father.*
> *Mwinsa, get up.*
> *Let me gather the herd."*

She then heard the mortar still sounding right above the child.
So she sprayed one medicine, then another.
There was the child already pounding from under the ground. Little by little the head came out. Then the neck, and the song was heard again:

> *"Pound! At home I do not pound,*
> *Here I pound to celebrate my wedding.*
>> Yepu! Yepu!
> *If I pound, I go to God's."*

The child was now in full view. Finally she stepped outside.
I have finished.

[BENA MUKUNI]

49

How an Unborn Child Avenged Its Mother's Death

A MAN HAD TAKEN a wife, and now she had the joy of being with child, but famine was acute in the land.

One day, when hunger was particularly severe, the man, accompanied by his wife, was dragging himself along in the direction of her mother's home in the hope of getting a little food there. He happened to find on the road a tree with abundant wild fruit on the top. "Wife," he said, "get up there that we may eat fruit."

The woman refused, saying, "I, who am with child, to climb up a tree!"

He said, "In that case, do not climb at all."

The husband then climbed up himself and shook and shook the branches, the woman meanwhile picking up what fell down. He said, "Do not pick up my fruit. What! Just now you refused to go up!"

And she: "*Bana!* I am only picking them up."

Thinking about his fruit, he hurried down from the top of the tree and said, "You have eaten some."

And she: "Why! Of course, I have not."

Then, assegai in hand, he stabbed his wife. And there she died on the spot.

He then gathered up his fruit with both hands. There he sat eating it, remaining where the woman was stretched out quite flat.

All of a sudden he started running. Run! Run! Run! Without stopping once, he ran until he reached the rise of a hill.

There he slept, out of sight of the place where he had left the woman.

Meanwhile the child that was in the womb rushed out of it, dragging its umbilical cord. First, it looked round for the direction which its father had taken, then it started this song:

> "*Father, wait for me,*
> *Father, wait for me,*
> *The little wombless.*
> *Who is it that has eaten my mother?*
> *The little wombless . . . !*
> *How swollen are those eyes!*
> *Wait till the little wombless comes.*"

186

That gave the man a shake. . . . "There," he said, "there comes the thing which is speaking." He listened, he stared in that direction. . . . "This is the child coming to follow me after all that, when I have already killed its mother. It had been left in the womb."

Then rage took his wits away, and he killed the little child! . . . There he was, making a fresh start, and going on. Here, where the little bone had been left: "Little bone, gather yourself up! . . . Little bone, gather yourself up."

Soon it was up again, and then came the song:

"Father, wait for me,
Father, wait for me,
The little wombless.
Who is it that has eaten my mother?
The little wombless . . . !
How swollen are those eyes!
Wait till the little wombless comes."

The father stopped. . . . "Again the child that I have killed! It has risen and is coming. Now I shall wait for him."

So he hid and waited for the child, with an assegai in his hand. The child came and made itself visible at a distance as from here to there. As soon as it came, quick with the assegai! He stabbed it! Then he looked for a hole, shovelled the little body into it, and heaped branches up at the entrance.

Then with all speed he ran! With all speed! . . .

At last he reached the kraal, where the mother of his dead wife lived, the grandmother of the child.

When he came he sat down. Then his brothers and sisters-in-law come with smiling faces. . . . "Well! Well! You have put in an appearance!"

"We have," he says, "put in an appearance."

And a hut was prepared for him and his wife, who was expected.

Then the mother-in-law was heard asking from afar, "Well! And my daughter, where has she been detained?"

Said he, "I have left her at home. I have come alone to beg for a little food. Hunger is roaring."

"Sit down inside there, father."

Food was procured for him. So he began to eat. And, when he had finished, he even went to sleep.

Meanwhile, the child, on its part, had squeezed itself out of the hole wherein it had been put and, again, with its umbilical cord hanging on:

"Father, wait for me,
Father, wait for me,
The little wombless.
Who is it that has eaten my mother?
The little wombless . . . !

How swollen are those eyes!
Wait till the little wombless comes."

The people listened in the direction of the path. . . . "That thing which comes speaking indistinctly, what is it? . . . It seems to be a person. . . . What is it? . . . It looks, man, like a child killed by you on the road. . . . And now, when we look at your way of sitting, you seem to be only half-seated."

"We do not see him distinctly. . . . It cannot be the child, Mother; it remained at home."

The man had just got up to shake himself a little. And his little child, too, was coming with all speed! It was already near, with its mouth wide open:

> *"Father, wait for me,*
> *Father, wait for me,*
> *The little wombless.*
> *Who is it that has eaten my mother?*
> *The little wombless . . . !*
> *How swollen are those eyes!*
> *Wait till the little wombless comes!"*

Everyone was staring. They said, "There comes a little red thing. It still has the umbilical cord hanging on."

Inside of the hut there, where the man stood, there was complete silence!

Meanwhile the child was coming on feet and buttocks with its mouth wide open, but still at a distance from its grandmother's hut. "Straight over there!" noted everyone. The grandmother looked toward the road and noticed that the little thing was perspiring, and what speed! Then the song:

> *"Father, wait for me,*
> *Father, wait for me,*
> *The little wombless.*
> *Who is it that has eaten my mother?*
> *The little wombless . . . !*
> *How swollen are those eyes!*
> *Wait till the little wombless comes."*

Bakoo! It scarcely reached its grandmother's hut when it jumped into it . . . and up on the bed:

> *"Father, wait for me.*
> *Father, have you come?*
> *Yes, you have eaten my mother.*
> *How swollen those eyes!*
> *Wait till the little wombless comes."*

Then the grandmother put this question to the man: "Now what sort of song is this child singing? Have you not killed our daughter?"

She had scarcely added, "Surround him!" when he was already in their hands. His very brothers-in-law tied him. And then . . . all the assegais were poised together in one direction, everyone saying, "Now today you are the man who killed our sister. . . ."

Then they just threw the body away there to the west. And the grandmother picked up her little grandchild.

[BENA MUKUNI]

50

The Woman Who Killed Her Co-Wife

ONCE A MAN MADE a double marriage, one with a superior and one with an inferior wife. The inferior one then prepared a drug and caused the death of her mate, the owner of the place.

When she was dead, the people said, "Let us bury her in the village."

But the guilty woman said, "No, not in the village. That would not do, rather at the back of it. I feel the loss of my mate too much."

The mourning was kept up for a long while.

At last the chief said, "Let them eat, otherwise they will die."

When this word was uttered, the womenfolk said, "Let us go to do field work."

So they dispersed in order to go to the fields. But the guilty woman went up to the granary and took out some ears of corn. She then called to the dead woman, saying, "Come and thresh this." So saying she went and dug her mate out until she came forth from the grave in which she had been covered with earth, in order to go and thresh the corn.

When the dead wife had finished threshing it, she winnowed and sifted it, then took it to the grinding stone, and began to prepare this stone for use by beating it with a smaller one.

Meanwhile in the hut the living woman was cooking porridge. When she had finished stirring it, she said, "Come and have some food."

Go into the hut! That is what her mate would not do. So the living wife said, "Then go and grind. You are a fool."

The dead woman went to the stone and ground, singing all the while:

> *"First let me hand over to you little things,*
> *my lady.*
> *Lady Rows, let me hand over little things.*
> *Rows, I have left you the husband;*
> *break me in two, yes.*
> *Rows, I have left you the cowries;*
> *break me in two, yes.*
> *Rows, I have left you the children;*
> *break me in two, yes.*

Rows, I have left you the slaves;
  break me in two, yes.
Rows, I have left you the cotton goods;
  break me in two, yes.
Rows, I have left you the fowls;
  break me in two, yes.
Rows, I have left you the guinea-fowls;
  break me in two, yes.
Rows, I have left you the baskets;
  break me in two, yes.
Rows, I have left you the fire;
  break me in two, yes.
Rows, I have left you everything;
  break me in two, yes.
Let me hand over all the rows."

She disappeared before the people came to the village.

The following day the people again dispersed in order to go to the fields. The woman also went, but soon came back and went to the granary and began to take out grain. All of a sudden she started toward the place where she had covered her mate with earth, saying, "Now, now! Come, thresh and grind; the sun is sinking." And she went and dug her out.

The dead woman threshed and threshed. When she had finished threshing, she took the grain to the grinding stone, then once more began to beat it with another stone.

"Come along!" said her mate, "come and have some food."

"No," she said, "I do not want any. Food is not what is in my heart."

"Well!" said the other. "Where are the people who are going to look at you the whole day long? You died long ago." Then she added, "What, eat! That is what you will not do. . . . Then go and grind, dear, the sun is shining."

Then the dead woman bent over the stone and began to grind, singing:

"First let me hand over to you little things,
  my lady.
Lady Rows, let me hand over little things.
Rows, I have left you the husband;
  break me in two, yes.
Rows, I have left you the cowries;
  break me in two, yes.
Rows, I have left you the children;
  break me in two, yes.
Rows, I have left you the slaves;
  break me in two, yes.

Rows, I have left you the cotton goods;
break me in two, yes.
Rows, I have left you the fowls;
break me in two, yes.
Rows, I have left you the guinea-fowls;
break me in two, yes.
Rows, I have left you the baskets;
break me in two, yes.
Rows, I have left you the fire;
break me in two, yes.
Rows, I have left you everything;
break me in two, yes.
Let me hand over all the rows."

Meanwhile everyone left the fields and came back to the village.

The next morning people said, "Let us go to the fields." After having gone to the field, the woman once more came back before the sun was high and went up to the granary. After that her mate again threshed, took the grain to the stone, and began to grind, singing the same song as on the previous days.

At dawn the next morning people said once more, "Now let us go to work." But this time a number of people remained hidden in the grass. Then, fancy their surprise!, they saw the woman go up to the granary, start taking some ears of corn and, on coming down, go and unearth her mate. Seeing that, they said, "This time it is plain, this is the woman who killed her mate."

Then, as they saw the dead woman thresh the grain and go and bend over the millstone and heard her saying, "Let me begin to grind," and when they further heard the song, "First let me hand over . . ." then, by the ghosts! they were all in suspense.

"Now," said the dead woman, "let me move away from the stone."

At this moment they got hold of the murderer. . . . "Let me go," she said, "first hold a court of inquiry."

But they just went and dug up a poison and mixed it and made her drink it by force. Meanwhile her dead mate had vanished.

Bakoo! They made a heap of firewood, dug her heart out, and burned her over the fire.

Now, little iron, my little story stops. Little iron, that's all.

[BENA MUKUNI]

51

The Slave Girl Who Tried to Kill Her Mistress

A MAN CALLED AKPAN, who was a native of Oku, a town in the Ibibio country, admired a girl called Emme very much. She lived in Ibibio and he wished to marry her, as she was the finest girl in her kraal.

It was the custom in those days for the parents to demand such a large amount as dowry for their daughters that if, after they were married, they failed to get on with their husbands and could not redeem themselves, they were sold as slaves.

Akpan paid a very large sum as a dowry for Emme and she was put in the fatting-house until the proper time arrived for her to marry. Akpan told the parents that when their daughter was ready they must send her over to him. This they promised to do.

Emme's father was a rich man. After seven years had elapsed and Emme came out of the fatting-house to go to her husband, her father saw a very fine girl, also just out of the fatting-house, whose parents wished to sell her as a slave. He therefore bought her and gave her to his daughter as her hand-maiden.

The next day Emme's little sister, being very anxious to go with her, obtained the consent of her mother, and they started off together, the slave girl carrying a large bundle containing clothes and presents from Emme's father. Akpan's house was a long day's march from where they lived. When they arrived just outside the town, they came to a spring where people used to get their drinking water. No one was allowed to bathe there. Emme, however, knew nothing of this. The women took off their clothes to wash close to the spring, where there was a deep hole which led to the water *juju*'s house. The slave girl knew of this *juju* and thought that, if she could get her mistress to bathe there, her mistress would be taken by the *juju* and she would then be able to take her place and marry Akpan. So they went down to bathe and, when they were close to the water, the slave girl pushed her mistress in, and Emme at once disappeared.

The little sister began to cry, but the slave girl said, "If you cry any more I shall kill you at once and throw your body into the hole after your sister." She told the child that she must never mention what had happened to anyone, particularly not to Akpan, as she was going to take her sister's place and marry him, and that if she ever told anyone what she had seen, she would be killed at once. She then made the little girl carry her load to Akpan's house.

When they arrived, Akpan was very much disappointed at the slave girl's appearance, as she was not nearly as pretty and fine as he had expected her to be; but as he had not seen Emme for seven years, he had no suspicion that the girl was not really Emme for whom he had paid such a large dowry. He then called his society together to play and feast and, when they arrived, they were much astonished and said, "Is this the fine woman for whom you paid so great a dowry and whom you told us so much about?" And Akpan could not answer them.

The slave girl was then for some time very cruel to Emme's little sister and wanted her to die so that then her position would be more secure with her husband. Every day she beat the little girl, and she always made her carry the largest waterpot to the spring. She also made the child place her finger in the fire to use as firewood. When the time came for food, the slave girl went to the fire and took a burning piece of wood and burned the child all over her body with it. When Akpan asked her why she treated the child so badly, she replied that she was a slave whom her father had bought for her.

Now when the little girl took the heavy waterpot to the river to fill it, there was no one to lift it up for her, so that she could not get it up on her head. She therefore had to remain a long time at the spring and at last began calling for her sister Emme to come and help her.

When Emme heard her little sister crying for her, she begged the water *juju* to allow her to go and help her, so he told her she might go but that she must return to him again immediately. When the little girl saw her sister she did not want to leave her and asked to be allowed to go into the hole with her. She then told Emme how cruelly she had been treated by the slave girl, and her elder sister told her to have patience and wait, that a day of vengeance would arrive sooner or later.

After seeing her sister, the little girl went back to Akpan's house with a glad heart, but when she got to the house, the slave girl said, "Why have you been so long getting the water?" and took another stick from the fire and burned the little girl and starved her for the rest of the day.

This went on for some time, until, one day, when the child again went to the river for water. After all the people had gone, she cried out for her sister, but for a long time she did not come. There was a hunter from Akpan's town hidden nearby, watching the hole, and the water *juju* told Emme that she must not go. When the little girl went on crying so bitterly, Emme at last persuaded the *juju* to let her go to her sister, promising to return quickly. When she emerged from the water, she looked very beautiful with the rays of the setting sun shining on her glistening body. She helped her little sister with her waterpot and then disappeared into the hole again.

The hunter was amazed at what he had seen, and, when he returned, he told Akpan what a beautiful woman had come out of the water and had helped the little girl with her waterpot. He also told Akpan that he was convinced that the girl he had seen at the spring was his proper wife, Emme, and that the water *juju* must have taken her.

Akpan then made up his mind to go out and watch and see what happened. So in the early morning, the hunter came for him, and they both went down to the river and hid in the forest near the waterhole.

When Akpan saw Emme come out of the water, he recognized her at once, and he went home and considered how he should get her out of the power of the water *juju*. He was advised by some of his friends to go to an old woman who frequently made sacrifices to the water *juju*, and consult her as to what was the best thing to do.

When he went to her, she told him to bring her one white slave, one white goat, one piece of white cloth, one white chicken, and a basket of eggs. Then, when the great *juju* day arrived, she would take them to the water *juju* and make a sacrifice of them on his behalf. On the day after the sacrifice was made, the water *juju* would return the girl to her, and she would bring her to Akpan.

Akpan then bought the slave and took all the other things to the old woman and, when the day of sacrifice arrived, he went with his friend, the hunter, and witnessed the old woman make the sacrifice. The slave was bound up and led to the hole, the old woman called to the water *juju*, and she then cut the slave's throat with a sharp knife and pushed him into the hole. She then did the same with the goat and the chicken and she also threw the eggs and cloth on top of them. After this had been done, they all returned to their homes.

The next morning at dawn the old woman went to the hole and found Emme standing at the side of the spring. She told her that she was her friend and was going to take her to her husband. She then took Emme back to her own home and hid her in her room and sent word to Akpan to come to her house and to take great care that the slave woman knew nothing about the matter.

So Akpan left the house secretly by the back door and arrived at the old woman's house without meeting anyone.

When Emme saw Akpan, she asked for her little sister, so he sent his friend, the hunter, to bring her from the spring. The hunter met the child carrying her waterpot to get the morning supply of water and brought her to the old woman's house with him.

After Emme had embraced her sister, she told her to return to Akpan's house and to do something to annoy the slave woman, and then she was to run as fast as she could back to the old woman's house where, no doubt, the slave girl would follow her. There she would meet them all inside the house and would see Emme, whom she believed she had killed.

The little girl did as she was told, and as soon as she entered the house, she called out to the slave woman, "Do you know that you are a wicked woman and have treated me very badly? I know you are only my sister's slave, and you will be properly punished." She then ran as fast as she could to the old woman's house. When the slave woman heard what the little girl had said, she was quite mad with rage and seized a burning stick from the fire and ran after the child; but the little one got to the house first and ran inside, the slave woman following close upon her heels with the burning stick in her hand.

Then Emme came out and confronted the slave woman, and she at once recognized her mistress whom she thought she had killed, and she stood quite still.

Then they all went back to Akpan's house, and, when they arrived there, Akpan asked the slave woman what she meant by pretending that she was Emme and why she had tried to kill her. But, seeing she was found out, the slave woman had nothing to say.

Many people were then called to play and to celebrate the recovery of Akpan's wife, and when they had all come, he told them what the slave woman had done.

After this, Emme treated the slave girl in the same way as she had treated her little sister. She made her put her fingers in the fire and burned her with sticks. She also made her beat *fufu* with her head in a hollowed-out tree and, after a time, she was tied up to a tree and starved to death.

Ever since that time, when a man marries a girl, he is always present when she comes out of the fatting-house and takes her home himself, so that such evil things as happened to Emme and her sister might not occur again.

[EFIK-IBIBIO]

52

The Smart Man and the Fool

L ET US TELL another story; let us be off!"
"Pull away!"
"Let us be off!"
"Pull away!"

There were two brothers, the Smart Man and the Fool, and it was their habit to go out shooting to keep their parents supplied with food. Thus, one day, they went together into the mangrove swamp, just as the tide was going down, to watch for the fish as they nibbled at the roots of the trees. Fool saw a fish, fired at it, and killed it. Smart Man fired also, but at nothing, and then ran up to Fool and said, "Fool, have you killed anything?"

"Yes, Smart Man, I am a fool, but I killed a fish."

"Indeed, you are a fool," answered Smart Man, "for when I fired I hit the fish that went your way, so that the fish you think you killed is mine. Here, give it to me."

The fool gave Smart Man the fish. Then they went to their town, and Smart Man, addressing his father, said, "Father, here is a fish that your son shot, but Fool got nothing."

The mother prepared and cooked the fish, and the father and Smart Man ate it, giving none to Fool.

Then they went again; and Fool fired, and with his first shot killed a big fish.

"Did you hear me fire?" said Smart Man.

"No," answered Fool.

"No?" returned Smart Man. "See, then, the fish I killed."

·"All right," said Fool, "take the fish."

When they reached home they gave the fish to their mother and, after she had cooked it, Smart Man and his father ate it, but gave none to Fool. As they were enjoying the fish, a bone stuck in the father's throat. Then Smart Man called to Fool and bade him go for a doctor.

"No," said Fool, "I cannot. I felt that something would happen." And he sang:

197

> *"Every day you eat my fish,*
> *You call me Fool,*
> *And would let me starve."*

"How can you sing," said Smart Man, "when you see that our father is suffering?"

But Fool went on singing:

> *"You eat and eat unto repletion;*
> *A bone sticks in your throat;*
> *And now your life is near completion,*
> *The bone is still within your throat.*
>
> *"So you, smart brother, killed the fish,*
> *And gave the fool to eat?*
> *Nay! but now he's dead perhaps you wish*
> *You'd given the fool to eat."*

While Fool was still singing, the father died. Then the neighbours came and joined the family circle, and asked Fool how it was that he could go on singing now that his father was dead.

And Fool answered them, saying, "Our father made us both, one a smart man, the other a fool. The Fool killed the food, and they ate it, giving none to the Fool. They must not blame him, therefore, if he sings while they suffer. He suffered hunger while they had plenty."

And when the people had considered the matter, they gave judgment in favour of the Fool, and departed.

The father died, and so had been justly punished for not having given food to the Fool.

He who eats fish with much oil must suffer from indigestion.

And now I have finished my story.

Tomorrow may you chop palm-kernels.

[BAKONGO]

53

The Greed of the Old Man and His Wife

THERE WAS ONCE UPON A TIME an old man who lived in a kraal with his neighbours. And this old man had a wife and a small child, and he possessed a very fine ox.

One day he said to himself, "How shall I slaughter my ox?" And he said aloud to his wife, "My child! I will call the men and tell them that I am going to move. We can then slaughter our ox all by ourselves."

His wife agreed and, in the evening, the old man blew his horn as a signal to his friends that he had something to tell them. His neighbours came together, and he told them that he wished to move, as the air did not agree with him. The others consented, and in the morning he saddled his donkeys, separated his cattle from the rest, and started off, accompanied by his wife, who was carrying the child.

When they had gone some distance, they halted and erected their kraal, after which they rested.

At dawn on the second day the old man called his wife and asked her why they had not yet slaughtered their ox. The woman replied, "My husband! How shall we manage to slaughter the ox? There are two things to be considered—the first is that we have no herdsman and the second that I am carrying the baby."

The old man then said, "Oh, I know what we will do. I will stab the ox in the neck, then I will leave you to skin it, and I will carry the child to the grazing ground. But when you have skinned the animal, roast some meat so that it will be ready on my return."

The old man then killed the ox, after which he picked up his bow and quiver, put the child on his back, and drove the cattle to the grazing ground where he herded them.

In the afternoon, as the child was asleep, the old man put it down in the grass, and went to drive back the cattle, for they had wandered far. But when he returned to the spot where he had left the child, he was unable to find it, so he decided to set fire to the grass. "When the fire reaches the child, it will cry," he thought, "and I will run to the place and pick it up before it is burned."

He made a fire with his fire-sticks, and the fire travelled to where the child was. He ran to the spot, but when he reached it, he found that the child was dead.

The old man had left his wife in the morning skinning the ox. And while she was skinning it—she had just reached the dewlap—the knife slipped, and she stabbed herself in the eye. She went and lay down, and the birds came and finished the meat.

After the child was burned, the old man drove the cattle to the kraal, and when they were opposite to the gate, he heard his wife weeping, and saying, "Oh, my eye!" He therefore asked her who had told her the news.

"What news?" she inquired.

"The child has been burned," he replied.

The woman exclaimed, "Oh, my child!"

The old man then asked where his meat was, and his wife informed him that the birds had eaten it, whereupon he cried out, "Oh, my meat!"

They both wept, the old man crying, "Oh, my meat!" and the woman, "Oh, my child! Oh, my eye!"

Look well at these people. It was for their greed that they were punished. They lost their child and their ox, the woman lost her eye, and they had to return in shame to their former home.

[MASAI]

54

How Contradiction Came to the Ashanti

THERE WAS ONCE a certain man called Hate-to-Be-Contradicted, and because of that, he built a small settlement all by himself and went to live in it. And the creature called the duiker went to visit him, and he walked with him and sat down at the foot of a palm tree. Then some of the palm nuts fell down. The duiker said, "Father Hate-to-Be-Contradicted, your palm nuts are ripe."

Hate-to-Be-Contradicted said, "That is the nature of the palm nut. When they are ripe, three bunches ripen at once. When they are ripe, I cut them down; and when I boil them to extract the oil, they make three waterpots full of oil. Then I take the oil to Akase to buy an Akase old woman. The Akase old woman comes and gives birth to my grandmother who bears my mother who, in turn, bears me. When Mother bears me, I am already standing there."

The duiker said, "As for all that, you lie."

And Hate-to-Be-Contradicted took a stick and hit the duiker on the head, and killed it.

Next the little abedee antelope came along. Hate-to-Be-Contradicted went off with it and sat under the palm tree, and the same thing happened. And thus it was with all the animals. Finally, Kwaku Ananse, the spider, went and fetched his cloth and his bag, slung the bag across his shoulders, and went off to visit Hate-to-Be-Contradicted's kraal. He greeted him: "Father, good morning."

Hate-to-Be-Contradicted replied, "*Y'aku*, and where are you going?"

He replied, "I am coming to visit you."

And he took his stool and placed it under the palm tree.

Hate-to-Be-Contradicted said, "Cook food for the spider to eat."

And while it was cooking, Ananse and Hate-to-Be-Contradicted sat under the palm tree. Some of the palm nuts fell down, and Ananse took them and placed them in his bag. This he continued to do until his bag was full. The food was brought, and Ananse ate. When he had finished eating, some of the ripe palm nuts again fell down, and Ananse said, "Father Hate-to-Be-Contradicted, your palm nuts are ripe."

Hate-to-Be-Contradicted said, "It's their nature to ripen like that; when they are ripe, three bunches ripen at once. When they are ripe, I cut them down, and when I boil them to extract the oil, they make three waterpots full of oil, and I take the oil to Akase to buy an Akase old woman. The Akase old woman comes and gives birth to my grandmother who bears my mother so that she in turn may bear me. When Mother bears me, I am already standing there."

The spider said, "You do not lie. What you say is true. As for me, I have some okras standing in my farm. When they are ripe, I join seventy-seven long hooked poles in order to reach them to pull them down, but even then I cannot reach them. So I lie on my back, and am able to use my penis to pluck them."

Hate-to-Be-Contradicted said, "Oh, I understand. Tomorrow I shall come and look."

The spider said, "Surely."

While the spider was going home, he chewed the palm nuts which he had gathered and spat them out on the path. The next morning, when things began to be visible, Hate-to-Be-Contradicted set out to go to the spider's village. Now when the spider had arrived home the day before, he had gone and said to his children, "A certain man will come here who hates to be contradicted, and when he arrives and inquires for me, you must tell him that yesterday I had said I was going off somewhere, when my penis broke in seven places and I had to take it to a blacksmith to be repaired and, as the blacksmith could not finish it at the time, I have now gone to have the work finished."

Not long afterward Hate-to-Be-Contradicted came along. He said, "Where has your father gone?"

They replied, "Alas, Father went somewhere yesterday, and his penis got broken in seven different places. So he took it to a blacksmith, but he could not finish the job at the time, and Father has gone to have it completed. You, father, did you not see the blood on the path?"

Hate-to-Be-Contradicted said, "Yes, I saw it." He then asked, "And where is your mother?"

The spider's child replied, "Mother, too—yesterday she went to the stream, and her waterpot would have fallen and broken had she not saved it from doing so by just catching at it in time. But she didn't quite finish saving it from falling and has returned today to do so." Hate-to-Be-Contradicted did not say anything.

Now Ananse arrived. He said, "Cook some food that Hate-to-Be-Contradicted may eat." As the children were cooking the food, they used only one single little perch but an immense quantity of peppers. They made the soup-stew very hot. When they had finished, they set it down before Hate-to-Be-Contradicted. Hate-to-Be-Contradicted ate. Now the peppers pained him; he wanted to die. He said to one of Ananse's sons, "Ntikuma, where is that water?"

Ntikuma said, "Ah, the water which we have here in our waterpot is of three different kinds. That belonging to Father comes first, that of my mother's co-wife is in the middle, and that belonging to my own mother is at the bottom of the pot. I must draw for you only the water belonging to my own mother and if I do not take great care when drawing it, it will cause a tribal dispute."

Hate-to-Be-Contradicted said, "You little brat, you lie."

Straightway Ananse said, "Beat him so that he dies."

Hate-to-Be-Contradicted said, "Why should they beat me so that I may die?"

The spider said, "You say you hate to be contradicted, and yet you have contradicted some one. That is why I say they must beat you so that you may die."

So they beat Hate-to-Be-Contradicted until he died. Then Ananse cut up his flesh in little pieces and scattered them all about.

That is why many persons who hate to be contradicted are to be found in the tribe today.

[ASHANTI]

55

How It Came About That One Person Does Not Reveal the Origin from Which Another Person Comes

THERE WAS ONCE a hunter. After he got up in the morning he used to go to the bush to seek for game to kill so that he might get some to eat and some to sell.

Now one day he went to the bush and he heard Kokotee, the bush pig, call out to its kinsman, "Kokotee Asamoa!"

He replied, "Yes, brother, yes." Kokotee again called, "The time for work on our farms has arrived. Let us go to the blacksmith's forge that he may fashion the iron and put an edge on our cutting tools, so that, if we have to cut down any trees, we may be able to do so."

When the bush pig called to his brothers, the hunter crouched down and hid, and he heard all the conversation. Now Kokotee's brother asked, "And to what village shall we go to have the iron struck?"

Kokotee replied, "We shall go to the village called Across-the-Stream."

And his brother said, "What day?"

He replied, "Monday."

The hunter heard all this arrangement and set off for home. When he came home, he told the headman of Across-the-Stream the news, namely, what he had heard when he had gone to the bush. And the hunter said to the headman of the village, "Let the children go and cut logs and bring them, and when, on Monday, the bush pigs change themselves into people and come, we shall take them and fasten them to the logs."

The children went and cut the logs and brought them. The headman of the village went and told the village blacksmith to beat out iron staples for him. And the blacksmith asked the headman, "And all this quantity of iron staples which you say I must beat out—what are you going to do with them?"

And he told him the news—how a hunter had gone to the bush and come back to report that on Monday certain beasts would turn themselves into people in order to come to his forge to have tools forged. The blacksmith ran off to beat out the iron staples quickly. As soon as the chief had finished collecting the logs and staples, he caused the town crier to beat the iron gong, saying, "On Monday, be it woman, or be it man, no one must go anywhere."

Monday arrived, and in the morning an old woman said to the hunter, "Go and grind peppers, salt, and onions at the place where the beasts will peel off their skins and lay them down. Do you also, when you go there, take the peppers and rub them on. When the beasts come there, and we catch them, should some escape and go to take their skins again and put them on, then the peppers will hurt them, and they will throw the skins off and will become people again."

The hunter went off to the bush and he hid there. And he heard the bush pigs calling, "Kokotee Asamoa, Monday has arrived, let us go." So they all came. They peeled off their skins and put them down. Now one of the pigs, who was a doctor of herbs, was among them, and he took his skin and laid it elsewhere. The hunter watched them and let them go away. He went and took all the skins and rubbed on them the peppers which they had mashed, and then took the skins and put them in the stream, letting the water take them away. The skin of the medicine-man, however, which had been put aside from the rest, the hunter did not see.

The hunter went home, and the chief called the people gathered round the blacksmith's forge and made them come to his house. When these people came to the chief's house, they inquired of the chief, "Why have you called us?"

The chief said, "You were once my men, and you ran away to settle elsewhere. Today you have come back—that is the reason I say you must come, for I will not permit you to go away any more."

The beasts said to the chief, "What you have said we have heard. But we know that the Creator's hunter came and told you all about us. However, that does not matter. We and you will live together, although we know that what you say is false. Nevertheless that, also, does not matter; we thank that hunter. So we and you will live together. But there is one thing which we taboo, namely, that you disclose our origin, or that any of your subjects should disclose our origin. Should that happen, we shall break up this, your tribe, and depart."

Now at the time the chief went to call them, the medicine-man and some others ran away. And the medicine-man went to take his skin and he escaped; but the rest turned back. That was because they could not find their skins. The chief agreed to the conditions laid down by the beasts, and the human beings and the beasts lived happily together.

After a while the men of the village married some of the beasts' women-folk and they bore children. Now one day one of the beasts and one of the villagers were fighting with their fists. Thereupon the villager said to the beast, "Take yourself off from there—an animal like you who belongs to the bush-pig tribe!" No sooner had he said this than the eyes of all the beasts became red, and they went to the chief's house to tell him, saying, "The possibility about which we told you has now actually come about, so what are you going to do?"

The chief made them go and call the people who had caused the dispute. The chief looked closely into the matter and gave judgment that the beasts should drop the charge because, he said, it was a long time since they had come and this, moreover, was the first occasion on which anyone had ever said anything to them about their origin.

But the beasts said, "We do not agree."

And the chief said, "You will not listen, and you think that what this man said is a lie. Are you not bush pigs?"

And the beasts said, "Oh! We have heard."

Thereupon the beasts and the Across-the-Stream people fought. The beasts destroyed the village until there remained only about ten people. These begged for mercy and told the beasts that they had right on their side. The beasts listened, and then informed the people, saying, "A case already stated is not difficult to understand. Now if you and we are to live together, we taboo all allusion to our origin. If you ever think of or mention it again, then we will ask you to point out to us the very thicket whence we came to this place, that we may return thither."

And the people said, "We will never do such a thing again. What we have done has caused our tribe to be ruined; we shall never do so again."

So they caused a public proclamation to be made by beating the *odawuro* gong to the effect that no one should ever tell of another person's origin, lest the disclosure should cause the town to be ruined.

[ASHANTI]

56

Why a Girl Should Marry Him to Whom
She is Given in Marriage

THERE WAS ONCE a virgin named Kwaboaso. To whomsoever they gave her to marry she said, "I do not desire him." They gave her to a hunter, and she said, "Ugh! This man has ticks on him; I do not want him."

One day she went off to the plantation, saying she was going to cut plantains. She took a knife and struck at the plantain, when behold, the little folk were sitting on the plantains. They descended and came and caught Kwaboaso. They said, "You are the one who shakes your head, *pusu! pusu!* when they take you to give to anyone." And the fairies caught hold of her and said:

> *"Come let us squeeze her.*
> *We squeeze her, O!*
> *We squeeze Kwaboaso.*
> *Come, let us squeeze her.*
> *We squeeze her, O!"*

Now, when the hunter to whom they had given Kwaboaso heard Kwaboaso's voice, he said, "I am going to see what is the matter, for we don't take something bad to repay something bad." When he arrived, there was Kwaboaso and the fairies squeezing her. Then the hunter fired a gun at the fairies, and one fell down.

The eldest of them said to the others, "He has drunk palm wine and is intoxicated; place him yonder in the meantime, and then go on squeezing her." Again the hunter fired, and another fell. The eldest again said, "The brave fellow has drunk palm wine and is overcome; take him and lay him aside there." The hunter killed all the little folk except the eldest. The eldest called out to the hunter, "Come, oh, come on! I will not do anything to you."

The hunter went over to her. The eldest of the fairies said, "Look in my room there and you will see the medicine for the gun and all the bullets which you have fired. Take what belongs to you and take Kwaboaso as well. But before you leave, go and cut bananas and, as you go, throw them away, so that when the other fairies wake up and come to catch you they will stop

207

to pick them up, one by one, and you will have gone long, long, long ago."

And, accordingly, the hunter went and cut bananas, and he took Kwaboaso as well, and, when he reached the path, he threw one banana away. He continued doing so all the way home. And when only a short time remained before they would reach home, behold! the fairies were pursuing them. And he threw down the only banana left, and the fairies went after it, and eventually turned back. And the hunter restored Kwaboaso to her blood relations. Then the hunter went off to his own house.

Now the hunter was living there when he saw messengers had arrived at his place, and he said, "What is the news?"

The messengers said, "Kwaboaso says she has asked the head of the village to intercede for her, saying that now she is willing to marry you."

The hunter said, "I thank you for the words from the mouth of the headman of the village, but I cannot marry the girl, for I still have ticks on my body."

That is why the elders say, "When they take you to give you in marriage to anyone, marry him, for you do not know whether some day when you are in need, he will not rescue you."

[A S H A N T I]

57

How It Came About That Children Were
First Whipped

THEY SAY that once upon a time a great famine came, and that Father Ananse, the spider, and his wife Aso, and his children, Ntikuma, Nyi-wankonfwea (Thin-Shanks), Afudotwedotwe (Belly-Like-to-Burst), and Tikonokono (Big-Big-Head), built a little settlement and lived in it. Every day the spider used to go and bring food—wild yams—and they boiled and ate them.

Now one day, Father Ananse went to the bush and he saw that a beautiful dish was standing there. He said, "This dish is beautiful."

The dish said, "My name is not 'Beautiful.'"

The spider then asked, "What are you called?"

It replied, "I am called 'Fill-Up-Some-and-Eat.'"

The spider said, "Fill up some so that I may see." The dish filled up with palm-oil soup, and Ananse ate it all.

When he had finished, he asked the dish, "What is your taboo?"

The dish replied, "I hate a gun wad and a little gourd cup."

The spider took the dish home, and went and placed it on the ceiling. He went off to the bush and brought food, and Aso, when she had finished cooking, called Ananse. He said, "Oh, yours is the real need. As for me, I am an old man. What should I have to do with food? You and these children are the ones in real need. If you are replete, then my ears will be spared the sounds of your lamentations."

When they had finished eating, Ananse the spider passed behind the hut, and went and sat on the ceiling where the dish was. He said, "This dish is beautiful."

It replied, "My name is not 'Beautiful.'"

He said, "What is your name?"

It said, "I am called 'Fill-Up-Some-and-Eat.'"

Ananse said, "Fill up some for me to see." And it filled up a plate full of ground-nut soup, and Ananse ate. Every day when he arose it was thus.

Now Ntikuma noticed that his father did not grow thin in spite of the fact that they and he did not eat together, and so he kept watch on his father to see what the latter had got hold of. When his father went off to the bush, Ntikuma climbed up on top of the ceiling and saw the dish. He called his mother and brothers and they, too, went on top. Ntikuma said, "This dish is beautiful."

It said, "I am not called 'Beautiful.' "

He said, "Then what are you called?"

It said, "My name is 'Fill-Up-Some-and-Eat.' "

He said, "Fill up a little that I may see." And the dish filled up to the brim with palm-oil soup.

And now Ntikuma asked the dish, "What do you taboo?"

The dish said, "I hate a gun wad and a small gourd cup."

Ntikuma said to Afudotwedotwe, "Go and bring some for me."

And he brought them, and Ntikuma took the gun wad and touched the dish and also the little gourd cup and touched the dish with it. Then they all descended.

Father Spider meantime had come back from the bush with the wild yams. Aso finished cooking them. They called Ananse.

He replied, "Perhaps you didn't hear what I said—I said that when I come home with food, you may partake, for you are the ones in need." Aso and her children ate.

Father Spider washed and then climbed up on the ceiling. He said, "This dish is beautiful." Complete silence! "This dish is beautiful!" Complete silence! Father Spider said, "Ah! It must be on account of this cloth not being a beautiful one; I shall go and bring the one with the pattern of the Oyoko clan and put it on." And he descended to go and fetch the Oyoko-patterned cloth to wear. He put on his sandals and again climbed up on the ceiling. He said, "This dish is beautiful." Complete silence! "This dish is beautiful." Complete silence! He looked round the room and saw that a gun wad and a little gourd cup were there.

Ananse said, "It's not one thing, it's not two things—it's Ntikuma." Ananse smashed the dish, and came down. He took off the Oyoko-patterned cloth, laid it away, and went off to the bush. As he was going, he saw that a very beautiful thing called Mpere, the whip, was hanging there. He said, "Oh, wonderful! This thing is more beautiful than the last. This whip is beautiful."

The whip said, "I am not called 'Beautiful.' "

The spider said, "Then what are you called?"

It said, "I am called 'Abiridiabrada,' or 'Swish-and-Raise-Welts.' "

And Ananse said, "Swish a little for me to see." And the whip fell upon him *biridi, biridi, biridi!* Father Spider cried, "*Pui! pui!*"

A certain bird sitting nearby said to Ananse, "Say '*Adwobere*, cool-and-easy-now.' "

And Ananse said, "*Adwobere*, cool-and-easy-now."

And the whip stopped beating him. And Ananse brought this whip home; and he went and placed it on the ceiling.

Aso finished cooking the food and said, "Ananse, come and eat."

He replied, "Since you are still here on earth, perhaps you have not a hole in your ears and don't hear what I said—I shall not eat." Ananse climbed up above and went and sat down quietly. Soon he came down again and he went and hid himself somewhere.

Then Ntikuma climbed up aloft. He said, "Oh, that father of mine has brought something home again!" Ntikuma called, "Mother, Nyiwankonfwea, Afudotwedotwe, come here, for the thing father has brought this time excels the last one by far!" Then all of them climbed up on the ceiling. Ntikuma said, "This thing is beautiful."

It replied, "I am not called 'Beautiful.' "

He said, "What is your name?"

It said, "I am called 'Swish-and-Raise-Welts.' "

He said, "Swish a little for me to see." And the whip descended upon them and flogged them severely.

Ananse stood aside and shouted, "Lay it on, lay it on! Especially on Ntikuma, lay it on him!" Now when Ananse had watched and seen that they were properly flogged, he said, "*Adwobere*, cool-and-easy-now." Ananse came and took the whip and cut it into small pieces and scattered them about.

That is what made the whip come into the tribe. So it comes about that when you tell your child something and he will not listen to you, you whip him.

[ASHANTI]

58

Why It Is That the Elders Say We Should Not Repeat Sleeping-Mat Confidences

THEY SAY that once upon a time Nyankonpon Kwame, the sky-god, cleared a very large plantation and planted okras, onions, beans, garden-eggs, peppers, and pumpkins. The weeds in the garden became thick and nettles grew up. The sky-god then made a proclamation by *odawuro* to the effect that his plantation was overgrown with weeds and that anyone who could weed it without scratching himself might come forward and take his daughter, Abena Nkroma, in marriage. The first one who went to try scratched himself where the nettles tickled, and they hooted at him. The next one who tried was also hooted at. All men went and tried and all failed.

Now Kwaku Ananse, the spider, said, "As for me, I am able to do it." The sky-god's plantation was situated on the side of the path, and that path was the one people used to take when going to the market every Friday. The spider, because he knew this fact, used only to go and clear the weeds every Friday. When he was hoeing, the people who passed by used to greet him, saying, "Hail to you at your work, Father Spider!"

Then he would answer, "Thank you, *Aku*." They would continue, "A plantation which no one has been able to clear—do you mean to say you are weeding it?"

The spider would answer, "Ah, it's all because of one girl that I am wearing myself out like this. Her single arm is like this." And he would then slap and rub his arm where it was tickling him, and when he did so, he would get relief from the irritation. Then another person would pass there and hail him at his work, and he would again slap the place that was itching. For example, if it was his thigh, he would say, "That single girl! They say her thigh is like this," and he would slap and rub his own thigh.

In this manner he finished clearing the plantation. Then he went off to tell the sky-god how he had finished the weeding of his farm. The sky-god asked the messenger, "Has he really finished?"

The messenger said, "Yes."

The sky-god asked him, "Did he scratch himself?"

He said, "No, he did not scratch himself."

Then the sky-god took Abena Nkroma and gave her to Ananse in marriage.

One night Ananse and his bride went to rest and the bride questioned him, saying, "However was it that you of all people were able to clear father's plantation of weeds? A plantation like that—from which everyone who tried turned back! However were you able to clear it?"

Then the spider said, "Do you suppose that I am a fool? I used to hoe, and when anyone passed by and said to me, 'Ananse, are you clearing this farm which no one else has ever been able to clear?' I would thereupon slap with my hand any place on my skin that was tickling me and scratch it, and declare to the person that your thigh, for example, was like the thigh of a buffalo, and that it was beautiful and polished. That is how it came about that I was able to weed the plantation."

Thereupon Abena, the ninth child, said, "Then tomorrow I shall tell father that you scratched yourself after all."

But the spider spoke to her, saying, "You must not mention it. This is a sleeping-mat confidence."

Abena, the ninth child, said, "I know nothing whatever about sleeping-mat confidences, and I shall tell my father." Abena Nkroma took her sleeping-mat away from beside Ananse and went and lay down at the other end of the room.

Now Ananse's eyes grew red and sorrowful, and he went and took his *sepirewa*, and he struck the strings and sang:

> "*Abena, the ninth child, this is not a matter*
> *about which to quarrel.*
> *Let us treat it as a sleeping-mat confidence.*
> *'No!' she says. She has a case against me,*
> *But some one else has a case*
> *which is already walking down the path.*"

Then the spider went and lay down. After Ananse had lain there for some time, he rose up again. He said, "Abena Nkroma." Not a sound save the noise of the cicada chirping *dinn!* Ananse said, "I've got you!"

He took a little gourd cup and splashed it full with water and poured it over Abena Nkroma's sleeping-mat. Then Ananse went and lay down. After he had lain there a while, he said, "*Ko!* Abena Nkroma, whatever is this! You have wet the sleeping-mat, you shameless creature! Surely you are not at all nice. When things become visible, I shall tell everyone. It was true then— what they all said—that when anyone went to your father's plantation, he would say, 'A girl who wets . . . ! I am not going to clear a nettle plantation for such a person.' "

Then Abena said to him, "I implore you, desist, and let the matter drop."

But the spider said, "I will not leave it, for my case came first. You said you would tell your father. I said, 'Desist'; but you said, 'No.' Because of that I will not drop the case."

And Abena, the ninth child, said, "Leave my case, and your case, too, about which I spoke. I shall drop it, for if you do not leave mine, my eyes will die for shame."

Then Ananse said, "I have heard. Since you so desire, let it be a sleeping-mat confidence. So the matter ends there."

That is how the elders came to say, "Sleeping-mat confidences are not to be repeated."

[ASHANTI]

59

Why You Should Let Your Kinsman Accompany You When He Asks to Go Along

THERE WAS ONCE a certain woman, and she bore three children. The youngest among them was suffering from yaws.

The eldest of the brothers asked their mother to let them have gold dust that they might go trading. The youngest of them said he would like to go too, but they declared that he should not go with them. The mother, however, said that they and he must go together. Then their mother gave the elder sons gold dust to the value of five pounds and the youngest son gold dust to the value of two pounds. When things became visible, they set out.

The elder brothers went in front and left the child to follow behind. The child came along slowly. The elder ones met a certain man who was bringing fish. He said to them, "Buy!"

They answered, "Go on and you will meet a certain child. Make him buy. If he refuses to buy, take him and return with him to his mother."

The fellow went on and, sure enough, he met the child. He said, "Some elders whom I met said you are to buy this fish."

The child said, "Must I buy when those who are my elders did not buy?"

The fellow said, "They say if you will not buy I must beat you and must take you back and give you to your mother."

The child said, "How much is it?"

The fellow said, "An *osua*'s weight of gold dust." The child paid for it and received it.

He went on and overtook the elder brothers at a certain village. They had cooked vegetables but they did not have any meat to go with them. The child said, "Here is a fish which I bought." They put it in the soup-stew. When they had finished cooking, the elders gave him the head of the fish. When the child was about to break it, he saw red gold within, and he tied it up in the edge of his cloth.

The next day, when things became visible, the elders set out, and, as they went along, they met a man, and a cock rested on the top of things which he was carrying. As soon as he came up with the elders, he said, "Buy this cock."

They replied, "Go on, and you will meet a child. Make him buy it and, if he will not buy it, beat him."

Of a truth he met the child. He said, "Your elder kinsmen said that you are to buy this cock, and that if you do not buy it, I am to beat you and take you and give you to your mother."

The child replied, "Here, take what I have." The fellow, on his part, handed him over the cock.

After a while they reached a village. In the whole village there were no cocks to crow. The next morning, when things became visible, the cock, which belonged to the child, crowed. The headman of the village said, "Child, bring the cock and let me buy it."

The child said, "The price is an *osua*-and-*suru*'s weight of gold dust."

The headman paid the amount. The next day, when things became clear, they started off again.

As they were going along, the elders met a man carrying a cat. He said, "Buy this cat."

The elders said, "Take it along, and you will meet a certain child. Make him buy it. Should he say he will not buy, beat him and take him back to his mother."

The fellow passed on and met the child. He said, "Your elders say that you are to buy this cat and that if you do not buy it, I must beat you and take you back to your mother."

The child said, "How much?"

The fellow said, "An *osua*-and-*suru*'s weight of gold dust."

The child paid the price. He went on and came up with his elders at another village.

Now the mice used to nibble the feet of the headman there whenever he attempted to sleep. When the child with the cat arrived at this village, he went to the chief's house and the cat caught the mice which were there. The headman said, "I will buy this cat from the person to whom it belongs."

The child said, "It is mine."

The headman said, "How much?"

The child said, "An *osua*-and-*suru*'s weight of gold dust." The headman picked up the gold dust and put it in the child's hand.

The next day, when things became visible, they again set out. The elders went ahead and on the way they met thieves who had stolen the corpse of a certain chief. The thieves said, "You must buy this corpse."

The elders said, "Take it, and go on and you will meet a child. Give this corpse to him to buy. If he says he will not buy it, beat him, and take him and give him back to his mother."

The thieves went on and they met the child. They said, "Your elders say that you are to buy this corpse."

The child said, "Eh! What should I buy a corpse for? I could not carry it. Whatever I do with it, it will not be of any good to me."

The thieves said, "Your elders said that if you do not buy it, we must beat you and take you and give you back to your mother."

The child said, "How much?"

They said, "An *osua*-and-*suru*'s weight of gold dust."

The child paid the price, took the corpse, and laid it in the bush.

Then he set off and came to a certain village and went to a house to beg for food. The master of the house said, "There is none."

The child said, "Grandfather, I implore you!"

The master of the house said, "There is none."

The child said, "Grandfather, I implore you!"

The master of the house said, "Why does this child trouble me like this? Our chief is dead. We are fasting, and this is the eighth day, but, search as we may, we cannot find his corpse."

Then an old woman sitting nearby said, "Give him some food."

Thereupon a woman gave the child food and meat. When the child had finished eating, he said, "Master of the house, I have seen the chief's body. Yesterday as I was coming, some thieves made me buy it for an *osua*-and-*suru*'s weight of gold dust."

The woman ran off. *Yiridi! yiridi! yiridi!* was the sound of her running, and she told the village elders the news. They took the child and he went and showed them the body. Then they brought it and buried it properly. They said, "Now you will succeed to the chieftaincy." So the child became chief.

Now when his elder brothers heard about him, they came and claimed blood relationship with him. The child, however, said, "Clear out! I don't know you! Be off!" And he made his slaves drive them away.

That is why we say, "If you are going anywhere, and if your younger brother says he will go with you, take him along."

⌊ ASHANTI ⌋

60

If Someone Does Good to You, You Should
Do Good in Return

IT IS SAID that once there was a female eagle and that in her wanderings she came upon a certain old woman who had a sore on her leg. And the eagle said, "Gracious me! That is an unusual kind of sore. With a sore like that, however hard you try, are you able to walk?"

The old woman said, "Oh, just a very little."

The eagle said, "You people! Nowadays, if I were to do something good for you today, tomorrow you would do something bad to thank me."

The old woman said, "Oh! I would not do that."

The eagle said, "If you will not behave like that, I will help you." After a pause the eagle commanded, "Shut your eyes, and then open them."

And the old woman shut her eyes and opened them.

The eagle then said, "Look at your sore."

And the old woman stooped to look—not a trace of it remained. Then the eagle made her close her eyes again; she opened them, and she saw that all the forest had been cleared.

The eagle said, "Close your eyes again."

The old woman closed them and then opened them, and she saw that houses were firmly built there. And the eagle made her close her eyes again. She opened them to see a town of large size. There it was—huge!

The eagle said, "Old woman, it's yours."

The old woman said, "Thanks, thanks! I give you thanks! What must I give to thank you?"

The eagle said, "I do not want even a trifling thing. As for me, all that I desire is that silk-cotton tree that stands there."

The old woman said, "This thing you ask for—it is nothing—take it."

Then the eagle flew off, alighted on the tree, and wove a nest and laid two eggs which she deposited in it. And she hatched the two eggs, and went off to seek for something for her children to eat.

Then the old woman's grandchild, who lived with her, began to whimper: "*Ehe! Ehe!*"

The old woman said, "What's the matter?"

The child said, "Let me chew an eagle's child."

The old woman said, "Where am I to get an eagle's child?"

The small grandchild commenced again—"whimper! whimper!"

The old woman said, "What's the matter?"

The child said, "Let me chew an eagle's child, for if I don't have one to chew I shall die."

The old woman said, "Ah! Must this my grandchild die for want of an eagle's child to chew? Go, take axes, and strike the silk-cotton tree and bring me the eagle's children."

The village folk went there, the axes sounded *pinpin! pinpin! pinpin!* It was just when the tree was going down, that the elder of the eagle's children jumped up and stood on the edge of the nest and raised a cry. It called the mother:

> "Sango, *the bird* e!
> Sango, *the bird, the eagle's child!*
> Sango, *the bird* e!
> Sango, *if she went to eat, come back!*
> Sango, *the bird* e!
> Sango, o! o!"

The mother heard that her child was crying; she rose up and the sound of her wings flapping was *fa!* She came, she said *"Sanguri!"* And the silk-cotton tree, which was nearly severed, came together again, and all the people who had been striking it were swallowed up. The eagle took the food which she had brought and gave it to her children. Then she bade them good-bye and said, "I am going. If the old woman comes to take you away, let her take you."

And the old woman said, "Go and strike down the tree and bring the creatures for my grandchild to chew."

And they went there a second time. *Pinpin! pinpin! pinpin!* It was just as the tree was to go to the ground that the eagle's child came out and stood on the edge of the nest, and called its mother:

> "Sango, *the bird* e!
> Sango, *the bird, the eagle's child!*
> Sango, *the bird* e!
> Sango, *if she went to eat, come back!*
> Sango, *the bird* e!
> Sango, o! o!"

It called its mother, and called, and called, and called—there was no answer—and now the tree spoke as it hit the ground. *"Brim!"* it said.

They took away the eagle's children. They gave one to the old woman, but the one that remained flew away and alighted on a *wawa-wawa* tree. The first one the old woman roasted and gave to her grandchild, who added it to the roasted plantain she was eating.

Not long afterward, the eagle came. When she reached the tree which they had felled, she saw one of her children sitting there. She asked it what had happened, and it told her the news. The eagle set off for the old woman's village. When she arrived there, the old woman's grandchild was eating one of her children. She said, "Old woman, I congratulate you." Then she came out from the old woman's house and commenced her magic at the outskirts of the town. She said *"Sanguri!"* and every person disappeared; and again she said *"Sanguri!"* and every house broke up at once and not a dwelling remained. *"Sanguri!"*—the village once again became the forest. *"Sanguri!"* and the old woman's sore came back. And the eagle said, "Old woman, you have seen." That is why the elders say, "If some does good to you, thank him by doing good to him and do not return evil to thank him."

[ASHANTI]

61

Untombinde, the Tall Maiden

THE DAUGHTER OF THE KING Usikulumi said, "Father, I am going to the Ilulange next year." Her father said, "Nothing goes to that place and comes back again: it goes there for ever." She came again the next year and said, "Father, I am going to the Ilulange. Mother, I am going to the Ilulange." He said, "nothing goes to that place and comes back again: it goes there for ever." Another year came round. She said, "Father, I am going to the Ilulange." She said, "Mother, I am going to the Ilulange." They said, "To the Ilulange nothing goes and returns again: it goes there for ever." The father and mother at last consented to let Untombinde go.

She collected a hundred virgins on one side of the road, and a hundred on the other. So they went on their way. They met some merchants. The girls came and stood on each side of the path, on this side and that. They said, "Merchants, tell us which is the prettiest girl here; for we are two wedding companies." The merchants said, "You are beautiful, Utinkabazana; but you are not equal to Untombinde, the king's child, who is like a spread-out surface of good green grass; who is like fat for cooking; who is like a goat's gall-bladder!" The marriage company of Utinkabazana killed these merchants.

They arrived at the river Ilulange. They had put on bracelets and ornaments for the breast, and collars, and petticoats ornamented with brass beads. They took them off, and placed them on the banks of the pool of the Ilulange. They went in, and both marriage companies sported in the water. When they had sported a while, a little girl went out first and found nothing there, neither the collars, nor the ornaments for the breast, nor the bracelets, nor the petticoats ornamented with brass beads. She said, "Come out; the things are no longer here." All went out. Untombinde, the princess, said, "What can we do?" One of the girls said, "Let us petition. The things have been taken away by the Isik*q*uk*q*umadevu." Another said, "You, Isik*q*uk*q*umadevu, give me my things, that I may depart. I have been brought into this trouble by Untombinde, the king's child, who said, 'Men bathe in the great pool: our first fathers bathed there.' Is it I who bring down upon you the Intontela?" The Isik*q*uk*q*umadevu gave her the petticoat. Another girl began, and besought the Isik*q*uk*q*umadevu: she said, "You, Isik*q*uk*q*umadevu, just give me my things, that I may depart. I have been brought into this trouble by Untombinde, the king's child; she said, 'At the great pool men bathe: our first fathers used to bathe there.' Is it I who have brought down upon you Intontela?" The whole marriage company began until every one of them had done the same. There remained Untombinde, the king's child, only.

The marriage party said, "Beseech Usik*q*uk*q*umadevu, Untombinde." She refused, and said, "I will never beseech the Isik*q*uk*q*umadevu, I being the king's child." The Isik*q*uk*q*umadevu seized her, and put her into the pool.

The other girls cried, and cried, and then went home. When they arrived, they said, "Untombinde has been taken away by the Isik*q*uk*q*umadevu." Her father said, "A long time ago I told Untombinde so; I refused her, saying, 'To the Ilulange, nothing goes to that place and returns again: it goes there for ever.' Behold, she goes there for ever."

The king mustered the troops of young men, and said, "Go and fetch the Isik*q*uk*q*umadevu, which has killed Untombinde." The troops came to the river, and fell in with it, it having already come out of the water, and being now on the bank. It was as big as a mountain. It came and swallowed all that army; and then it went to the very village of the king; it came, and swallowed up all men and dogs; it swallowed them up, the whole country, together with the cattle. It swallowed up two children in that country; they were twins, beautiful children, and much beloved.

But the father escaped from that house; and he went, taking two clubs, saying, "It is I who will kill the Isik*q*uk*q*umadevu." And he took his large assegai and went on his way. He met with some buffalo, and said, "Whither has Isik*q*uk*q*umadevu gone? She has gone away with my children." The buffalo said, "You are seeking Unomabunge, O-gaul'-iminga. Forward! Forward! *Mametu!*" He then met with some leopards, and said, I am looking for Isik*q*uk*q*umadevu, who has gone off with my children." And the leopards said, "You are looking for Unomabunge, O-gaul'-iminga, O-nsiba-zimak*q*embe. Forward! Forward! *Mametu!*" Then he met with an elephant, and said, "I inquire for Isik*q*uk*q*umadevu, who has gone away with my children. It said, "You mean Unomabunge, O-gaul'-iminga, O-nsiba-zimak*q*embe. Forward! Forward! *Mametu!*" Then he came to Unomabunge herself: the man found her crouched down, being as big as a mountain. And he said, "I am seeking Isik*q*uk*q*umadevu, who is taking away my children." And she said, "You are seeking Unomabunge; you are seeking O-gaul'-iminga, O-nsiba-zimak*q*embe. Forward! Forward! *Mametu!*" Then the man came and stabbed the lump; and so the Isik*q*uk*q*umadevu died.

And then there came out of her cattle, and dogs, and a man, and all the men; and then Untombinde herself came out. And when she had come out, she returned to her father, Usikulumi, the son of Uthlokothloko. When she arrived, she was taken by Unthlatu, the son of Usibilingwana, to be his wife.

Untombinde went to take her stand in her bridegroom's kraal. On her arrival she stood at the upper part of the kraal. They asked, "Whom have you come to marry?" She said, "Unthlatu." They said, "Where is he!" She said, "I heard said that King Usibilingwana has begotten a king." They said, "Not so: he is not here. But he did beget a son; but when he was a boy he was lost." The mother wept, saying, "What did the damsel hear reported? I gave birth to one child; he was lost: there was no other!" The girl remained. The father, the king, said, "Why has she remained?" The people said, "Let her depart." The king again said, "Let her stay, since there are sons of mine here; she shall become their wife." The people said, "Let her stay with the mother." The mother refused, saying, "Let her have a house built for her." Untombinde therefore had a house built.

It came to pass that, when the house was built, the mother put in it sour milk, and meat, and beer. The girl said, "Why do you put this here?" She said, "I used to place it even before you came." The girl was silent, and lay down. And in the night Unthlatu came; he took out from the sour milk, he ate the meat, and drank the beer. He stayed a long time, and then went out.

In the morning Untombinde uncovered the sour milk: she found some had been taken out; she uncovered the meat: she saw that it had been eaten; she uncovered the beer: she found that it had been drunk. She said, "O, Mother placed this food here. It will be said that I have stolen it." The mother came in; she uncovered the food, and said, "What has eaten it?" She said, "I do not know. I too saw that it had been eaten." She said, "Did you not hear the man?" She said, "No."

The sun set. They ate those three kinds of food. A wether was slaughtered. There was placed meat; there was placed sour milk; and there was placed beer in the house. It became dark, and Untombinde lay down. Unthlatu came in; he felt the damsel's face. She awoke. He said, "What are you about to do here?" She said, "I come to be married." He said, "To whom?" The girl said, "To Unthlatu." He said, "Where is he?" She replied, "He was lost." He said, "But since he was thus lost, to whom do you marry?" She said, "To him only." He said, "Do you know that he will come?" He said, "Since there are the king's other sons, why do you not marry them, rather than wait for a man that is lost?" Then he said, "Eat, let us eat meat." The girl said, "I do not yet eat meat." Unthlatu said, "Not so. As regards me too, your bridegroom gives my people meat before the time of their eating it, and they eat." He said, "Drink, there is beer." She said, "I do not yet drink beer; for I have not yet had the *imvuma* slaughtered for me." He said, "Not so. Your bridegroom too gives my people beer before they have had anything killed for them." In the morning he went away; he speaking continually, the girl not seeing him. During all this time he would not allow the girl to light a fire. He went out. The girl arose, going to feel at the wicker door, saying, "Let me feel, since I closed it, where he went out?" She found that it was still closed with her own closing; and said, "Where did the man go out?"

The mother came in the morning, and said, "My friend, with whom were you speaking?" She said, "No; I was speaking with no one." She said, "Who was eating here of the food?" She said, "I do not know." They ate that food also. There was brought out food for the third time. They cooked beer and meat, and prepared sour milk. In the evening Unthlatu came, and felt her face, and said, "Awake." Untombinde awoke. Unthlatu said, "Begin at my foot, and feel me till you come to my head, that you may know what I am like." The girl felt him; she found that the body was slippery; it would not allow the hands to grasp it. He said, "Do you wish that I should tell you to light the fire?" She said, "Yes." He said, "Give me some snuff then." She gave him snuff. He said, "Let me take a pinch from your hand." He took a pinch, and sniffed it. He spat. The spittle said, "Hail, king! Thou black one! Thou who art as big as the mountains!" He took a pinch; he spat; the spittle said, "Hail, chief! Hail, thou who art as big as the mountains!" He then said, "Light the fire." Untombinde lighted it, and saw a shining body. The girl was afraid, and wondered, and said, "I never saw such a body." He said, "In the morning whom will you say you have seen?" She said, "I shall say that I have seen no one." He said, "What will you say to that your mother, who gave birth to Unthlatu, because she is troubled at his disappearance? What does your mother say?" She replied, "She weeps, and says, 'I wonder by whom it has been eaten. Would that I could see the man who eats this food.'" He said, "I am going away." The girl said, "And you, where do you live, since you were lost when a little child?" He said, "I live underground." She asked, "Why did you go away?" He said, "I went away on account of my brethren: they were saying that they would put a clod of earth into my windpipe; for they were jealous, because it was said that I was king. They said, 'Why should the king be young, while we who are old remain subjects?'"

He said to the girl, "Go and call that your mother who is afflicted." The mother came in with the girl. The mother wept, weeping a little in secret. She said, "What then did I say? I said, 'It is my child who was lost, who had the smooth body.'" He then said, "What will you say to my father?" She said, "I will say, 'Let the whole country brew beer.'"

The father said, "What is the beer to do?" The mother said, "I am going to see the people; for I used to be queen. I was deposed because I had no child." So the beer was brewed; and the people laughed, saying, "She sends for beer. What is she going to do, since she was the rejected one, and was deposed?" The beer was ready; the people came together; the soldiers went into the cattle enclosure; they had shields, and were all there. The father looked on and said, "I shall see presently what the woman is about to do."

Unthlatu came out. The eyes of the people were dazzled by the brightness of his body. They wondered, and said, "We never saw such a man, whose body does not resemble the body of men." He sat down. The father wondered. A great festival was kept. Then resounded the shields of Unthlatu, who was as great as all kings. Untombinde was given a leopard's tail; and the mother the tail of a wild cat; and the festival was kept, Unthlatu being again restored to his position as king. So that is the end of the tale.

[ZULU]

IV

Man and His Fate

62

The Wonder-Worker of the Plains

O NCE THERE WAS a man and a woman to whom were born first a boy and then a girl. When the bride-price had been paid for the girl and she was married, the parents said to the son, "We have a herd for you to dispose of. It is now time for you to take a wife. We will choose you a pretty wife, one whose parents are honest people."

The son, however, firmly refused. "No," he said, "do not bother. I do not like any of the girls who are here. If I absolutely have to marry, I shall choose for myself what I want."

"Do as you will," said the parents, "but if you are unhappy later on, it will not be our fault."

Then the boy set out, left the country, and travelled far, very far, into an unknown region. Finally, he came to a village where he saw some young girls, some of them crushing corn and others cooking. Secretly he made his choice, and said to himself, "That one there is the one I like." Then he went to the men of the village and said, "Good day, fathers!"

"Good day, young man!" they answered. "What is it that you wish?"

"I want to look at your daughters, for I want to take a wife."

"Well, well," they said, "we shall show them to you, and then you can choose."

So they led all of their daughters past him and he indicated the one he wanted. She gave her consent right away.

"Your parents, we expect, will pay us a visit and bring us the bride price, is that right?" asked the young girl's parents.

"No, not at all," answered the young man, "I have my bride-price with me. Take it; here it is!"

"Then," they added, "they will, we trust, come later in order to conduct your wife to you?"

"No, no, I fear they would only pain you with the hard admonitions they would give the girl. Let me, myself, take her along right away."

The parents of the young girl gave their consent to this request, but they took her aside in the hut once more to give her advice on how to conduct herself. "Be good to your parents-in-law and take diligent care of your husband!" Then they offered the young couple a younger daughter who could help with the housework. But the woman refused. Two, ten, twenty were then offered for her to choose from. All the girls were first examined before being offered to her.

"No," she insisted, "I do not want them. Give me instead the buffalo of the country, our buffalo, the Wonder-Worker of the Plains. Let him serve me."

"How can you ask for him?" they said. "You know that our life depends on him. Here he is well taken care of, but what would you do with him in a strange country? He will starve, die, and then all of us will die with him."

Before she left her parents, she took with her a pot containing a package of medicinal roots, a horn for bleeding, a little knife for making incisions, and a gourd full of fat.

Then she set out with her husband. The buffalo followed them, but he was visible to her alone. The man did not see him. He did not suspect that the Wonder-Worker of the Plains was the servant accompanying his wife.

As soon as they had come to the husband's village, they were received with joyful cries: "*Hoyo, hoyo!*"

"Now look at him!" said the old ones. "So you have found a wife after all! You did not want one of those whom we suggested to you, but that makes no difference. It is well as it is. You have acted according to your own will. If, however, at some time, you have enemies, you will have no right to complain."

The man then took his wife into the fields and showed her which were his and which were his mother's. The girl noted everything carefully and returned with him to the village. On the way she said, "I have lost my pearls in the field; I must return to look for them at once." In reality, however, she wanted to see the buffalo. She said to him, "Here is the boundary of the fields. Stay here! And there, too, is the forest in which you can hide."

"You are right," he replied.

Now whenever the wife wanted any water, she merely went to the cultivated fields and set the pitcher down in front of the buffalo. He ran with it to the lake, filled it, and brought the vessel back to his mistress. Whenever she wanted wood, he would go into the brush, break trees with his horns, and bring her as much as she needed.

The people in the village were surprised at all these things. "What strength she has!" they said. "She is always back from the well right away; in the twinkling of an eye she has gathered a bundle of dry wood." But no one suspected that a buffalo assisted her as a servant.

The wife did not, however, bring the buffalo anything to eat, for she had only one plate for herself and her husband. At home, of course, they had had a separate plate for the Wonder-Worker and fed him carefully. Here, therefore, the buffalo was hungry. She would bring him her pitcher and send him to fetch water. This he did willingly, but he felt great pangs of hunger.

One day she showed him a corner in the brush which he was to clear.

During the night the buffalo took a hoe and prepared a vast acreage. Everyone commented, "How clever she is! And how fast she has done her work!"

One evening the buffalo said to his mistress, "I am hungry and you give me nothing to eat. Soon I shall not be able to work any more!"

"*Aie*," said she, "what shall I do? We have only one plate at the house. The people at home were right when they said that you would have to start stealing. So, steal! Go into my field and take a bean here and there. Then, again, go farther. Do not, however, take them all from the same spot, thus the owners may not be too much aware of it and will not fall over in terror right away."

That night, accordingly, the buffalo went to the field. He devoured a bean here and a bean there, jumped from one corner to the other, and finally fled back to his hiding place. When the women came into the fields the next morning, they could not believe their eyes. "Hey, hey, what is going on here? We have never seen anything like this! A wild beast has destroyed our plants! One can even follow his spoor. Ho, the poor land!" So they ran back and told the story in the village.

In the evening, the young woman said to the buffalo, "To be sure, they were very much terrified, but not too much, nevertheless. They did not fall on their backs. So keep on stealing tonight!" And so it continued. The owners of the devastated fields cried out loud and then turned to the men and asked them to summon the watchmen with their guns.

Now, the husband of the young woman was a very good marksman. He, therefore, hid in an ambush in his field and waited. The buffalo, however, thought that someone might be lying in wait for him where he had stolen the night before, so he went to his mistress's beans, the place where he had pastured the first time.

"Say," cried the man, "this is a buffalo! One has never seen any like him here. This is a strange animal, indeed." He fired. The bullet entered the temple of the buffalo, close to the ear, and came out exactly opposite on the other side. The Wonder-Worker of the Plains turned one somersault and fell dead.

"That was a good shot!" exclaimed the hunter and announced it to the village.

But the woman now began to cry out in pain and writhe. "Oh, I have stomach-aches, oh, oh!"

"Calm yourself," she was told. She seemed sick, but in reality she only wanted to explain why she was crying thus, and why she was so terrified when she heard of the buffalo's death. She was given medicine, but she poured it out when nobody else saw her.

Now everyone set out, women with baskets, and men with weapons, in order to cut up the buffalo. The young wife alone remained in the village. Soon, however, she followed them, holding her belly, whimpering and crying.

"What is wrong with you, that you come here," said her husband. "If you are sick, stay at home!"

"No, I did not want to stay in the village all by myself."

Her mother-in-law scolded her, saying that she could not understand what she was doing and that she would kill herself by this. When they had filled the baskets with meat, she said, "Let me carry the head!"

"But no, you are sick, it is much too heavy for you."

"No," said she, "let me do it!" So she shouldered it and carried it.

After they had arrived at the village, however, instead of stepping into the house, she went into the shed where the cooking-pots were kept and set down the buffalo's head. Obstinately, she refused to move. Her husband looked for her in order to bring her into the hut. He said she would be much better off there, but she only replied to him harshly, "Do not disturb me!"

Then her mother-in-law came and admonished her gently. "Why do you torture yourself?"

And she replied crossly, "Will you not let me sleep even a little?"

Then they brought her some food, but she pushed it away. Night came. Her husband went to rest. He did not sleep, however, but listened.

The woman now fetched fire, cooked some water in her little pot, and poured into it the package of medicine which she had brought with her from her home. Then she took the buffalo's head and, with the knife, made incisions in front of the ear, at the temple, where the bullet had struck the animal. There she set the bleeding horn and sucked, sucked with all the force of her body, and succeeded in drawing first a few lumps of clotted blood, and then liquid blood. Thereupon she exposed the place to the steam which rose from the cooking-pot, after having, however, smeared it completely with the fat that she had saved in the gourd. That soothed the spot. Then she sang as follows:

"*Ah, my father, Wonder-Worker of the Plains,*
They told me: You would go through the deep darkness; that in all directions you would stumble through the night, Wonder-Worker of the Plains;
You are the young wonder-tree plant, grown out of ruins, which dies before its time, consumed by a gnawing worm. . . .
You made flowers and fruit fall upon your road, Wonder-Worker of the Plains!"

When she had finished her invocation formula, the head moved, the limbs grew again, the buffalo came to life once more, shook his ears and horns, rose up, and stretched his limbs. . . .

But at this point the man, who could not sleep in the hut, stepped out and said, "Why does my wife have to cry so long? I must see why she pours out all these sighs!" He entered the shed and called for her, but in great anger she replied, "Leave me alone!" Thereupon, however, the buffalo's head fell to the ground again, dead, pierced as before.

The man returned to the hut; he had understood nothing of all this and had seen nothing. Once again the woman took the pot, cooked the medicine, made the incisions, placed the bleeding horn in the proper spot, exposed the wound to the steam, and sang as before:

"Ah, my father, Wonder-Worker of the Plains,
Indeed they have told me: You would go through the deep darkness; that in
all directions you would stumble through the night, Wonder-Worker of
the Plains;
You are the young wonder-tree plant, grown out of ruins, which dies before
its time, consumed by a gnawing worm. . . .
You made flowers and fruit fall upon your road, Wonder-Worker of the
Plains!"

Once again, the buffalo rose up, his limbs grew together again, he felt himself coming to life, shook his ears and horns, stretched himself—but then again came the man, disquieted, in order to see what his wife was doing. Then she became very angry with him, but he settled down in the shed in order to watch what was going on. Now she took her fire, her cooking pot and all the other things and went out. She pulled up grass to kindle the embers and began for the third time to resuscitate the buffalo.

Morning had already broken when her mother-in-law came—and once more the head fell to the ground. Day came, and the buffalo's wound began to grow worse.

Finally, she said to all of them, "I would like to go bathing in the lake all alone."

They answered her, "But how will you get there since you are sick?"

She went on her way anyhow and then came back and said, "On my way I came upon someone from home. He told me that my mother is very, very sick. I told him to come here to the village but he refused and said, 'They would offer me food and that would only delay me.' He went on right away and added that I should hurry lest my mother die before my arrival. Therefore, good-bye, I am going away!"

Of course, all this was a lie. She had thought of the idea of going to the lake so that she could invent this story and have a reason for carrying the news of the buffalo's death to her people.

She went off, carrying the basket on her head and singing all along the road the end of the song about the Wonder-Worker of the Plains. Wherever she passed, the people would band together behind her to accompany her into her village. Arrived there, she announced to them that the buffalo no longer lived.

Then they sent out messengers in all directions in order to gather together the inhabitants of the country. They reproached the young woman earnestly, saying, "Do you see now? We told you so. But you refused all the young girls and wanted absolutely to have the buffalo. Now you have killed all of us!"

Things had advanced thus far when the man, who had followed his wife into the village, also arrived. He rested his gun against a tree trunk and sat down. They greeted him by shouting, "Be saluted, criminal, be saluted! You have killed us all!" He did not understand this and wondered how one could call him a murderer and a criminal.

"To be sure, I have killed a buffalo," said he, "but that is all."

"Yes, but this buffalo was your wife's assistant. He drew water for her, cut wood, worked in the field."

Completely stunned, the man said, "Why did you not let me know that? I would not have killed him then."

"That is how it is," they added. "The lives of all of us depended on him."

Thereupon all of the people began to cut their own throats. First, the young woman, who, as she did it, called out:

"Ah, my father, Wonder-Worker of the Plains!"

Then came her parents, brothers, sisters, one after the other.

The first one said:

"You shall go through darkness!"

The next:

"You shall stumble through the night in all directions!"

The next:

"You are the young wonder-tree plant which dies before its time."

The next:

"You made flowers and fruit fall upon your road!"

All cut their throats and they even slew the little children who were still being carried in skins upon the back. "Why should we let them live," they said, "since they would only lose their minds!"

The man returned home and told his people how, by shooting the buffalo, he had killed them all. His parents said to him, "Do you see now? Did we not tell you that misfortune would come to you? When we offered a fitting and wise woman for you, you wanted to act according to your own desire. Now you have lost your fortune. Who will give it back to you, since they are all dead, all of your wife's relatives, to whom you have given your money!"

This is the end.

[BARONGA]

63

The Enchanted Guinea-Fowl

A CERTAIN MAN once upon a time set his bird line and sent his daughter, saying, "Go and look at my line while I go to dig." So his daughter went to see the line. She found a guinea-fowl caught in it, and the guinea-fowl sang:

> *"Little girl, little girl,* kirijakija,
> *What have you come to do?"*

Then said the girl, "I have come to look at the snare." And the guinea-fowl asked her, "Whose snare is it?" And the girl said, "I have come to look at my father's snare." Thereupon the guinea-fowl said to her, "Go and tell your father that I will bring a white bead and a white sheep if he will let me go."

So the girl went back and told her father, and her father abused his daughter, saying, "You are a bad child," and sent his son instead.

So his son went to look at his father's line and he too found the guinea-fowl in the line. And the guinea-fowl asked him, asked him in song:

> *"Little boy, little boy,* kirijakija,
> *What have you come to do?"*

Thereupon said the little boy, "I have come to look at my father's line." And the guinea-fowl said, "Go and tell your father that I will bring a white chicken and a white sheep and a white bead if he will let me go."

So the boy went back and told his father in these words.

Next the man sent his wife. His wife found the guinea-fowl, and the guinea-fowl addressed her in the same terms as he had used to the children.

Then anger overcame the man, and he went himself and found the guinea-fowl in the line. The guinea-fowl addressed his same song as before. But the man seized the guinea-fowl firmly, and the guinea-fowl said to him, "Though you seize me, seize me: here in the evening I shall seize mine."

The man then brought him home and plucked him. As he did this, the guinea-fowl said to him, "Though you pluck me, pluck me: here in the evening I shall pluck mine."

The man cooked the bird, and the guinea-fowl said to him, "Though you cook me, cook me: here in the evening I shall cook mine."

But he was cooked and ready to be eaten. Then the man summoned people, and the people came for food, came that they might eat the guinea-fowl which had been cooked. They all rejoiced with a careless joy and served up the guinea-fowl. Suddenly the guinea-fowl flew up with a quick flutter and these men were left with their joy.

Now if the man had been wise enough to take the white bead and the sheep and the white chicken, he could have eaten this guinea-fowl. This was the guinea-fowl of God.

[LANGO]

64

The Adventures of Mrile

IN THE COURSE OF TIME, a man had three sons. Once, the oldest one went with his mother to dig up eddo tubers. As they were thus occupied, he saw a seed-bulb. And he said, "Why, there is a seed-bulb as handsome as my little brother." But his mother said to him, "How can a seed-bulb be as handsome as a human child?" He, however, hid the seed-bulb, and the mother tied up the eddoes to carry them home. The boy hid the seed-bulb in the hollow of a tree and, using a magic formula, said, "*Msura Kwivire-vire tsa kambingu na kasanga.*"

The following day he went there again. The seedling had now become a child. Whenever his mother cooked food, he carried some to it, again and again. Every day he carried food there, but he himself grew leaner and leaner. His father and mother noticed how lean he had grown and asked him, "Son, what is it that makes you so lean? Where is the food going that we always cook for you? Your younger brothers have not become so lean!" Then one of his younger brothers decided to watch the food being cooked. He saw his older brother receive his share served on a plate, and that he did not eat it but carried it away as though to save it. His brothers followed him at a distance to spy on him and saw how he put it into the hollow of a tree. Thereupon they returned home and said to their mother, "We saw how our brother put the food there into the hollow of a tree and brought it to a child living there." And she said to them, "Whose child would inhabit the hollow of a tree?" Thereupon they said to her, "Come on, we will go and direct you there, you-who-have-nursed-us!" And they led their mother there and showed her the place. And behold! there in the hollow of the tree was a little child! So his mother approached the child and killed it.

After she had killed the child, the older brother Mrile carried food there as usual but did not find the child; instead he found it slain. Thereupon he went home and wept copiously. Then his parents asked him, "Mrile, why do you cry?" And he answered, "It is because of the smoke." So they said, "Sit down here at the lower end." Yet his tears still continued unrestrained. Again they said to him, "Why do you cry all the time?" And he answered, "It is nothing but the smoke." Then they responded, "Take your father's

237

chair along with you and go into the courtyard and sit down!" He took the chair, sat down on it in the courtyard, yet the tears continued.

Suddenly he said, "Chair, raise yourself up high like my father's rope whereby he suspends the honey barrel in the virgin forest and in the steppe." About this time his younger brothers entered the courtyard. They saw how he was travelling upward toward the sky. They informed their mother, "Mrile has travelled up toward the sky." But she said, "Why do you talk about your oldest brother travelling up towards the sky? Is there a road, pray, whereon he could ascend?" But they again spoke to her, "Come and see, you-who-have-nursed-us!" So his mother came to investigate and found that he had indeed ascended high up.

Thereupon his mother cried:

> *"Mrile return,*
> *Return, my child,*
> *Return!"*

But Mrile answered:

> *"I shall return no more,*
> *I shall return no more,*
> *Mother, Ah, I,*
> *I shall return no more,*
> *I shall return no more."*

Thereupon his younger brother cried:

> *"Mrile, return,*
> *Return, our brother,*
> *Return!*
> *Come home,*
> *Come home!"*

But he said:

> *"Oh, I,*
> *I shall return no more,*
> *I shall return no more,*
> *My brothers,*
> *I shall return no more,*
> *I shall return no more."*

Thereupon his father came and spoke:

> *"Mrile, here is your food,*
> *Here is your food,*
> *Mrile, here it is!*
> *Mrile, here is your food,*
> *Here is your food!"*

But he answered, saying:

> "*I want no more,*
> *I want no more,*
> *My father, Ah, I,*
> *I want no more,*
> *I want no more.*"

Thereupon his tribal companions came and sang:

> "*Mrile, come home!*
> *Come home!*
> *Mrile, come!*
> *Come home!*
> *Come home!*
> *Mrile, come!*"

Thereupon his uncle came and sang:

> "*Mrile, come home,*
> *Come home!*
> *Mrile, come!*
> *Come home,*
> *Come home!*"

But he sang in reply:

> "*Ah, I,*
> *I shall return no more,*
> *I shall return no more.*
> *Uncle, Ah, I,*
> *I shall return no more,*
> *I shall return no more!*"

And he disappeared, so that they could not see him any more.

After a while, Mrile encountered wood-gatherers. He greeted them, "Wood-gatherers, good day! Please show me the way to Moon-King." But they answered him, "Gather some wood, then we will direct you there." So he cut some firewood for them. Then they told him, "Just go straight ahead, and you will encounter some grass-cutters!" So he went on and soon encountered some grass-cutters. "Grass-cutters, good day!" They returned the greeting. "Please show me the road to Moon-King." But they said to him, "Cut some grass first, then we will direct you there." So he cut some grass for them. Thereupon they told him, "Just go straight ahead, and you will encounter some tillers." So he went on and soon encountered some tillers. "You who are tilling there, good day!" And they said to him, "Good day!" "Please show me the road to Moon-King!" But they said to him, "First till for us, then we will direct you there." So he tilled for them. Thereupon they told him, "Just go straight ahead and then you will encounter some herds-men." He went on and soon encountered some herdsmen. "You, tending the herd there, good day!" "Good day!" "Please direct me to Moon-King!" But they told him, "Watch the herd for us for a while, and we will direct you there!" So he helped them with the grazing for a while.

Then they said to him, "Just go straight ahead to the bean-harvesters!" "You there, harvesting beans, good day! Please direct me to Moon-King!" "Help us pick beans a little, then we will direct you there!" So he picked some beans. Thereupon they said, "Just go further along this road to the mil-let-reapers!" Soon he encountered some millet-reapers. "You, millet-reapers, greetings! Please direct me to Moon-King!" "Help us first reap some millet, then we will direct you there!" "Now go further along the road to the peo-ple who seek banana stalks!" These, in turn, he saluted: "You, banana-stalk seekers, greetings! Please direct me to Moon-King!" "Help us seek banana stalks first, then we will direct you there!" So he found them some banana stalks. Then they told him, "Just go straight ahead, until you come to the people who carry water!" "You water-carriers, greetings! Please show me the way to Moon-King!" "Go straight ahead to the people who are just eat-ing in their own houses!" "You, house-owners, greetings! Please direct me to Moon-King!" "Come, first eat something, then we will direct you there."

After a while he encountered people who ate raw food. They were the people of the Moon-King. And he said to them, "Why do you not cook with fire?" But they answered him thus, "What is that, fire?" He said to them, "One cooks food with it until it is done." Then they said to him, "We know nothing about fire!" And he said to them, "If I prepare you some tasty food by means of fire, what will you give me?" The Moon-King said, "We shall rent you large cattle and some small stock." And Mrile said to them, "Good, gather a lot of dry wood for me, and I will bring you the fire." So they gathered some wood, but they went behind the house where they were not seen by other people. Mrile, then, brought forth a fire-drill and a fire-board and struck fire, there, behind the house. They then lit the firewood and he placed green bananas in it for roasting. Then he said to Moon-King, "Try to eat these bananas which I have roasted in the fire." Moon-King ate the banana and noticed how nice it tasted. Thereupon Mrile put meat in to cook and said to him, "Now you must eat cooked meat too!" And Moon-King noticed how tasty it was. Then he cooked for them all kinds of eatable things, all well done. Finally, Moon-King had the people called and he said to them, "A medicine-man has come from below there, from below there!"

Now Moon-King spoke, "Tribute shall be paid to this man to buy his fire from him." Then they asked him, "What shall be paid you?" And he said, "Let one person bring a cow, another a goat, another something from the granary!" So they carried all these things to him. Then he distributed fire among them, whereon they went to cook their food.

After a while he reflected: "How can I reach home again, if I cannot send a message there?" So he ordered all the various birds to come to him. They came to the place where he was staying. Then he spoke to Raven: "If I send you to my homeland as a messenger, what will you say when you get there?" Raven said, "I shall speak thus: '*Coorooh, coorooh, coorooh!*'" So he chased him away. Then Rhinoceros-Bird came. "You, Rhinoceros-Bird, if I send you, how will you speak to them?" He answered, "I shall say, '*Ngaa, ngaa, ngaa!*'" So he chased him away, and Hawk appeared. "You, Hawk, if I send you into the homeland as a messenger, what will you say there?" Hawk answered thus: "*Chiri—i—i—o!*" So he chased him away too. Thereupon he spoke to Buzzard: "If I send you, what will you say?" Buzzard answered, "I shall say, '*Cheng, cheng, cheng!*'" So he chased him away. And thus he examined in turn all the birds, every species around there, without finding a bird who understood anything. Then, finally, he called Mocking-Bird. "You, Mocking-Bird, if I send you, what message will you deliver?" Mocking-Bird answered:

> *"Mrile will come the day after tomorrow,*
> *The day after tomorrow;*
> *Mrile will come the day after tomorrow,*
> *The day after tomorrow,*
> *The day after tomorrow.*
> *Save some fat for him in the spoon!*
> *Save some fat for him in the spoon!"*

Thereupon Mrile said, "Well, that is good, go ahead!"

Then Mocking-Bird went and reached the gate to the court of Mrile's father, and he sang thus:

> *"Mrile wants me to tell you:*
> *He will come the day after tomorrow,*
> *The day after tomorrow,*
> *He will come the day after tomorrow.*
> *The day after tomorrow,*
> *Save some fat for him in the spoon!"*

And Mrile's father set out into the courtyard saying, "My, what is this being that shouts in the courtyard and tells me that Mrile will come the day after tomorrow? For, surely, he has perished long ago!" He drove him away and the bird disappeared.

Then Mocking-Bird went to Mrile and said, "I have been there." But Mrile spoke to him thus: "No, you have not been there. If you have been there—what does one find there, in my homeland?" And he said to him, "Go a second time, and when you get there, be sure to pick up my father's stick and come back therewith, so that I can be certain you have been there." So Mocking-Bird returned for a second time, picked up the stick and carried it to Mrile. The children in the house saw him take it, but they could not snatch it away from him.

Then Mocking-Bird brought it to Mrile. Thereupon Mrile was certain that Mocking-Bird had really been there. Now Mrile said, "Well, I shall now set out on my journey home." Moon-King let him go with his cattle.

So he started out with his cattle. On the way he grew tired. Now he had a bull with him, and the bull spoke to him and said, "Since you are so tired out, if I take you upon my back, what will you do? If I take you upon my back, will you eat me when they slaughter me?" And Mrile answered him, "No, I will not eat you." So he climbed on the bull's back, and the bull supported him. Finally he arrived, singing:

> "*No possessions do I lack,*
> *The stock is mine*, hae!
> *No possessions do I lack,*
> *The cattle are mine*, hae!
> *No possessions do I lack,*
> *The small stock are mine*, hae!
> *No possessions do I lack,*
> *Mrile comes home*, hae!
> *No possessions do I lack.*"

And so Mrile came home. When he arrived at home, his father and mother smeared him with fat. Then he spoke to them thus: "This bull you shall feed until he grows old. Even when he grows old, I shall not eat his meat." But when the bull grew old, the father slaughtered him; thereupon the mother said, "Should this bull, that my son has taken so great trouble with, be devoured without his eating therefrom?" And she hid the fat, she hid it in the honey pot. When she knew that the meat had been used up, she ground flour, took the fat and added it thereto. So she brought it to her son, and Mrile tasted it. When he had tasted it with his mouth, the meat spoke to him: "Do you dare to consume me, me who have taken you on my back?" And it said to him, "Therefore be consumed, as you consume me!"

Then Mrile sang:

> "*My mother, I told you:*
> *Serve me not the meat of the bull!*"

But when he tasted it for a second time, his foot sank into the ground. And he sang:

> "*My mother, I told you:*
> *Serve me not the meat of the bull!*"

Thereupon he consumed the meal completely. Suddenly, he was swallowed up.

And this is the end of the story.

[CHAGA]

65

The Handsome Ogre-Girl of the Pool

SOME MEN ONCE WENT out hunting. When they had walked some distance, they met a girl who was decked with chains that dangled to and fro. One of the men saluted her, and she returned the salutation. He said to her, "Give me food!"

"Take it, here is some!"

"I do not want any!"

"What do you want, then?"

"I want to take you home as my wife to our village."

"Wait, then, and I'll fetch my mother!" She called, "Mother!"

"*Wau!*"

"Here is a man who wants to take me to wife!"

The man saw how the water of a pool began to surge, and it rose up and down violently. He saw a head resembling a flame of fire appearing above the surface of the water. Then the man and his friends took fright and fled, throwing away their provisions and their bows and all their clothes. They ran to their camp and said, "In this neighbourhood we do not wish to sleep. We are very frightened, and tomorrow we shall go back home."

They returned home to their village and said to the people there, "We have seen a girl and her mother who live in the water. And the girl is very good-looking, but her mother, oh! oh!"

"What does she look like?"

"She is an ogre!"

"Let us go and take that girl to wife; we are not afraid of ogres," said some.

They got their equipment and set out into the wilderness. A boy who was quite small joined them. They remonstrated at length with the boy and told him to turn back, but he refused. They went on and came to the place where, on the preceding day, the other men in fright had thrown their things away. They said, "Never mind! Let us go on and bring the girl back home with us!"

They went on and found the girl. They greeted her: "*Wakra*, girl?"

"Aah!"

"Give us food!"

"There is food in the calabash."

243

"We do not really want food."

"What do you want, then?"

"We want to take you home with us to our village."

"Well, wait, then, and I shall fetch my mother, so that she may see you!"

"Your mother, why should you call her?"

"I summon her so that she may come and see him who wishes to take me to wife."

"Well, call her, then!"

"Mother!"

"*Wau!*"

"Come here that you may see the man who wants to take me to wife!"

They saw how the water began to surge, high, then higher. They saw a head looking out of the pool, and it looked like fire. They all ran away, only the small boy remained. In their flight they threw away the calabashes containing their provisions. And they repaired to the camping-place from which they had started. The ogre-mother pursued the men for some distance, and then she slowly returned and became very small. Then she said to the boy, "Good-day, son-in-law!"

"Aah!" said the girl.

"I understand that some man wanted to take you to wife, but this one is a child," the ogress said to her daughter.

The boy said, "So I am, mother, but never mind that!"

"Well, sit down, then, and talk with your wife, and come tonight over there to my hut."

When evening arrived, the wife said to him, "Get up and let us go to the hut!"

"But where are we to sleep? Will that be in the water?"

"There is a hut." She took him by the arm. "Close your eyes! And open them when we are inside the hut!"

The boy shut his eyes and then opened them again, and found that he was in a hut free from water. And the woman, his mother-in-law, was sitting there weaving a bag and looking like a Kamba woman. She said to him, "You go and lie down on the bed over there and sleep!" And they went and lay down. And in the morning they went to the garden. The boy went to make a new garden for his mother-in-law. When he came back, she asked, "Do you wish to return home?"

"Yes!"

"Then take your belongings and be off!" And to her daughter she said, "In case, when you get home, your husband should happen to die, you must give instructions that he is not to be buried, but that they must throw him outside. And when he begins to putrefy, you are to take a maggot which you shall put into a honey jar. That maggot you must smear every day with fat. You must go on smearing it with fat and, eventually, it will grow into a child. That child you must go on smearing with fat, and then it will increase in growth, and you must give it milk. And by and by you will see that it is your husband who has returned."

"I will do as you say," answered the girl. The next morning they returned to the husband's home.

When the people saw the boy arriving with the girl, they wailed and said, "Alas, alas! That beautiful girl has become the wife of a child. Has anyone ever seen the like." And they looked about for medicine to kill the boy, but found that they were unable to kill him in that manner. Then they said, "We will show you something else."

And they took their bows and went to hunt bush buck. The boy's brother went and took up his station for the hunt in a spot out in the wilderness, and the boy placed himself opposite him. The brother shot him. Then he called for help, "Come here, all of you! I happened to shoot Syani when I aimed to kill a bush buck."

"Seeing it was you who did it, there can be no case against you, as you were his brother." They put the body of the boy down in the wilderness and returned home.

In the evening they said to the girl, "Syani is dead."

She asked, "In what way was he killed?"

"By his brother."

She wailed a great deal. Then she ceased, and asked the brother, "How did you manage to kill him?"

"I was aiming to kill a bush buck."

"Well, I do not care for other men. I am now going to live alone."

She wept for two months. After that she asked where they had put her husband in the wilderness. She went there and found a maggot. She took it, brought it home, and put it into a honey jar. She smeared it with fat and continued to do so daily. It grew into a child and could grow no further within the jar. Then she took the child out and put it underneath her bedstead in the *we*. Her husband's brother lived there in the hut, but they did not sleep together.

The boy grew apace. She made food for him and brought it to him under the bed. The man asked her, "Who is it that you are feeding over there underneath the bed?"

"It is rats, it is just rats that are always hanging about there."

One day the boy went outside the hut, and then she noticed that he had grown into a big man. She gave him sword, quiver, and bow, and said to him, "It was this child that was killed when they were hunting bush buck. To-night he will take revenge."

"Good!"

Now the brother had gone to drink beer at some villages far away. He returned in the evening, speaking with the beer. As he reached the gate of his fence, he heard someone talking with the wife within. He said, "Who is that?"

The wife answered, "Come here, and you will see him!"

He took his stick in order to beat the man. He walked in, and when he got to the door of the hut, he was shot by the brother whom he had killed and who now took his revenge. He dropped to the ground, was slashed with the sword, and died.

The next morning the husband and his wife moved away from the place. They went and settled at a place called Kavithe.

[AKAMBA]

66

The Town Where None Might Go to Sleep

A CERTAIN WOMAN had two daughters. One was married to a man who lived in a town where no one was allowed to go to sleep, the other to one in a town where no one might spit.*

One day the woman cooked a dish of sweetmeats to take to the daughter who lived in the town where no one was allowed to go to sleep. As soon as the dish was ready she started off and, when she arrived, all the household said to her, "Welcome, welcome!" Food was prepared for her, for the son-in-law said, "See, my mother-in-law has come."

But the daughter said, "O parent, no one may sleep here. Do not eat too much lest sleepiness should overcome you."

But the mother said, "I knew long before you were born that sleep was not permitted here."

"Oh, very well then," replied the daughter, "I'll say no more." And the mother ate every bit of the food that was brought to her.

That night, although she lay down, she managed to keep awake. In the morning the daughter took up her jar to go to the stream for water and said to her mother, "See here, I have put the breakfast on to boil. Please keep up the fire while I am away."

But when the daughter had gone, although her mother managed to replenish the fire for a time, drowsiness overcame her in the end, and she lay down and fell fast asleep. Just then a neighbour came to get fire and, when she saw the sleeping woman, she exclaimed, "Alas! So-and-so's mother-in-law is dead."

Then the drummers were sent for, and soon the whole town had assembled at the house and a grave had been dug. The drums were saying:

> "Birrim, birrim, *get a corpse mat,*
> *Death's in the son-in-law's house.*"

But the daughter heard from where she was, and she cried out:

> "*Stay, oh, stay, don't get a corpse mat,*
> *We are accustomed to sleep.*"

And when she had come to her house, she roused her mother, and said, "Wake up, wake up." Then the mother awoke with a start and the people

* See glossary.

were terrified, but they soon saw that it was nothing to be afraid of, and the whole town began to learn how to sleep.

Now the mother returned to her own home, and one day she cooked more sweetmeats and decided to visit her other daughter, the one living in the town where no one might spit.

When she arrived, the household said, "Welcome, welcome!" And the son-in-law said, "My mother-in-law has come." So he killed a fowl and sent her a dish of rice. The daughter said to her mother, "Do not eat too much. You know that in this town no one is allowed to spit."

The mother replied, "Thanks for the information! I knew that before ever you were born."

"Very well," said the daughter, and she took no more notice. The mother ate until she was full.

Now when night came, she wanted very much to spit, but she did not know where she could do so without being found out. At last she went to the place where the horses were tied, and she spat, and covered the place with some of the cut grass there. But the earth was not used to this, and the part spat upon rose up and began to complain, saying:

"Umm, umm, *I am not used to this,*
Umm, umm, *I am not used to this.*"

Soon all the people came and said, "Who has spat here?" Then they said, "Bring out the magic gourds, the small one and the large, and let everyone come here and step over them; and the gourds will catch hold of the one who has spat." So all the people of the town stepped over them, but no one was seized and they were surprised. Then someone said, "See here, there is a stranger amongst us, let her come and step over the gourds."

Immediately when she had come and had lifted up a leg to step over, the gourds seized her, and everyone said, "It is she who has spat, it is she who has spat!" And the gourds began singing these words:

"*The things which clasp and hold on,*
The mother-in-law has got them."

She could not sit down, for they held on to her body.

Now, the spider, that interfering person, met her, and said, "O mother-in-law, how lucky you are to have gourds which sing such a beautiful song. I should like to have them."

So she replied, "Very well, spit on the ground and say that it was not you who did it."

And when he had done so, he said, "There! But it is not I who have done it, if it is I, O you magic gourds, seize me."

And immediately the gourds loosed the woman and seized him. Then they began singing:

> *"The things which clasp and hold on,*
> *The spider of spiders has got them,"*

and the spider felt exceedingly pleased, and began to dance.

But soon he got tired and said, "O mother-in-law, you thing to be avoided, come and take your gourds." But she refused to do so.

Then the spider climbed a tree, and when he got high up he threw himself down on his buttocks, so as to smash the gourds. But they moved to one side, and so the spider's back was broken and he died. Then the magic gourds returned to where they had come from, and all the townspeople began to spit, for they saw that there was no harm in it.

[HAUSA]

67

The City Where Men Are Mended

ALL THE GIRLS of the town had assembled and had gone to the forest to pick herbs. While they were doing this, it began to rain; from the east it came, and they ran and got inside the hollow of a baobab tree, and the devil closed it up. When the rain had ceased, the devil said that each must give him her necklace and cloth before he would release her, and all gave them to him except one girl who refused to do so. So she had to remain, but the others went off home.

Now the tree had a small hole at the top, and the girls who had returned told the girl's mother, so she started off and came to see the place where her daughter was. Then she returned home and prepared food, and in the evening she went back to the tree and said, "Daughter, daughter, stretch out your hand and take this food." So she stretched out her hand through the hole, and the girl got it and ate it, and then the mother went home again.

Now it happened, a hyena had heard all this and, later on, he returned and said, "Daughter, daughter, stretch out your hand and take this food." But she replied, "That is not my mother's voice," and she would not. So the hyena went to a blacksmith and said, "Alter my voice for me, so that it will resemble that of a human being," and the other said, "If I do improve your voice for you, even before you have arrived at the foot of the tree you will have eaten whatever you have found. However," he continued, "I'll do it for you," and he did so. But as the hyena was returning, he saw a centipede, and he said, "Does one ignore what he finds in the morning?" So he took the centipede and ate it. Then he went to the tree and said, "Daughter, daughter, stretch out your hand and take this food." But she replied, "That is not my mother's voice."

So the hyena became angry, and he returned to the blacksmith and was about to eat him, but the other said, "Stop, stop, stop, you must not eat me," and he continued, "Why do you want to eat me?" Then the hyena replied, "Because you did not alter my voice properly." Then the smith said, "Stop, I will do it properly." So he altered the hyena's voice and then the hyena returned to where the girl was and said, "Daughter, daughter, stretch out your hand and take this food." This time she stretched out her hand, and, when she had done so, the hyena seized it and pulled the girl out of the tree and ate her, leaving only the bones. Then he went away.

Now the girl's mother brought the food in the evening. But when she came, she saw her daughter's bones, and she burst out crying there. Then she went home and got a basket, and she returned and collected the bones and took the road to the city where men were mended.

She travelled on and on, and after a time she came to a place where food was cooking itself, and she said, "O food, show me the road to the city where men are mended." Then the food said, "Stay here and eat me," but she replied, "I have no appetite, I do not wish to eat you." So the food said, "When you have gone a certain distance, take the road on the right hand and leave that on the left."

After a time she came upon meat which was grilling itself, and she said, "O meat, show me the road to the city where men are mended." Then the meat said, "Stay here and eat me," but she replied, "I have no appetite, I do not wish to eat you." So the meat said, "When you have gone so far, take the road on the right hand and leave that on the left."

So she started again, and as she was travelling, she came upon *fura* which was mixing itself in a pot, and she said, "O *fura*, show me the road to the city where men are mended." Then the *fura* said, "Stay here and eat me," but she replied, "I have no appetite, I do not wish to eat you." So the *fura* said, "When you have gone a certain distance, take the road on the right hand and leave that on the left."

She travelled on again and, at last, there she was in the city where men were mended. Then the people said, "What has brought you here?" And she replied, "The hyena has eaten my child." "Where are the bones?" they asked. And she put down her basket and said, "See, here they are." So they said, "Very well, tomorrow your daughter will be mended."

When morning broke, they said to her, "Go out and tend the cattle," so she unloosed the cattle and took them off to feed. Now these cattle had no food except the fruits of the *adduwa* tree, and when she had picked off the fruits above and had thrown them down, she picked out the ripe ones and gave them to the cattle, but she herself chose the green ones to eat. She fed them thus until the evening, and then they returned home, and as they reached the enclosure, the biggest bull began bellowing:

> "*This woman has a good heart,*
> *Mend her daughter well.*"

So the daughter was mended well, and the mother returned to her hut, for the people said to her, "Sleep here, and tomorrow you will go home." So next day the daughter was brought and restored to her mother, and they went home.

Now the mother had a rival wife, who also had a daughter, but a very ugly one, and, when the mother had returned home, the rival said that she too would kill her daughter, and go to the city where men were mended.

So she took her daughter, and put her in a mortar, and began to pound her up. Then the daughter cried out, "O Mother, are you going to kill me?" But she went on pounding, and at last she took out the bones, and she brought a basket and put the bones into it, and then she took the road to the city where men were mended.

She travelled on and on, and after a time she came to a place where food was cooking itself, and she said, "O food, show me the road to the city where men are mended." Then the food said, "Stay here and eat me," but she replied, "*Opp*, do you need to invite me to eat you?" So she stayed and ate the food.

After a time she came upon meat which was grilling itself, and she said, "O meat, show me the road to the city where men are mended." Then the meat said, "Stay here and eat me," and she replied, "*Opp*, do you need to invite me to eat you?" So she stayed and ate up the meat.

She started again, and as she was travelling, she came upon *fura* which was mixing itself in a pot, and she said, "O *fura*, show me the road to the city where men are mended." Then the *fura* said, "Stay here and eat me," and she replied, "*Opp*, do you need to invite me to eat you?" So she stayed an ate up the *fura*.

So on she travelled again and, at last, there she was in the city where men are mended. Then the people said, "What has brought you here?" And she replied, "The hyena has eaten my child." "Where are the bones?" they asked. And she put down her basket and said, "See, here they are." So they said, "Very well, tomorrow your daughter will be mended."

When morning broke, they said to her, "Go out and tend the cattle," so she unloosed the cattle and took them off to feed. Now when she had picked off the fruits of the *adduwa* tree, and had thrown them down, she picked out the green ones, and gave them to the cattle, and she herself chose the ripe ones to eat. She fed them thus until the evening, and then they returned home, and as they reached the enclosure, the biggest bull began bellowing:

> *"This woman has a bad heart,*
> *Mend her daughter ill."*

So she tied up the cattle, and went to her hut, for the people said to her, "Sleep here, and tomorrow you will go home." In the morning, the daughter was created with one leg, one buttock, one hand, the whole consisted of only one side. Half a nose was there, the other half was missing. And when the mother came and said that she was going home, the daughter was brought out to her, and they went off along the road.

When they had emerged from the forest, the mother said, "I am not your mother," and she started off at a run, and went and hid in some grass. But the daughter followed the footprints, and went on and on until she had found her, and said, "Arise, let us go on." Then the mother said, "Go away, you are not my child." But the other said, "Ah, it is you who are not my mother."

Once more the mother started off at a run and entered their own town and went into her hut and shut the door. But the daughter came to the door and called out, "O Mother, I have come." But the other remained silent. "O Mother, I have come," said the daughter again, and she opened the door, and went to her mother. So they lived together, and the rival wife had to put up with the fact that the other's daughter was beautiful while her own was hideous.

[HAUSA]

68

M'wambia and the N'jenge

[BANTU]

ONCE UPON A TIME there was a man who married a woman, and she bore him a male child. Then he married a second wife, and she also bore him a male child. After a while the first wife died.

Now the name of the eldest son was M'wambia, and the name of the second was also M'wambia, and he was known as M'wambia the Younger, to distinguish him from his brother.

When the two boys were about twelve and ten years old, it happened that the animal known as the N'jenge came from the wilds and ate the food in the fields. Thereupon the two brothers went into the woods, and M'wambia the Elder made a snare to catch the N'jenge, and M'wambia the Younger also made a snare at a little distance away. Now a N'jenge came into the snare of M'wambia the Younger, and he released it and killed it and ate it. And a N'jenge also came into the snare of M'wambia the Elder, but he released it and did not kill it. He let it go free into the woods, and the two boys returned to the village and said nothing to their father.

One day the mother of M'wambia the Younger went into the fields and gathered sugar-cane, put it into her basket on her back, and brought it to the house. The father took a large piece and gave it to his elder son, but to the younger he gave a small piece. Then the younger brother said, "Why have you given me a small piece and my brother a big piece?"

And he said, "Because you have a mother while the mother of your brother is dead."

Then M'wambia the Younger said to his father, "Come into the woods."

Then he showed him the two snares, and told him how he had killed the N'jenge which he had caught, and how M'wambia the Elder had let him go. And the father was very angry and upbraided his elder son, because the N'jenge was very fat. He chose a tree, tall, with a straight stem, and made him climb up into it. Then he took spikes and stuck them into the ground around the tree with the points leaning inward toward the tree; and he made the points sharp, so that if the boy descended or fell down the points would run into him and he would die. He went away and left M'wambia the Elder in the tree.

Now M'wambia stayed in the tree for twenty days, and at the end of that time, a N'jenge came and said, *"Mangi Kihuti!"*

And M'wambia said, "I am not Mangi, I am M'wambia."

And the N'jenge took one spike and carried it away, and ten N'jenge came and each took one spike and carried it away. Then the N'jenge whom M'wambia had set free came, and he said, "*Mangi.*"

And the boy said, "I am M'wambia," and he told him how he had set him free. The N'jenge, when he heard this, carried away all the remaining spikes and M'wambia gradually unloosed the grip of his arms around the stem of tree and slid to the bottom.

Next the N'jenge made a hole open in his side, and out came a big sheep. M'wambia took some fat to eat. At first he could not eat it, for he was so weak and was very sick; but afterward he ate a little, and then a little of the leg. Then the next day, he ate another piece of the leg. Thus the sheep provided him with food for four days. At the end of that time, the N'jenge opened his side again and there came out a goat, and that gave him food for four days, and then there came out two goats, and these lasted three days, for M'wambia had grown stronger and bigger. There then came an ox, and the N'jenge ate too, and M'wambia grew still bigger and stronger.

Finally, the N'jenge said, "Go among the long grass and jump." And M'wambia went among the long grass and jumped twice, and N'jenge said, "You are not yet strong enough." So they ate another ox, and then the N'jenge said, "Go and jump again." So M'wambia went and jumped four times. Finally, he said to the boy, "What would you like to possess?"

And he said, "A goat."

And the N'jenge opened his side and gave him one hundred female goats which had not borne, one hundred female goats which had borne, one hundred young goats who knew their mother, one hundred male goats, one hundred fat male goats, one hundred sheep which had not borne, one hundred sheep which had borne, one hundred young sheep who knew their mother, one hundred male sheep, one hundred fat male sheep, one hundred cows which had not borne, one hundred cows which had borne, one hundred calves, one hundred oxen, one hundred fat oxen.

And the N'jenge said to M'wambia again, "What do you want?"

And M'wambia replied, "Women."

And the N'jenge gave him two hundred goats and two hundred oxen to buy women. So M'wambia bought one hundred women. And the N'jenge said again, "What do you want?"

And he said, "I want nothing more."

Then he went to the Gura River, and he built a big village for his wives and his oxen and his goats. But no children were yet born, so M'wambia went and tended the goats, and he sat on a hillside where he could see them all, for they were many.

Now the mother of M'wambia the Younger said to her young daughter, "Take a bag and go and get vegetables." So the child went to get the vegetables but could see none; and she walked and walked, and at last she saw

M'wambia sitting on the hillside herding goats, and she called out, "That is our M'wambia who was lost." But he said nothing. And then she called out again, "That is our M'wambia who was lost."

So he spoke to her and he asked, "How are they all at home, my father and my father's brother?"

She said, "They are well."

She saw his village and his wives and his cattle. Then he took a goat and killed it and cut it up and put it into her bag. She walked twelve hours and came to her home. As she came to the homestead she called out to her mother, "Bring me a cooking-pot in which to cook the vegetables." And her mother brought a little one, and she said, "Bring me a big one." And she brought a bigger, and the girl said, "That is not big enough."

And the mother said, "Do you want the one in which we cook meat?" And she said, "Yes."

And her mother asked, "What kind of vegetables have you that you want so large a pot?" The mother opened the bag and saw the meat, and she said, "You have stolen a goat."

And the girl said, "I have not stolen it; it is from M'wambia."

And her mother said, "Do not tell a lie. M'wambia is lost."

And the girl said, "I have seen him, and the day after tomorrow you shall come and see him too." And she told how she had seen him and his many possessions.

So the next day they cooked the meat and ate it, and on the day after they all went together to see M'wambia. All went—his father and his father's brother, and the mother and the father's other wife, and M'wambia the Younger, and the girl, and all the family. And when they came to where M'wambia the Elder was, they saw him sitting on the hill herding goats. And there was a river between them, and M'wambia the Elder took a string and he tied a goat to the end of the string and threw it across the river. And the father took hold of it to go to him. As he was being pulled across the river he was drowned because he had been cruel to his son. But the others got across safely, and when they came to the village of M'wambia the Elder and saw his many goods, they stayed there and made their home with him.

And, after a while, M'wambia said, "I have many men and women to do work in my homestead." And he gave his relations work to do—one had to mind the full-grown goats, one had to mind the young goats, and one had to work in the fields. And he said, "I will go away for a while and see if they do their work well." And he went to another village and slept there for five days.

And when he came back to his homestead he saw some fat, and he said, "What is this fat on the ground?" And he looked and saw on the wall the head of N'jenge, and he knew that his friend the N'jenge had come to the village while he was away and that his relatives had killed him. And he said no word to them, but he said to himself, "My luck is gone, because the N'jenge is dead with whom I am of one heart."

And he took a stone and a knife and made his knife very sharp, and he killed all the women and all the men, and all the goats and all the cattle. Then he took the knife and plunged it into his own breast, for the N'jenge, his luck, was dead.

[AKIKUYU]

69

The Child and the Eagle

A WOMAN HAD A CHILD. One day she went to work in the fields. While she was going to her work the child cried. When it stopped crying she suckled it, and after she had finished suckling it she laid it down in the shade. Then she went on hoeing.

Once again the child cried, and a bird came—an eagle—and sat upon it. It soothed the child with its wings. Then the child which was crying became silent. When she saw this the woman was greatly alarmed and said, "Dear me! How terrible! The eagle is eating my child!" As she went toward it the eagle flew away. Then she suckled her child, and after she had done suckling it she put it upon her back. When she had finished hoeing, she left off work and returned to the village.

On her arrival there, she did not tell her husband of the marvel which she had seen but kept it to herself. The next morning, the woman again went to work in the field with her child. The same thing happened—once again she laid the child to sleep in the shade. After a time the child cried. Then she beheld the eagle alight on the child and quiet it. The woman was amazed and said, "What is that eagle doing? It is sitting upon my child, but it neither bites nor scratches it—no, and then the child is quiet. Truly an astounding thing!" Once again the woman went to her child. When the eagle saw her coming, it flew off and went to sit on a tree. The woman took her child and was greatly alarmed.

She returned to the village and, on her arrival, told her husband about it, saying, "A great marvel!"

Her husband asked, "What about?"

The woman said, "Today is the second day I have seen the most amazing thing there where I hoe. I put my child to sleep in the shade, and as soon as it cried an eagle came, and when it alighted it stooped over the child and soothed it with its wings. Today is the second day that I have seen that bird act thus. Its name is 'eagle.' "

Thereupon the husband refused to believe her, saying, "No, you are lying; there never was such a thing." The wife said no more.

Late in the afternoon the woman took her hoe and went to work in the field. On her arrival she laid her child in the shade. The child cried. Thereupon the woman thought, "Now I will go and call my husband, who disputed my word and said that I lied." So the woman ran. When she arrived where her husband was, she cried, "Come on! It is you who disputed, saying there never was such a thing. Let us go now and see."

The man took his bow and three arrows. On his arrival at the field, the woman said to him:

"Sit down here. I will put the child to sleep in the shade yonder, and then, when you see the bird coming, hide yourself." The woman left the child and went some distance away, and the man hid himself there. Then the child cried very loudly. As the man watched, he saw the eagle come and sit upon the child. Then the man was greatly alarmed and charged his bow with two arrows, that he might pierce the eagle sitting on his child. Then he shot, but at that moment the eagle dodged, and both arrows pierced his child.

Now that is the explanation of the origin of murder. The eagle was a kind person; nevertheless the father of the child wished to kill it. Then the eagle cursed him, and said, "Now is kindness among men at an end, because you killed your child. Beginning with you, and going on to all people, you shall kill each other."

To this day people kill each other.

[BAILA]

70

The Fat Woman Who Melted Away

THERE WAS ONCE a very fat woman who was made of oil. She was very beautiful and many young men applied to her parents for permission to marry her and offered a dowry; but the mother always refused. She said it was impossible for her daughter to work on a farm as she would melt in the sun. At last a stranger from a far-distant country fell in love with the fat woman, and he promised, if her mother would give her to him, that he would keep her in the shade. At last the mother agreed, and he took his wife away.

When he arrived at his house, his other wife immediately became very jealous because when there was work to be done, firewood to be collected, or water to be carried, the fat woman stayed at home and never helped, as she was frightened of the heat.

One day when the husband was absent, the jealous wife abused the fat woman so much that she finally agreed to go and work on the farm, although her little sister, whom she had brought from home with her, implored her not to go, reminding her that their mother had always told them, ever since they were born, that she would melt away if she went into the sun.

All the way to the farm the fat woman managed to keep in the shade. When they arrived at the farm the sun was very hot, so the fat woman remained in the shade of a big tree. As soon as the jealous wife saw this, she again began to abuse her and asked her why she did not do her share of the work. At last she could stand the nagging no longer and, although her little sister tried very hard to prevent her, the fat woman went out into the sun to work and immediately she began to melt away. Very soon there was nothing left of her but one big toe which had been covered by a leaf. This her little sister observed and, with tears in her eyes, she picked up the toe which was all that remained of the fat woman, and, having covered it carefully with leaves, she placed it in the bottom of her basket. As soon as she arrived at the house, the little sister placed the toe in an earthen pot, filled it with water, and covered the top up with clay.

When the husband returned, he said, "Where is my fat wife?" and the little sister, crying bitterly, told him that the jealous woman had made her go out into the sun and that she had melted away. She then showed him the pot with the remains of her sister and told him that her sister would come to life again in three months' time quite complete in body, but that he must send away the jealous wife, so that there should be no more trouble. If he refused to do this, the little girl said she would take the pot back to their mother, and when her sister became complete again, they would remain at home.

The husband then took the jealous wife back to her parents who sold her as a slave and paid the dowry back to the husband, so that he could get another wife. When he received the money, the husband took it home and kept it until the three months had elapsed. Then the little sister opened the pot and the fat woman emerged, quite as fat and beautiful as she had been before. The husband was so delighted that he gave a feast to all his friends and neighbours and told them the whole story of the bad behaviour of his jealous wife.

Ever since that time, whenever a wife behaves very badly, the husband returns her to her parents, who sell the woman as a slave. Out of the proceeds of the sale they give the husband the amount of dowry which he paid when he married the girl.

[EFIK-IBIBIO]

71

The Cherry-Pickers

ONCE UPON A TIME some girls went to pick cherries, and one of them said to one of her comrades, "Let us pick cherries with our eyes shut." Now the rest of her comrades picked without shutting their eyes, and they picked red cherries, but she picked hers unripe. And she said, "Girls, let us open our eyes," and she saw that the cherries of her comrades were red. So she said, "My comrades, wait: let me go and pick some good cherries." And her comrades said, "Go." However they deceived her and went their ways and defecated. Then she asked, "Are you there?" And the dung replied, "We are." But it was the dung which replied. So she tried to follow her comrades and sang:

> *"I went with those girls: they left me*
> *at the cherries.*
> *They made me stay on the dung and on*
> *the rock,*
> *The dung cried* ah-loo-rookok,
> *Ah-loo-rookok was cried on the rock."*

After a while she came to a marsh, and the marsh caused her to trip and fall and upset her cherries. But the marsh gave her a fish in exchange for her cherries. So the girl sang:

> *"Behold, this marsh upsets my cherries:*
> *My cherries I got on the rock, where*
> *the girls left me:*
> *I went with those girls: they left me*
> *at the cherries.*
> *They made me stay on the dung and on the rock,*
> *The dung cried* ah-loo-rookok,
> *Ah-loo-rookok was cried on the rock."*

The marsh then gave her another fish, but a kite snatched the fish away. So the girl sang:

> *"Behold, this kite snatches my fish:*
> *My fish I got from that marsh which upset*
> *my cherries:*

My cherries I got on the rock, where
*   the girls left me:*
I went with those girls: they left me
*   at the cherries.*
They made me stay on the dung and on the rock.
The dung cried ah-loo-rookok,
Ah-loo-rookok *was cried on the rock."*

Then the kite gave her a feather. And the girl went along and found a boy who was dancing with a spray of grass. The boy saw that the feather was pretty and tried to grab the feather, and it was badly broken. So the girl sang:

"Behold, this boy breaks my feather:
My feather I got from that kite that snatched
*   my fish:*
My fish I got from that marsh which upset
*   my cherries:*
My cherries I got on the rock, where
*   the girls left me:*
I went with those girls: they left me
*   at the cherries.*
They made me stay on the dung and on the rock.
The dung cried ah-loo-rookok,
Ah-loo-rookok *was cried on the rock."*

So the boy thereupon gave her a withe. The girl went on and came upon a place where a man hit his cow with his penis. The girl laughed at him. "Why do you hit your cow with your penis? Have you no stick?" So the man seized her withe and hit his cow with it and the withe broke. Then the girl sang:

"Behold, this man breaks my withe:
My withe I got from the boy who broke my feather:
My feather I got from that kite that snatched
*   my fish:*
My fish I got from that marsh which upset
*   my cherries:*
My cherries I got on the rock, where
*   the girls left me:*
I went with those girls: they left me
*   at the cherries.*
They made me stay on the dung and on the rock,
The dung cried ah-loo-rookok,
Ah-loo-rookok *was cried on the rock."*

The man gave her milk and she went on. Next the girl found a place where the children drank cattle-dung. There the children tried to take her milk, and upset it all. So the girl sang:

"*Behold, these children upset my milk:*
My milk I got from the man who broke my withe:
My withe I got from that boy who broke my feather:
My feather I got from that kite that snatched
    my fish:
My fish I got from that marsh which upset
    my cherries:
My cherries I got on the rock, where
    the girls left me:
I went with those girls: they left me
    at the cherries.
They made me stay on the dung and on the rock,
The dung cried ah-loo-rookok,
Ah-loo-rookok *was cried on the rock.*"

The children gave her a razor. And next the girl found a place where they shave their heads with a potsherd, and she laughed. "Why do you shave with a potsherd?" Thereupon the man seized her razor and the razor broke. So the girl sang:

"*Behold, this man breaks my razor:*
My razor I got from those children who upset
    my milk:
My milk I got from that man who broke my withe:
My withe I got from that boy who broke my feather:
My feather I got from that kite that snatched
    my fish:
My fish I got from that marsh which upset
    my cherries:
My cherries I got on the rock where
    the girls left me:
I went with those girls: they left me
    at the cherries.
They made me stay on the dung and on the rock,
The dung cried ah-loo-rookok,
Ah-loo-rookok *was cried on the rock.*"

These people gave her a cow. Thereupon the girl went on and found a place where they eat bones with the dogs, and she said, "Take this cow and eat it." Then they killed her cow and ate it, they and their children. So the girl sang:

"Behold, these men kill my cow:
  My cow I got from that man who broke my razor:
  My razor I got from those children who upset
    my milk:
  My milk I got from that man who broke my withe:
  My withe I got from that boy who broke my feather:
  My feather I got from that kite that snatched
    my fish:
  My fish I got from that marsh that upset
    my cherries:
  My cherries I got on the rock, where
    the girls left me:
  I went with those girls: they left me
    at the cherries.
  They made me stay on the dung and on the rock,
  The dung cried ah-loo-rookok,
  Ah-loo-rookok was cried on the rock."

They gave her a dog in exchange for her cow. But the dog killed a man,
and they arrested her as the owner of the dog. And the girl said, "Take me
to the pasturage that I may defecate." And they told her, "Go aside here."
But she said, "My dung smells offensive: let me go aside at a distance." So she
escaped from there, fearing vengeance for the man whom the dog had killed.

⌈ LANGO ⌉

72

Ngomba's Basket

FOUR LITTLE GIRLS one day started to go out fishing. One of them was suffering sadly from sores which covered her from head to foot. Her name was Ngomba. The other three, after a little consultation, agreed that Ngomba should not accompany them, and they told her to go back.

"Nay," said Ngomba, "I will do no such thing. I mean to catch fish for mother as well as you."

Then the three girls beat Ngomba until she ran away. But she determined to catch fish also, so she walked and walked, she hardly knew whither, until at last she came to a large lake. Here she commenced fishing and singing:

> "*If my mother*
> [She catches a fish and puts it in her basket]
> *Had taken care of me*
> [She catches another fish and puts it in her basket]
> *I should have been with them*
> [She catches another fish and puts it in her basket]
> *And not here alone.*"
> [She catches another fish and puts it in her basket]

But a murderer, a *mpunia*, had for some time been watching her, and now he came up to her and accosted her:

"What are you doing here?"

"Fishing. Please, don't kill me! See, I am full of sores, but I can catch plenty of fish."

The *mpunia* watched her as she fished and sang:

> "*Oh, I shall surely die!*
> [She catches a fish and puts it in her basket]
> *Mother, you will never see me!*
> [She catches another fish and puts it in her basket]
> *But I don't care*
> [She catches another fish and puts it in her basket]
> *For no one cares for me.*"
> [She catches another fish and puts it in her basket]

266

"Come with me," said the *mpunia*.

"Nay, this fish is for mother, and I must take it to her."

"If you do not come with me, I will kill you."

> "*Oh! Am I to die*
> [She catches a fish and puts it in her basket]
> *On the top of my fish?*
> [She catches another fish and puts it in her basket]
> *If mother had loved me*
> [She catches another fish and puts it in her basket]
> *To live I should wish.*"
> [She catches another fish and puts it in her basket]

"Take me and cure me, dear *mpunia*, and I will serve you."

The *mpunia* took her to his home in the woods and cured her. Then he placed her in the paint-house and married her.

Now the *mpunia* was very fond of dancing, and Ngomba danced beautifully, so that he loved her very much and made her mistress over all his prisoners and goods.

"When I go out for a walk," he said to her, "I will tie this string round my waist; and that you may know when I am still going away from you, or returning, the string will be stretched tight as I depart, and will hang loose as I return."

Now Ngomba pined for her mother and, therefore, entered into a conspiracy with her people to escape. She sent them every day to cut the leaves of the *mateva* palm and ordered them to put the leaves in the sun to dry. Then she set them to work to make a huge *ntenda*. When the *mpunia* returned, he remarked to her that the air was heavy with the smell of *mateva*.

Now Ngomba had made all her people put on clean clothes, and when they knew that the *mpunia* was returning, she ordered them to come to him and flatter him. So now they approached him, some calling him "father" and others "uncle"; others told him how he was a father and a mother to them. And he was very pleased and danced with them.

The next day when the *mpunia* returned, he again said he smelt *mateva*.

Then Ngomba cried, and told him that he was both father and mother to her and that, if he accused her of smelling of *mateva*, she would kill herself.

He could not endure this sadness, so he kissed her and danced with her until all was forgotten.

The next day Ngomba determined to try her *ntenda*, and to see if it would float in the air. Four women lifted it high and gave it a start upwards, and it floated beautifully. Now the *mpunia* happened to be up in a tree, and he espied this great *ntenda* floating in the air; and he danced and sang for joy, and wished to call Ngomba, that she might dance with him.

That night he smelt *mateva* again, and his suspicions were fully aroused. When he thought how easily his wife might escape him, he determined to kill her. Accordingly, he gave her some palm wine to drink which he had drugged. She drank it, and she slept as he put his *sommo* into the fire. He meant to kill her by pushing this red-hot wire up her nose.

But when he was almost ready, Ngomba's little sister, who had changed herself into a cricket and hidden herself under the bed, began to sing. The *mpunia* heard her and felt forced to join in and dance, and thus he forgot to kill his wife. But, after a time, the cricket ceased singing, and then he began to heat the wire again. The cricket then sang again, and again the *mpunia* danced and danced, and in his excitement he tried to wake Ngomba to dance also. But she refused to awaken, telling him that the medicine he had given her made her feel sleepy. Then the *mpunia* went out to get some palm wine, and as he went Ngomba drowsily asked him if he had made the string fast. He called all his people, dressed himself, and made them all dance.

The cock crew. The iron wire was still in the fire. Then the *mpunia* made his wife get up and fetch more palm wine.

Then the cock crew again, and it was daylight.

When the *mpunia* had left her in the morning, Ngomba determined to escape that very day. She called her people and made them try the *ntenda* again. When she was certain that it would float, she put all her people and the *mpunia*'s ornaments into it. Then she got in and the *ntenda* began to float away over the tree-tops in the direction of her mother's town.

When the *mpunia*, who was up a tree, saw it coming toward him, he danced and sang for joy, and only wished that his wife had been there to see this huge *ntenda* flying through the air. It passed just over his head and then he saw plainly that the people in it were his people. So he ran after it in the tops of the trees until he saw it drop in Ngomba's town. And he determined to go there also and claim his wife.

The *ntenda* floated round the house of Ngomba's mother, and astonished all the people there, and finally settled down in front of it. Ngomba cried to the people to come and let them out. But they were afraid and did not dare, so that she came out herself and presented herself to her mother.

Her relations at first did not recognize her, but after a little while they fell upon her and welcomed her as their long-lost Ngomba.

Then the *mpunia* entered the town and claimed Ngomba as his wife.

"Yes," her relations said, "she is your wife, and you must be thanked for curing her of her sickness."

While some of her relations were entertaining the *mpunia*, others were preparing a place for him and his wife to be seated. They made a large fire, and boiled a great quantity of water, and dug a deep hole in the ground. This hole they covered over with sticks and a mat. When all was ready they led the *mpunia* and his wife to it and requested them to be seated. Ngomba sat near her husband, who, as he sat down, fell into the hole. The relations then brought boiling water and fire, and threw this over him until he died.

[BAKONGO]

73

The Beautiful Girl Who Had No Teeth

THERE WAS ONCE a man who had three sons, none of whom had a wife. One day the father went out to see if he could find a suitable girl for his eldest son, and he found a beautiful girl at a village nearby. That night, when he returned home, he called his eldest son and said, "I have found a beautiful girl for you, and tomorrow I want you to take the cattle to her father."

Early next morning the son went out with five of the best cattle and presented them to the girl's father. On his arrival the girl took his sticks and the young boys took the cattle to the kraal. The girl's father then said, "Have you come to take my daughter?" To this the man replied that he had. The girl's father then called his daughter and said, "Here is your husband, you must go with him to his home today."

The girl replied that she was ready, and she and the man departed together for his home. On the road home the girl began to sing:

"I am a beautiful girl but I have no teeth."

Her husband became alarmed and said, "Open your mouth that I may see if what you say is true." To his surprise he found that what she said was true and that she had only a black ridge where her teeth should have been.

The husband then said, "I was not told of this, and I must return you to your father." They returned to the girl's home and there the husband demanded the return of his cattle as his wife had no teeth. The cattle were returned and the disappointed man went home. On his arrival his father asked, "Where is the girl, my son?"

The son replied, "I could not bring her home because she had no teeth."

The second son, on hearing this, asked his father, "May I not go myself to see if the girl has no teeth, because I too want a wife?" The father agreed, and the next day the second son set off with the five head of cattle. Presenting them to the girl's father, he said, "I have come for your daughter. I have come early so that I need not sleep here tonight but may return home with your daughter this evening."

The man informed his daughter of the wishes of the young suitor and the girl replied, "Very well, but I must first give my husband some food." After the meal the girl suggested that they depart at once, and they proceeded along the road. When she and the second son reached the same place on the road as before the girl began to sing:

"I am a beautiful girl but I have no teeth."

On hearing this the young man asked her to open her mouth that he might see for himself. To his surprise he found that what she said was true and he immediately returned her to her father. "Here is your daughter," he said, "she has no teeth and I want my cattle returned." The girl's father sadly agreed, and the second son returned to his home.

On his return his father said, "Where is the girl?"

The son replied, "I thought my brother was lying, but it is true. She has no teeth and I returned her to her father."

The youngest son now rose and asked his father if he might go and see for himself, and the father agreed.

The eldest brother asked in disgust, "Do you think that we are mad and stupid because we left the girl?"

"No, no," answered the youngest brother, "but I should like to see a girl who has no teeth."

The next day the youngest brother took the cattle and went to the girl's kraal, where he presented the cattle and asked for the girl. The old man, seeing such a young man, said, "You are very young to want a wife and, besides, both your brothers tried but returned my daughter. However, you may take her if you so wish." Calling his daughter, he told her she must return with this new man to his home. The girl agreed and, after first giving her new husband some food, they proceeded down the road.

At the same place as before the girl again sang:

"I am beautiful but I have no teeth."

"Open your mouth," said the young man anxiously. On seeing the black ridge within her mouth he showed some surprise, but only said, "Never mind, let us go on our way." Arriving at a river the girl began to sing the same song, but the young man said nothing. When in the middle of the stream, he called to the girl to come near to him and, clasping her tightly by the neck with one hand, he told her to open her mouth; with the other hand he scrubbed the girl's mouth with sand.

To his joy he found that beneath the coating of black shone forth a set of beautiful teeth, and, filled with happiness, he brought his wife to his father's kraal. The other two brothers on seeing the girl, rushed to their father saying, "Come father, come and see your mad son, he has brought this girl home, although she is even now singing her song about her teeth."

The father came, but said nothing, and the youngest brother called one of his sisters and told her to take his newly acquired wife to his mother's hut. The girls of the village who had heard about this strange girl gathered about her and began to make jokes, so that when the newcomer laughed they might see if the story about her teeth were true. To their surprise they found that the girl had very good teeth.

Meanwhile the youngest son told his father that he had brought the girl home as his wife. The father was disappointed. "Yes, my son," he said, "that's all very well, but you have lost all my cattle. What can we do with this girl? I hear she has no teeth and therefore cannot eat." The son did not reply, for at that moment his sister came in and told her father that the newcomer had teeth, for she had seen them. The father said, "Are you sure?" Being convinced that it was so, he went to his son and said, "Very well, my son, we shall see your wife tomorrow."

The next day the father entered the hut where the girl was and said, "I want you to open your mouth. I will give you a sheep for this favour." The girl did as she was bid and the man saw for himself that she had teeth. The woman in whose hut the girl rested then trilled with her lips, and all three went out to the main yard, where the father called the elder sons and said, "What stupid boys you are! Look, this girl has fine teeth, and it has fallen to your youngest brother to find this out and to take her to wife."

The two eldest brothers became very ashamed and would not look at the girl. A few days later large pots of beer were made and all the friends and neighbours came to pay their respects to the new arrival. All spoke of her beauty and her excellent teeth, but the two brothers never saw for themselves, their shame being too great.

The story is finished.

[BAVENDA]

74

The Girl Who Was Sacrificed by Her Kin and Whom Her Lover Brought Back from Below

THE SUN WAS VERY HOT and there was no rain, so the crops died and hunger was great. This happened one year; and it happened again a second, and even a third year, that the rain failed. The people all gathered together on the great open space on the hilltop, where they were wont to dance, and they said to each other, "Why does the rain delay in coming?" And they went to the Medicine-Man and they said to him, "Tell us why there is no rain, for our crops have died, and we shall die of hunger."

And he took his gourd and poured out its contents. This he did many times; and at last he said, "There is a maiden here who must be bought if rain is to fall, and the maiden is named Wanjiru. The day after tomorrow let all of you return to this place, and every one of you from the eldest to the youngest bring with him a goat for the purchase of the maiden."

On the day after the morrow, old men and young men all gathered together, and each brought in his hand a goat. Now they all stood in a circle, and the relations of Wanjiru stood together, and she herself stood in the middle. As they stood there, the feet of Wanjiru began to sink into the ground, and she sank in to her knees and cried aloud, "I am lost!"

Her father and mother also cried and exclaimed, "We are lost!"

Those who looked on pressed close and placed goats in the keeping of Wanjiru's father and mother. Wanjiru sank lower to her waist, and again she cried aloud, "I am lost, but much rain will come!"

She sank to her breast; but the rain did not come. Then she said again, "Much rain will come."

Now she sank in to her neck, and then the rain came in great drops. Her people would have rushed forward to save her, but those who stood around pressed upon them more goats, and they desisted.

Then Wanjiru said, "My people have undone me," and she sank down to her eyes. As one after another of her family stepped forward to save her, someone in the crowd would give to him or her a goat, and he would fall back. And Wanjiru cried aloud for the last time, "I am undone, and my own people have done this thing." Then she vanished from sight; the earth closed over her, and the rain poured down, not in showers, as it sometimes does, but in a great deluge, and all the people hastened to their own homes.

Now there was a young warrior who loved Wanjiru, and he lamented continually, saying, "Wanjiru is lost, and her own people have done this thing." And he said, "Where has Wanjiru gone? I will go to the same place." So he took his shield and spear. And he wandered over the country day and night until, at last, as the dusk fell, he came to the spot where Wanjiru had vanished. Then he stood where she had stood and, as he stood, his feet began to sink as hers had sunk; and he sank lower and lower until the ground closed over him, and he went by a long road under the earth as Wanjiru had gone and, at length, he saw the maiden. But, indeed, he pitied her sorely, for her state was miserable, and her raiment had perished. He said to her, "You were sacrificed to bring the rain; now the rain has come, and I shall take you back." So he took Wanjiru on his back as if she had been a child and brought her to the road he had traversed, and they rose together to the open air, and their feet stood once more on the ground.

Then the warrior said, "You shall not return to the house of your people, for they have treated you shamefully." And he bade her wait until nightfall. When it was dark he took her to the house of his mother and he asked his mother to leave, saying that he had business, and he allowed no one to enter.

But his mother said, "Why do you hide this thing from me, seeing I am your mother who bore you?" So he suffered his mother to know, but he said, "Tell no one that Wanjiru has returned."

So she abode in the house of his mother. He and his mother slew goats, and Wanjiru ate the fat and grew strong. Then of the skins they made garments for her, so that she was attired most beautifully.

It came to pass that the next day there was a great dance, and her lover went with the throng. But his mother and the girl waited until everyone had assembled at the dance, and all the road was empty. Then they came out of the house and mingled with the crowd. When the relations saw Wanjiru, they said, "Surely, that is Wanjiru whom we had lost."

And they pressed to greet her, but her lover beat them off, for he said, "You sold Wanjiru shamefully."

Then she returned to his mother's house. But on the fourth day her family again came and the warrior repented, for he said, "Surely they are her father and her mother and her brothers."

So he paid them the purchase price, and he wedded Wanjiru who had been lost.

[AKIKUYU]

75

The Wicked Girl and Her Punishment

THERE WAS ONCE a certain girl who loved a youth, but her parents said that they would not give her to him in marriage. He was always coming and begging them to let him marry her, but they would say, "We shall not give her to you."

Now one day the girl came to him and said, "I have come to you to ask you to give me your knife so that I may go and kill my mother. Then we can run away to some other town and be married."

But he said, "No, no, we must not do that."

Again she came and said, "Give me your knife, that I may go and kill my mother."

But again he replied, "No, no, you must not kill your mother because of me." And he continued: "Go home and stay there. Those who can give your parents presents can give you some also."

Five days passed and then the girl asked, "Will you give me your knife to cut pumpkins?"

Now the boy had forgotten, and he pulled out his knife and gave it to her, and immediately upon receiving it, she went and cut her mother's throat. Then she ran to the youth and said, "Now, you see I have done it. If we do not flee, you and I will be killed. Look at the blood on your knife; I have cut my mother's throat with it."

So they started off. The youth took a bow and arrows and sent the girl in front of him, and they escaped from the city.

They pressed on and on toward the forest. They slept there that night and the next morning they pushed on again. When they reached the centre of the forest, the girl was seized with an internal pain, and she fell down and died. Then the youth drew out one of his arrows and fitted it to the bow and stood and guarded her body.

Soon the beasts of the forest all assembled to eat her, but he would not allow them to do so, but said that nothing should touch her unless he should first be killed.

The eagle came and alighted in front of the youth and said, "Let us feast." But he said, "No, no, did I not promise that I would not leave her? Shall I allow you to eat her body?"

274

The eagle replied, "Do not put your trust in women, they are not truthful."

But the youth said, "I do not agree, I trust this one."

Then the eagle said, "Have you a flask?"

And the youth said, "I have."

The eagle said, "Give me it," and he took it and flew off.

Soon he returned with water in the flask and said, "Have you a knife?" And the youth said, "Yes."

Then the eagle said, "Separate her teeth." And he plucked out two feathers from his wings and stirred them around in the water. So the girl's mouth was opened, the water was poured in, and immediately the girl rose up.

Then the eagle said to the youth, "See these feathers—keep them, some day when you have gone to another city and have obtained something to eat, you will repay us for our feast which we have lost today."

So the youth and the girl went off again and reached a city. They came to the house of an old woman which they entered, and they remained there until the afternoon. They even slept there.

The next morning they heard weeping, and they were told that the king's mother had died. Then the youth arose and said, "Let me go and see what can be done." So he started off and came to where the death had taken place, and when he had come, he went up to a man and said, "Can you obtain for me an interview with the king?"

"The king's heart is broken," the man replied. "Is anyone going to bother him now?"

But another one said, "Here, do you know what his business is? Go and ask the king indeed."

And the king, when he heard, said, "Tell the youth to come."

So he was summoned, and he came and said, "If I bring your mother back to life, what will you give me?"

Then one of the attendants said, "Have you ever seen anyone who has died come back to life?"

But the king said, "Leave him alone, perhaps he has some magic," and he continued, addressing the youth, "I will give you ten slaves." He said, "See, this house also will I give you, and these horses."

So the youth said, "Very well, bring me water in a flask." And water was obtained and brought to him.

Then he walked around to the back of the house and stirred the eagle's feathers in the water and brought it back, and said, "Now open the king's mother's mouth." Immediately after the water had been poured down her throat, she rose up and remained alive, so the youth's presents were brought and given to him. Then he returned to his house and remained in the town and, whenever anyone died, someone would come and summon him to give the dead person the charm so as to bring him back to life again.

Now after a time, one of the king's slaves made the girl fall in love with him, and he said, "Look here, girl, since we know each other so well, will you not give me your husband's charm?"

And she said, "Very well." So when she went to bed and her husband talked, she remained silent; when he asked her anything, she did not reply.

Then her husband said, "What is the matter with you?"

And she replied, "Well, we have been together for some time now, but you have got something which you are keeping secret from me; you are always hiding it." Then he said, "Is it only that which has made you so quiet? Well, here it is; keep it for me." And he gave the girl the eagle's feathers. No sooner had she received them than she took a waterpot and said that she was going to the river for water. But instead of doing so, she went and gave the feathers to the king's slave who took them to his house.

Soon afterward, another death took place in the king's family and the youth was summoned as usual. He came and said to his wife, "Where is the thing which I gave you to keep for me?"

And she replied, "It is here somewhere, I put it just here."

They looked but did not find it; they looked again but did not find it.

Now the king's slave went and said to the king, "If I make him rise up again, how much will you give me?"

The king replied, "Everything that you want I will give you."

So the slave said, "Very well," and he made the dead man rise up.

When he had done this, the king's slave asked that the youth should be seized and given to him for a slave. The king said, "Very well, go and seize him."

So he went and caught the youth and took his wife for himself. The king's slave bound the youth and put handcuffs on him and took him to the forest and made him clear the ground.

Some time later the eagle came to where he was and said: "Where is that which you promised me? I told you that the woman was not faithful, but you said she was. Now let me do you another good turn. Tonight, hold your leg irons up to your thighs and go into the city and find me a cat." So the youth went and found a cat, and he returned and hid the cat until daybreak.

Then the eagle came again and said, "The reason we sought you, O Cat, is that we want you to get us a mouse."

The cat said, "Very well," and immediately she ran in where the youth had been cutting wood and caught a mouse.

Then the eagle said, "O Cat, and you, O Mouse, you know the smell of my feathers. Take the road, go into the city, and enter the house of the king's slave, and if the mouse sees any feathers, you, O Cat, take them and bring them here."

The cat and the mouse went to the city and entered the house of the king's slave. The mouse looked everywhere, in the pots, in the quiver, but did not see the feathers, and he went outside to the cat, and said, "I cannot see them."

Then the cat said, "Return, go and look again." And the cat entered and cried out "*Miyau*."

Then the sleepers said, "Thank goodness! She will catch that mouse which has prevented our sleeping." So they went to sleep, both the king's slave and his wife.

Then the mouse came and sniffed at the slave's mouth and saw where the feathers were, and he said to the cat, "Here they are! I see them!"

"Where do you see them?" asked the cat.

The mouse replied, "In his mouth."

Then the cat said, "Very well, go and bite him."

The mouse went and bit the slave, and he went *poof*. The feathers fell out of his mouth and the cat caught them and took them to the youth in the forest.

The next morning the eagle came again and said, "Where are they?"

The youth replied, "See them."

Then the eagle said, "Good! but let us have another understanding. Some day you must pay me back for my feast which I gave up."

Now it happened that on the next day one of the king's sons became ill and died, and the king's slave was sent for and told to work his magic. But he said that he had lost his charm.

Then the king said, "Summon the other one to come. Here is a horse, go quickly and bring the one who is in the forest." The youth was sent for quickly and was brought and when he had come, the king said, "See, we have summoned you. May God cause your power to return to you."

"How can one who lives out in the forest obtain magic?" asked the youth.

But the king said, "For God's sake, help us."

Then the youth said, "Very well, but what will you give me?"

The king replied, "Everything that is in the slave's house I will give you."

Then the youth prepared his charm and raised up the dead man, and the king said, "Go and seize the slave."

The youth went and caught the slave and his wife; he undid his own handcuffs and put them on the slave; he took another pair and put them on the wife; and then he took them to the place where he had been cutting wood and said that they were to stack it all in one place. Then he called to the eagle, telling him to come; and when he had arrived, the youth said, "Go, assemble all your relatives; tomorrow we shall meet at the clearing."

The next morning the eagles came together, all the birds assembled, and all the beasts of the forest also came. When all had arrived, the youth said, "Now set fire to the pile." So they set fire to it. The fire consumed all the wood and left a great mass of embers. Then he said to the slave and his wife, "Get up and fall into the fire." But they refused. Then he told his attendants to get up and drag them in; and they threw them into the fire. Every time that they got out, they were thrown in again, and at last they were cooked. The youth told the attendants to pull the bodies out of the fire to put them out in the open.

Then he said, "Eagle!"

And the bird replied *"Um!"*

"Now, see, here is your feast," the youth said, and then he mounted his horse and returned to the city.

It is certainly true that women are not to be trusted.

[HAUSA]

76

The Old Woman Who Stole Milk

THERE WAS IN TIMES of long ago a certain old woman; she was living with her daughter; she was the mother-in law. Her son-in-law offered her *amasi*, telling her to eat; for there was not much food, it was a famine. She refused the *amasi*. He offered her a cow, telling her to eat the milk: she refused, saying she could not eat the milk of her son-in-law.

In the digging season she was very hungry; she was in the habit of returning home at noon, and she would open her son-in-law's house, and pour out the *amasi* and eat it. But when the sun had set, her son-in-law said, speaking to his wife, "Go home and boil some maize, that we may mix it with the *amasi*, for the calabash is now full." On their arrival she boiled maize, and made a soft mass; the husband went and took the calabash; he found it empty; there was now nothing but whey in it. They and their children cried, being hungry; and the mother-in-law said, "My children's children will die, for a thief is eating their milk, through this great famine." The old woman did thus at all times. But the husband and wife did not know that the milk was taken by their mother.

One day the husband lay in wait, and caught their mother; but their mother cried, saying, "I did it for the first time this very day." Her son-in-law said, "Go and fetch for me water at a place where no frog cries; and I will not expose you to the people."

He gave her a water-vessel. She went on and on for a long time, passing many rivers; she came to rivers which she did not know; she asked, "Is there any frog here?" A frog answered, "*Khhwe*, I am here." She passed on, and came to another place; she saw a pool; she went to it and dipped water; a frog said, "*Khhwe*, I am here." She poured it out. She travelled acting thus, and the frogs answering in like manner, for there were frogs in every pool. She came to another pool and said, "Is there a frog here?" No frog answered. She sat down and dipped water. But when the vessel was nearly full (for it was a very large one), a frog said, "*Khhwe*, I am here." She poured out the water again, now crying and saying, "Woe is me, *mamo!* I merely took of my own accord the *amasi* of my son-in-law for food." She went on and came to a very great pool. There were many paths which went to the pool. She was afraid. There were many shady trees on the banks of the pool. She went to the pool and sat down; she said, "Is there any frog here?" There was no answer. She repeated her question. There was no answer. She dipped water into the vessel; the vessel was very full. When it was full, she drank very much, until the vessel was empty. She dipped again till it was full; she drank; she was no longer able to drink the whole, she had a pain in the stomach, for she was unable to leave off drinking, it was so nice.

But when she wished to arise and depart, she was unable to arise; she dragged the water-vessel, and went into the shade, and sat down there, for she was unable to walk. At length it was noon; there came a rock-rabbit, and said, "Who is this sitting in the shade of the king?" She said, "It is I, father. I was about to depart; but my limbs failed me." The rock-rabbit said, "You will soon see Ugungqu-kubantwana." She went and drank at the pool, and returned to the shade. A duiker came and said, "Who is this sitting in the shade of the king?" She said, "It is I, father. I was about to depart, but my limbs failed me." The duiker said, "You will soon see Ugungqu-kubant-wana." A leopard came and said, "Who is this sitting in the shade of the king?" She said, "It is I, father. I was about to depart, but my limbs failed me." The leopard said, "You will soon see Ugungqu-kubantwana." All animals came saying the same. And when at length it was about sunset, there came very many and great animals; all the animals said the same.

When the sun was setting, she heard a great noise—*gungqu, gungqu.* She was afraid and trembled. At length there appeared something greater than all the animals she had seen. When it appeared they all said with one accord, "This is Ugungqu-kubantwana." When it came in sight, while still at some distance, she said, "Who, who are you sitting in the shade of Ugungqu-kubantwana?" Then the old woman had no more any power to speak; it was now as though death had already come to her. Ugungqu-kubantwana asked a second time. The old woman replied, "It is I, my lord. I was thinking of departing, but my limbs failed me." She said, "You will soon see Ugungqu-kubantwana."

The creature went to the river; when she reached it, she knelt on her knees, and drank the pool; although it was very great, she drank until the mud at the bottom of the pool appeared. She then sat down. And there were oribis there, who were the officers of Ugungqu-kubantwana; there were also hyenas. Ugungqu-kubantwana said, "Let her be eaten." The hyenas agreed. But the oribis said, "She shall be eaten when she is fat, O chief." Again she said, "Let her be eaten." The oribis said, "It is now dark; she shall be eaten in the morning, O chief."

It was dark; they slept, and all the animals slept. But some animals put off sleeping because they wished that she should be eaten. At length it was midnight and all were asleep. But four oribis had not gone to sleep; they arose and took the old woman, and raised her and placed her on the back of three of them; the fourth oribi took the water-vessel. They ran during the night, and went and placed her on the border of her village. Then they returned with speed, saying, then they should get back before morning. And truly they soon arrived at the pool again.

One said to the other, "What shall we do? Let us devise a plan, that it may not appear that it is we who have enabled her to flee." The others said, "Since the animals which like to eat men are the leopard, the lion, other wild beasts, and hyenas—" Then one said, "Let us smear mud on the hyenas, for it is they who like to eat men; and the chief will agree and say, 'They have taken the game of the chief, and gone and eaten it at a distance.' For if we smear the leopard it will feel (for it is a very wrathful creature) and awake, and all the people will awake, and the chief say, it is we who have taken away the game, and gone to eat it." So all the other oribis agreed. They went and smeared the mud on the legs of the hyenas; and when they had cleansed themselves they went and lay down where they had lain.

In the morning all the animals arose and said, "Where is the game of the chief? She will kill the oribis, it was they who objected to its being eaten." The oribis at once awoke, saying, "The chief will look at the feet of all the people. If they have not gone anywhere, they will be clean. But if they have gone, there will be seen mud on their feet and on their legs." The chief agreed, and said to the oribis, "Make haste at once, and look for the muddy legs, and let them be seized and brought to me." All the animals stood forth, and looked at each other; there was found mud on the hyenas. The oribis said, "It is the hyenas who have taken and eaten her, for they are animals which like to eat men." The hyenas were seized and taken to the chief. She seized the three hyenas, and ate them.

The old woman remained at the border of the kraal; at length she saw some one belonging to her home; he told her son-in-law; he went and fetched her and the water-vessel. The son-in-law continually drank the water which his mother-in-law had brought.

It came to pass on the day the water was finished the old woman said, "Since I went and fetched water, do you go and fetch for me the liver of an *ingogo.*" Many loaves were made for him to eat on his journey, for it was a great way off. In the morning, carrying the loaves, he set out on his journey, sleeping in the open air; at length he arrived at the new moon, and found very many *izingogo,* leaping on the bank of a river, at play. He approached them, he too now running and now going on his hands and feet. The old *izingogo* said, "There is our *ingogo.*" The young ones said, "What kind of *ingogo* is that, which has hair like a man; and little eyes like a man; and little ears like a man?" The old ones said, "It is an *ingogo:* by such and such things we see it is nought but an *ingogo;* by such and such things we see it is nought but an *ingogo;* by such and such things we see it is nought but an *ingogo.*" So the little ones were silent. But when they were by themselves they laughed, saying, "That is not an *ingogo.*" At length they returned to their homes.

On his arrival the man had noticed that there was at the kraal a grandmother, who was now old. In the morning the others said, "Go, fellow, we are going to hunt." He said, "I am tired; I shall not go today." All the old ones went; the young ones said, "Let us come home by and by, and find that you have already fetched firewood for cooking." The little ones said, "We do not like to leave our grandmother alone with the person who has come." So they went to hunt. At length they returned; on their arrival the little ones were sitting still; the old ones were angry, and said, "We are already come from hunting; but you have not been to fetch firewood." The little ones were silent. The game was cooked. They ate and lay down.

In the morning they said, "Let us go and hunt." He went with them. They went and hunted, and returned in the afternoon; they found the little ones too now returning from fetching wood. They cooked their game. The newly arrived *ingogo* said, when the game was dressed, "Just put aside a leg for me, for I have a pain in my stomach. I cannot just now eat meat." They assented, and put aside a leg for him. They lay down.

In the morning they asked him how his stomach was. He said, "It is still painful." They said, "Let us go and hunt." So they went, and he remained alone with the little ones. As soon as the hunters were gone, he said, "Do you go and fetch me some water from the river, that I may drink." They took a water-vessel and went with it. But the vessel leaked, having a hole in the bottom. They arrived at the river, and dipped water; the vessel leaked. They took a long time in returning from the river. But the moment they had gone, the *ingogo* arose and took a spear, and killed the grandmother of the *izingogo* who were absent. He cut open the chest and bowels; the liver appeared; he took it out; he looked on every side; he looked upwards and saw an *uvati;* he took it down and fled.

When the sun was setting the little *izingogo* returned; when they were in the lower part of the village, they saw much blood which had run on the path, now dry, for he had stabbed the old *ingogo* in the morning. They at once ran home; on their arrival they entered the house; but the house was very long, and not very light inside; they found their grandmother dead. They went out, running with all their might, crying, and looking in the direction whither they had gone to hunt. When they saw the old ones, the little ones cried out again and again, saying, "What kind of an *ingogo* is that who has eyes like a man?" The old ones said, "What has happened?" The little ones replied, "He has killed grandmother." They ran, they threw down their game; they carried their spears in their hands. They asked, "In what direction has the man gone who we thought was an *ingogo?*" The little ones said, "We saw him not; we had gone to fetch water; on our return we found grandmother dead; but saw no more of him."

They followed his track by the blood where it had gone dropping in the path. They ran; when it was dark they slept in the open country. In the morning they awoke and ran with all their might. When it was noon, the man who was carrying the liver looked and saw much dust behind him. He ran very fast. But the real *izingogo* were more swift than he; for he was a man; they were animals. At midday they saw him. It was as though they flew through catching sight of him. He saw that they would soon catch him. He ascended a very long steep place; when he was at the top, they were reaching the bottom; he descended; he found very much long and thick grass; he took the *uvati*, and sat down, and churned it, and kindled a fire, and set the grass on fire; it surrounded the steep hill; the *izingogo* fled, for they feared the fire; they went back from the mountain by the way they came. And he ran forward until it was dark without seeing them.

He slept. In the morning he awoke and fled. That night he slept at another village on the high land. In the morning he awoke and ran. At noon he looked behind him, and saw the *izingogo* coming to him running. And those who had lagged behind, being tired, now when they saw him ran rapidly; it was again as if their fatigue was at an end. Again he saw they were about to catch him. He churned the *uvati*, and kindled fire, and burnt the grass: when they saw the fire burning, they halted. He ran and saw them no more; until he had slept twice in the way he did not see them. On the third day, the day he would reach his own people, he saw them at noon; they pursued him; he hastened and approached near the villages, and then they turned back.

The *izingogo* returned to their own home. On their arrival they took the grandmother, and boiled her in a large pot. They took a whole day cooking her. Until it was morning they kept up the fire, and during the morning they kept up the fire. At noon they took her out of the pot, and placed her on the feeding-mats; she remained there till she was cold. The old ones said to the little ones, "Let us eat your grandmother, then we shall not die." So they ate her up.

The son-in-law of the old woman reached his home; on his arrival he gave her the liver. She said, "You have done well, my child."

EXPLANATIONS BY THE ZULU NARRATOR

Ugungqu-kubantwana was so called because she was the mother of all animals, for she was their chief; and as regards the pool, the animals used to go to it first and drink, and leave water for her; for she could not drink first, for all the water would have been exhausted before the animals had drunk if she had drunk first; and as to her body, on one side there was a country, on the other rivers and great forests; but the rivers which were in her the animals did not like to drink, for they were like common water; that pool at which they all drank was, as it were, milk; therefore they did not drink at other rivers, they drank at the pool. She was called Ugungqu because when she was still at a distance she was heard coming, for when she was moving there was heard a great noise, and they heard that she was coming by the *gungqu, gungqu.*

The *izingogo* were apparently men; but it came to pass by their own choice they lived in the open country, until they were called animals, for they lived in the open country, and therefore they ate man. But when there arrived a man who came from other men who practised the same habits as themselves, they rejoiced, saying, he too was an *ingogo*, because he did as they did. But the discernment of the children, who were now sharp, was greater than that of the older ones, for they were on their guard against him, saying, "It is not an *ingogo*." And even though the old ones were angry and beat them, they denied notwithstanding they were beaten. They used to go and play on the bank of the river; on their arrival they contended by leaping, saying that he who could not leap was not an *ingogo;* the little ones leaped too; and if there came a man feigning to be an *ingogo*, they would go with him to the bank, and tell him to leap like them; for it is said, when they leaped they were light, because they ate red earth.

The *izingogos* used to go on all fours; they had tails; but they talked like men.

[ZULU]

77

The Wife Who Ate the Wrong Porridge

WHAT DO YOU THINK? This is what they did. They went looking for wives, saying, "Let us go and try to marry."

One of them went looking for a wife everywhere. Every one rejected him. At last he, too, like the others, succeeded in making a marriage such as it was.

Well! He brought his wife into the house.

Now, when he married her, he said, "Look here, woman, you will eat porridge of small millet, and no other."

"All right," answered the woman.

"And I," added the man, "I shall eat only kafir-corn porridge."

"All right," said the woman again.

So, after that, they simply ate porridge, the woman millet, the man kafir corn.

Alas! One day the woman, making a mistake, happened to eat the kafir-corn porridge. The man came. "You have eaten my porridge," he said, "yet I told you to eat only millet porridge." Whereupon he picked up an axe and struck the woman. Then he dragged her, drag! drag! drag! and went and threw her away to the west.

After that the man went alone, wandering about.

One day he said to himself, "We are going for a ramble in the bush." He went there and killed game. He then remembered that one woman had been left in the village over there. So he said to himself, "Let us go and marry her."

He went there, received her in marriage, brought her to his home, and said to her, "Look here! You know what killed my former mate. . . . Now don't you ever dare to eat kafir-corn porridge; you shall eat millet porridge, that's all."

"No fear," said the woman, "I shall eat no kafir-corn porridge."

The following day he thought of resuming his expedition to the bush. Leaving his bride alone in the hut, he said, "Now I shall have a walk into the bush." And away he went.

Well! At night when it was quite dark, the new bride heard the sound *kwe! kwe! kwe!* drag! drag! drag! "That must be," she thought, "the former wife, the one that was killed, struck with an axe!"

There she was already at the door, drag! drag! drag! Then she knocked *nku! nku! nku!* knock! knock! knock! Then a song in Ramba:

"Open, open, little bird.
Open, open, little bird.
O mother! Be satisfied with millet.
A little porridge of kafir corn is a little bird."

The new bride went to open for her. The old one dragged herself into the hut, and said:

"Put it on the fire, put it on the fire, little bird.
Put it on the fire, put it on the fire, little bird.
O mother! Be satisfied with millet.
A little porridge of kafir corn is a spirit."

The old wife herself went ahead and put the pot on the fire. They both then remained quiet. Did you ever! The pot boiled, and the new bride then clearly recognized the former one, and heard:

"Stir the porridge, stir the porridge, little bird.
Stir the porridge, stir the porridge, little bird.
O mother! Be satisfied with millet.
A little porridge of kafir corn is a spirit."

The old bride then got up herself to bring kafir-corn meal from the big jar, put it with her own hands in the pot, stirred and stirred her porridge, and then put it in a dish. Just imagine! She actually put two fingers into it, saying:

"Let us eat, let us eat, little bird.
Let us eat, let us eat, little bird.
O mother! Be satisfied with millet.
A little porridge of kafir corn is a spirit."

She just ate alone. Her new mate went so far as to put a finger into the porridge, but she did not eat. So the woman repeated:

"Let us eat, let us eat, little bird.
Let us eat, let us eat, little bird.
O mother! Be satisfied with millet.
A little porridge of kafir corn is a spirit."

She finished her porridge alone. Her mate had not said a word. The woman then moved away. There! She was going. Drag yourself! Drag yourself! Then she stopped at the door to say:

"Shut behind me, shut behind me, little bird.
Shut behind me, shut behind me, little bird.

> *O mother! Be satisfied with millet.*
> *A little porridge of kafir corn is a spirit."*

Now she was out! There she went toward her hole and buried herself in it.

The next day the man returned from the bush, and his wife came to meet him. "Dear me!" she said, "here in the hut where you have left me there is a thing which comes at night. It is impossible to sleep. It keeps one awake with songs."

"What is it like?" asked the man.

"You will see it tonight," answered the woman.

Night came. "Now," asked the man, "how about that thing you were speaking of?"

"We shall see it, sure enough," said the woman.

Then it was dark. The woman was already there. The people inside heard *kwe! kwe! kwe!* drag! drag! There she was already knocking at the door:

> *"Open, open, little bird.*
> *Open, open, little bird.*
> *O mother! Be satisfied with millet.*
> *A little porridge of kafir corn is a spirit."*

Heaven help us! The present wife moved to go and open the door. The husband caught hold of her. "Do not go!" he said.

"I will go," she said.

So the little woman got away from his grip and went to open the door. The first wife then came in, dragging herself along.

> *"Put it on the fire, put it on the fire, little bird.*
> *Put it on the fire, put it on the fire, little bird.*
> *O mother! Be satisfied with millet.*
> *A little porridge of kafir corn is a spirit."*

She put the pot on the fire, and then sat down. When the pot boiled, she said:

> *"Stir the porridge, stir the porridge, little bird.*
> *Stir the porridge, stir the porridge, little bird.*
> *O mother! Be satisfied with millet.*
> *A little porridge of kafir corn is a spirit."*

Then she herself stirred the porridge, took it out of the pot and put two fingers in it, singing:

> *"Let us eat, let us eat, little bird.*
> *Let us eat, let us eat, little bird.*
> *O mother! Be satisfied with millet.*
> *A little porridge of kafir corn is a spirit."*

Good gracious! She ate and ate her porridge. Then she again began to drag herself along, but this time in the direction of the bed, saying:

"Let us sleep, let us sleep, little bird.
Let us sleep, let us sleep, little bird.
O mother! Be satisfied with millet.
A little kafir corn porridge is a spirit."

She then began to stretch herself on the bed in which lay her husband who had struck her with an axe. Seeing that, the second little wife rushed outside.

When people came, the next morning, they found in the hut only a corpse, and this already swollen.

And this little story, too, that's all. It ends there.

[BENA MUKUNI]

78

The Twin Brothers

ONCE A WOMAN, after prolonged labour, gave birth to twins, both sons. And each one, as he was brought forth, came into this world with a valuable fetish. One the mother called Luemba, the other Mavungu. And they were almost full-grown at their birth, so that Mavungu, the first-born, wished to start upon his travels.

Now about this time the daughter of Nzambi was ready for marriage. The tiger came and offered himself in marriage; but Nzambi told him that he must speak to her daughter himself, as she should only marry the man of her choice. Then the tiger went to the girl and asked her to marry him, but she refused him. Then the gazelle, and the pig, and all created things that had breath, one after the other, asked the daughter in marriage; but she refused them all, saying that she did not love them. And they were all very sad.

Mavungu heard of this girl, and determined to marry her. And so he called upon his charm, and asked it to help him. He took some grass in his hands, and changed one blade of grass into a horn, another into a knife, another into a gun, and so on, until he was quite ready for the long journey.

Then he set out, and travelled and travelled, until at last hunger overcame him, when he asked his fetish whether it was true that he was going to be allowed to starve. The charm hastened to place a sumptuous feast before him, and Mavungu ate and was satisfied.

"Oh, fetish!" Mavungu said. "Are you going to leave these beautiful plates which I have used, for the use of any commoner that may come along?" The charm immediately caused all to disappear.

Then Mavungu travelled and travelled, until at length he became very tired, and had to ask his charm to arrange a place for him where he might sleep. And the charm saw to his comfort, so that he passed a peaceful night.

And after many days' weary travelling he at length arrived at Nzambi's town. And Nzambi's daughter saw Mavungu and straightway fell in love with him, and ran to her mother and father and cried, "I have seen the man I love, and I shall die if I do not marry him."

Then Mavungu sought out Nzambi, and told her that he had come to marry her daughter.

"Go and see her first," said Nzambi, "and if she will have you, you may marry her."

And when Mavungu and the daughter of Nzambi saw each other, they ran towards each other and loved one another.

They were led to a fine *shimbec;* and while all the people in the town danced and sang for gladness, Mavungu and the daughter of Nzambi slept there. And in the morning Mavungu noticed that the whole *shimbec* was crowded with mirrors, but that each mirror was covered so that the glass could not be seen. And he asked the daughter of Nzambi to uncover them, so that he might see himself in them. And she took him to one and opened it, and Mavungu immediately saw the perfect likeness of his native town. And she took him to another, and he there saw another town he knew; and thus she took him to all the mirrors save one, and this one she refused to let him see.

"Why will you not let me look into that mirror?" asked Mavungu.

"Because that is the picture of the town whence no man who arrives there returns."

"Do let me see it!" urged Mavungu.

At last the daughter of Nzambi yielded, and Mavungu looked hard at the reflected image of that terrible place.

"I must go there," he said.

"Nay, you will never return. Please don't go!" pleaded the daughter of Nzambi.

"Have no fear!" answered Mavungu. "My fetish will protect me."

The daughter of Nzambi cried very much, but could not move Mavungu from his purpose. Mavungu then left his newly-married wife, mounted his horse, and set off for the town from whence no man returns.

He travelled and travelled, until at last he came near to the town, when, meeting an old woman, he asked her for fire to light his pipe.

"Tie up your horse first, and come and fetch it."

Mavungu descended, and having tied his horse up very securely, he went to the woman for the fire; and when he had come near to her she killed him, so that he disappeared entirely.

Now Luemba wondered at the long absence of his brother Mavungu and determined to follow him. So he took some grass, and by the aid of *his* fetish changed one blade into a horse, another into a knife, another into a gun, and so on, until he was fully prepared for his journey. Then he set out and, after some days' journeying, arrived at Nzambi's town.

Nzambi rushed out to meet him, and calling him Mavungu, embraced him.

"Nay," said Luemba, "My name is not Mavungu; I am his brother, Luemba."

"Nonsense!" answered Nzambi. "You are my son-in-law, Mavungu." And straightway a great feast was prepared. Nzambi's daughter danced for joy and would not hear of his not being Mavungu. And Luemba was sorely troubled, and did not know what to do, as he was now sure that Nzambi's daughter was Mavungu's wife. And when night came, Nzambi's daughter would sleep in Luemba's *shimbec;* but he appealed to his charm, and it enclosed Nzambi's daughter in a room, lifting her out of Luemba's room for the night and bringing her back in the early morning.

Luemba's curiosity, too, was aroused by the many closed mirrors that hung about the walls; so he asked Nzambi's daughter to let him look into them. And she showed him all excepting one. This she told him was the one that reflected the town whence no man returns. Luemba insisted upon looking into this one and when he had seen the terrible picture he knew that his brother was there.

Luemba determined to leave Nzambi's town for the town whence no man returns; and so after thanking them all for his kind reception, he set out. They all wept loudly, but were consoled by the fact that he had been there once already, and returned safely, so that he could of course return a second time. Luemba travelled and travelled, until he also came to where the old woman was standing, and asked her for fire.

She told him to tie up his horse and come to her to fetch it, but he tied his horse up only very lightly, and then fell upon the old woman and killed her.

Then he sought out his brother's bones and the bones of his horse, and put them together, and then touched them with his charm. And Mavungu and his horse came to life again. Then together they joined the bones of hundreds of people together and touched them with their charms, so that they all lived again. And they set off with all their followers to Nzambi's town. And Luemba told Mavungu how he had been mistaken for him by his father-in-law and wife, and how by the help of his charm he had saved his wife from dishonour. Mavungu thanked him, and said it was well.

But a quarrel broke out between the two brothers about the followers. Mavungu said they were his, because he was the elder; but Luemba said that they belonged to him, because he had given Mavungu and them all life. Mavungu then fell upon Luemba and killed him; but his horse remained by his body. Mavungu then went on his way to Nzambi's town and was magnificently welcomed.

Now Luemba's horse took his charm and touched Luemba's body, so that he lived again. Then Luemba mounted his horse and sought out his brother Mavungu and killed him.

And when the town had heard the whole story, they all said that Luemba had done quite rightly.

[BAKONGO]

79

Kenkebe

THERE WAS ONCE a great famine in a certain country, and the people were obliged to eat wild plants to keep themselves alive. Their principal food during this time was *nongwes* which they dug out of the ground.

There was living at that place a man called Kenkebe, and one day his wife said to him, "My husband, go to my father and ask him to give us some corn."

The man said, "Yes, I will go."

So he rose up early in the morning and went on until he arrived at his father-in-law's village, where he was received with every mark of kindness. A very large ox was killed for his entertainment. It was so large that it was six days before it was all eaten. His father-in-law asked of him the news.

He said, "There is no news to tell to friends. All the news is this—that at my home there is not a grain to be eaten. Famine is over our heads. Will you give us some corn, for we are dying?"

His father-in-law gave him seven bags full of millet, and his wife's sisters went with him to carry them. When they came to a valley close by his home, he told his sisters-in-law that they could now go back to their father.

They said, "How will you manage to carry all those bags alone?"

He replied, "I shall be able to carry them all now, because we are not far from my home."

So the girls went back to their father.

Then he carried the bags, one by one, and hid them in a cave under a great rock that was there. Afterward he took some of the millet and ground it. When it was ground very fine he made it into cakes just like *nongwes*. Then he dug some real *nongwes* out of the ground and went home to his wife.

He said to her, "There is a great famine at your father's also. I found the people there eating themselves."

He told his wife to make a fire. Then he pretended to cut a piece of meat out of his thigh and said, "So are they doing at your father's village. Now, my wife, let us do the same."

His wife cut a piece from her leg and roasted it, but the piece that Kenkebe put on the fire was some meat that he had brought home with him.

Then Kenkebe's little boy said, "Why does my father's meat smell nice in roasting and my mother's meat does not smell nice?"

Kenkebe answered, "It is because it is taken from the leg of a man."

After this he gave his wife some *nongwes* to roast. He took for himself some of those he had made of corn.

The little boy said, "Why do my father's *nongwes* smell nice in roasting, and my mother's do not smell nice?"

Kenkebe said, "It is because they were dug by a man."

After eating, he went outside, but he had dropped one of his *nongwes* by the fire. When he went out, the boy found it. He broke it in two and gave half to his mother.

He said, "There is a difference between our *nongwes* and those of father."

His mother said, "Yes, my child, this one is made of corn."

The next morning, just at the very beginning of dawn, Kenkebe got up and went away with a pot in his hand. The boy was awake and saw his father go out. So he called to his mother and said, "Mother, mother, wake! My father is going away with the pot in his hand!"

So she got up and they followed after Kenkebe. They saw him go to the cave where he took some corn out of one of the bags and began to grind it. Then they went on top of the rock, and rolled a big stone over.

When Kenkebe saw the stone coming he ran away, but it followed close behind him. He ran down the valley, but the stone kept running too. He jumped into a deep hole in the river. Down went the stone, too. He ran up the hill and up went the stone. He ran over the plain but, whenever he turned to look, the stone was just there behind him. So it continued all that day. At night he reached his own house and then the stone stopped. His wife had already come home and had brought with her one of the bags of corn.

Kenkebe came in crying.

His wife said to him, "Why do you cry as if you were a child?"

He said, "Because I am very tired and very hungry."

She said, "Where are your clothes and your bag?"

He replied, "I was crossing a river, and I fell down. The stream carried away my mantle, my bag, and my kerries, indeed everything that was mine."

Then his wife gave him his mantle, which she had picked up when he was running away, and she said to him, "You are foolish to do such things. There is no food for you tonight."

The next morning Kenkebe rose early and went out to hunt with his two dogs. The name of the one was Tumtumse, and the name of the other was Mbambozozele. He found an eland with a young calf which he drove to his place. He cut an ear off the calf and roasted it in the fire. It was fat, and he liked it so much that he cut the other ear off and cooked it also. Then he wished to kill the calf, but he said to himself, "If I kill this calf, I shall not be able to get milk from the eland."

So he called his two dogs and said to the one, "Tumtumse, my dog, if I kill this calf, will you imitate it and suck the eland for me?"

The dog said, "No, I shall bark like a dog."

Kenkebe said, "Get out of my sight and never come near me again, you ugly, useless animal."

He said to the other, "Mbambozozele, my dog, if I kill this calf, will you imitate it and suck the eland for me?"

The dog said, "I will do so."

Then he killed the calf and ate it. He took the skin and put it upon Mbambozozele, so that the eland thought it was her calf that sucked before Kenkebe milked her. But one day the dog was sucking too long, and Kenkebe wanted him to leave off. He tried to drink just a few drops more, when his master got angry and struck him with a stick. Thereupon the dog began to howl, and the eland saw how she had been deceived. At once she ran after Kenkebe and tried to stick him with her horns. He ran one way and the eland ran after him, then he ran another way, and still the eland chased him.

His wife came out and saw him running. She cried out to him, "Jump up quickly on the big stone." He did so, and the eland ran with such fury against the stone that it broke its head and fell down dead.

They then cut the eland up and wanted to cook it, but there was no fire. Kenkebe said to his son, "Go to the village of the cannibals that is on that hill over the valley and ask for some fire; but do not take any meat with you, lest they should smell it."

The boy went, but he hid a piece of meat and took it with him. When he got to the first house he asked for fire, but they sent him to the next. At the next they sent him farther, and so he finally had to go to the house that was farthest away. An old woman lived there. The boy gave her a little piece of meat and said, "Do not cook it until I am far away with the fire."

But as soon as the boy was gone she put it on the coals. The smell came to the noses of the cannibals and they ran to the place and swallowed the old woman, and the meat, and the fire, and even the ashes.

Then they ran after the boy. When he came near his own house, he cried out, "Hide yourselves, you that are at home!"

His father said, "My son is saying we must gather wood that will make coals."

His mother said, "No, he is saying that we must hide ourselves."

The boy cried again, "Hide yourselves!"

Then his mother hid herself in a bush. An old woman who was there covered herself with ashes, and Kenkebe climbed up into a tree, with the breast of the eland in his hand. The boy slipped into a hole which was by the side of the path.

The cannibals came to the place. First they ate the eland. Then one of them said, "Search under the ashes."

There they found the old woman, and they ate her. Then they said, "Search in the tree."

There they found Kenkebe. He cried very much, but they would not spare him. They ate him and the breast of the eland. Then the wise one said, "Look in the bush."

They looked there and found the wife of Kenkebe. They said, "We will eat her another time," and so they took her home with them. They did not look for the boy.

The woman made a plan to escape. She made beer for the cannibals and they all came to drink. They sat together in a big house, and drank very much beer. Then she said, "May I go out?"

They said, "You may go, but come back quickly."

She said, "Shall I close the entrance?"

They said, "Close it."

Then she took fire and put it on the house and all these cannibals were burned to death. So the woman escaped, and lived happily afterward with her son.

[XOSA]

80

The Giant of the Great Water

THERE WAS ONCE a small boy who was herding the goats, and his father came and pointed out to him some long and luxurious grass and told him to take the goats there to feed. So he pastured them there that day and took them there again the day following. Now the next day while the goats were feeding, the owner of the pasture appeared, and he said to the boy, "Why are you feeding your goats on my grass?" And the boy said, "It is not my doing, for my father told me to come here." And he said, "This evening I will go to your father's house and talk to him." Now the owner of the grazing ground was a man very big and tall, and his name was Mukun'ga M'Bura, so in the evening he came to the home of the boy and he said to the father, "Why were your goats eating my grass when you could see I had closed it to you?"

The father said, "That is my affair." Mukun'ga M'Bura said, "As you have done this, I will eat you and all your people." To this the father replied, "You shall do no such thing." So the young men made sharp their swords and got ready their spears, but Mukun'ga M'Bura was too strong for them, and he ate the father, and the young men, and the women, and the children, and the oxen, and the goats, and then he ate the house and the barns, so that there was nothing left. The only person who escaped was a little boy, who ran away and hid in the grass so that Mukun'ga M'Bura did not see him.

The boy made himself a bow and shot wild game and became very strong and built himself a house; and at last he said, when he was full-grown, "Why do I stay here? I am big and strong. Mukun'ga M'Bura, who killed my father and all my people, still lives."

So he took his sword and made it very sharp and went to the district where Mukun'ga M'Bura lived, and as he drew near he saw him coming up out of the great water where he lived. He shouted to him, "Tomorrow I will come and kill you." And he went back and ate more meat so as to be stronger than ever. The next day he went again, but Mukun'ga M'Bura was not to be seen. The third day he met him again, and he said, "You have killed all my people, so I will kill you," and Mukun'ga M'Bura was afraid and said to the warrior, "Do not strike me with your sword over the heart or I shall die, but open my middle finger," so the warrior did so, and he said, "Make a big hole, not a little one." And the warrior made a big hole, and out came first the father, whom Mukun'ga M'Bura had eaten, and then the young men, and the women, and the cattle, and the sheep, and the houses, and the food stores just as before. And the warrior said, "No, I will spare you, for you have restored my father, his people and his goods, but you must not eat them again." And the giant said, "They shall be safe."

The warrior and his people went back and rebuilt their homesteads, but the warrior thought to himself, "Now this Mukun'ga M'Bura is big and strong and very bad. He has eaten many people. He may come again and destroy my father."

So he called the young men and asked them to come and fight Mukun'ga M'Bura with him, and they all made ready for war and went to the home of Mukun'ga M'Bura. He saw them coming and said, "Why are you here to slay me? Have I not given you back your people?" But the warrior replied, "You are very evil; you have killed and eaten many people; therefore you shall die." Then they all fell upon him and slew him and cut off his head and hewed his body in pieces. But a big piece separated itself from the rest of the body, which was dead, and went back into the water, and the warrior returned to his home and told his brother that he had slain Mukun'ga M'Bura, all but one leg. "Tomorrow," he said, "I will go into the water and get that leg and burn it." And the mother besought him not to go, but the next day he went, and when he got to the place there was no water to be seen, only cattle and goats, for what remained of Mukun'ga M'Bura had gathered together his children and taken all the water and gone very far. The beasts, however, he had not taken but left behind. So the warrior went back and brought his people, and they gathered the cattle and goats together and took them back to their own homestead.

[AKIKUYU]

81

A Woman for a Hundred Cattle

ONCE UPON A TIME there were a man and a woman. They lived for many days in the land of Pata, and a son was born to them. Their fortune consisted of a hundred cattle. Beyond these they did not have a single calf; they had nothing but the cattle.

As time went by the son grew and became a big child, and when the boy was fifteen years of age, his father died. Several years later, his mother also died. So the young man had a heritage from both his parents—he inherited the hundred cattle which were left to him. He stayed in his home and observed the time of mourning for his parents. When he had finished mourning he felt an urge to look for a woman to marry.

He said to his neighbours, "I want to marry a woman, for my parents are dead and I am all alone now. I cannot stay alone. I must get married."

His neighbours said to him, "Surely, get married, for indeed you are lonely now. We shall look around for you so that you may find a suitable woman to marry."

He said, "Yes, be it so."

Later, he said, "I would like somebody to go out and look for a woman for me."

They said, "If God wills it!"

So one of the neighbours rose and went and looked for a woman whom the young man could marry, until he found one. Then he came and said to him, "I have found such a woman as you want, but she is not from this town."

He asked, "Where, then, does she live?" The neighbour said: "In a different town, pretty far away. I think it takes eight hours of travelling from here to get there."

He asked him, "Whose daughter is this girl?"

And the neighbour said to him, "She is the daughter of Abdallah, and her father is very rich. This woman owns six thousand cattle. The father has no other child, just this one daughter."

When the young man heard this, he was all full of desire to obtain this woman, and he said to his neighbour, "Would you go there tomorrow and carry my answer—which is that I am agreeable."

298

The neighbour said, "God willing, I will go there tomorrow." And at dawn, the matchmaker rose and travelled until he came to old Abdallah, and he carried the young man's message to him, and related all that had happened.

Finally the father answered him, saying, "I have heard your words, but I desire that anyone who wants to marry my daughter should give me a hundred cattle as a bride-price. If he gives such a bride-price I will give him my daughter for wife."

The matchmaker said, "God willing, I shall go and carry the answer to him."

The father said to him, "Yes, do that!"

The matchmaker rose and went back, and gave the young man the answer. He told him everything that had been discussed.

The young man said, "I have heard your words, but he wants a hundred cattle as a bride-price, and I have just a hundred cattle. If I give them all to him, what will my wife have to live on, if she comes to me? I have no other fortune but these hundred cattle which I have inherited from my father."

Finally his neighbour said to him, "Well now, if you do not want her, tell me so. Then I can go and carry back your reply; or if you want her, tell me so definitely."

The young man bowed his head and meditated and, when he raised his head again, he said, "It does not matter, go and say that I accept. I will go and fetch the hundred cattle and give them to him."

So the matchmaker got up and went to the father of the girl and said to him, "The young man is willing to pay the hundred cattle."

And the father said, "I am willing then that he should take my daughter." They talked over the details, and then someone was sent to bring the young man. The latter came and was amiably received, and they discussed the marriage. So the young man was wedded to the girl and paid the hundred cattle, and the wedding feast was celebrated.

Then the young man took his wife and travelled home. There they remained at first ten days; but when the provisions which they had taken along were used up, the young man had nothing for his wife to eat. Then he said to her, "Dear wife, now I have nothing left to eat. Formerly, I had my cattle. These I milked and thus I had my sustenance; but now I have given my cattle away for you and, therefore, I have nothing left. Dear wife, I will go now to my neighbours and from those who have cows I shall obtain some milk, however little it be, so that we shall have something to eat."

Then the woman said to him, "Yes, dear husband!"

So the young man went out and this now became his occupation. Every day he went out and milked other people's cows, so that he could have something to eat for himself and his wife. This he continued to do every day.

One day his wife went out and placed herself in front of her door just as a very handsome young man passed by. When he saw the woman standing by the door, he was seized with a desire to seduce her. Thereupon he sent a procurer to talk to the woman.

The woman said, "God is my witness that I have heard the message you convey to me, but you must wait a little longer, until I have made up my mind, and then I will let you know. I cannot answer yet." So the procurer rose and went home.

Three months later, the woman's father thought to himself, "I must go and pay a visit to my daughter and her husband." So he started on his journey and went his way until he came to his son-in-law's house. Arrived there, he knocked at the door. The daughter got up and answered, "Who is there?"

The old man said, "It is I, Abdallah."

The daughter rose and said to him, "Will you not come in?"

So he entered and exchanged greetings with his daughter, and she invited him into the hall, and the old man sat down there. The father asked the daughter how she was getting along, and she said, "Pretty well, my father."

Finally the daughter got up, went away from where her father was sitting and went into her room, cogitating and crying profusely, because there was not the slightest bit of food in the house that she could cook for her father. Then she left by the back door, and when she looked behind the yard, she noticed the young man who wanted to seduce her, and he called to her to come nearer. So she went over to him and said to him, "How are you getting along, sir?"

He said, "I once sent someone to you, and you said that you would come to me for a visit, but you have not come. Why are you so wavering? Since I saw you that day when you were standing by the door I have not been able to sleep any more; every day, when I lie down, I dream only of you in my sleep."

The woman answered him, saying, "God be my witness, I shall not harass you any more. If you long for me I shall come without delay. First, however, get a piece of meat for me, so that I can cook something to eat for my guest. I shall come afterward."

The young man asked her, "Who is your guest?"

The woman replied, saying, "It is my father whom I receive as a guest."

Thereupon he said, "You wait here, and I will bring you some meat right away."

So he rose and went out, and the woman remained standing there. A little later, he returned with a quarter of beef and said to her, "Here is the meat, but now do not put me off any longer."

She said, "God be my witness, I shall not put you off."

He stretched out his hand and gave her the meat, and the woman took it and went back into her house. Then he who had given her the meat paced up and down outside and waited for the fulfilment of the promise that the woman had made him.

After the woman returned, she took the meat, cut it into pieces, and put it into the pot. As soon as she had placed it in the pot, her husband came back and found his father-in-law sitting in the hall. As he saw his father-in-law sitting in the hall, his blood rose. He could not find a word to say, nor did he know what to do. He went closer until he came to where his father-in-law was sitting. He greeted him according to custom and asked him how he was getting along. After that he went to his wife and found her cooking meat and asked her, "My dear wife, what are you cooking there?"

She said, "I am cooking meat."

He asked, "Where did you get this meat from?"

She said, "I received it from the neighbours; they have given it to me." When her husband heard this he remained silent and became sad because he was so terribly poor.

Then he said to his wife, "My dear wife, what shall we do now that we have not only ourselves to feed but also a guest?"

His wife answered him, saying, "I do not know what we shall do."

Then the man said, "I will go out to the rich people where I milk the cows and tell them, 'I have a guest staying with me now, and I would like you to give me something, whatever it be, to cook for my guest.'" So he rose, went to the rich people where he worked, and apprised them of everything that had happened to him.

These rich people were sympathetic and gave him a little meat and a little milk, which he took. Then he went home.

At his house, in the meantime, his wife had finished cooking the meat that she had received from her would-be seducer. When her husband returned with the meat, the woman put out her hand, accepted it, and laid it on the floor. Then the husband rose and washed his hands and went into the hall. The woman in the kitchen withdrew the meat from the pot and placed it on the platter from which they were accustomed to eat.

Now the would-be seducer had remained where he was, walking up and down, until he saw that the time, which had been agreed upon with the woman, had passed. Then he said to his heart, "The best thing for me to do is to pass by the front door and look inside. Perhaps I shall see the woman." So he went off and passed by the door, and encountered the woman's husband and the father-in-law sitting and chatting. When the wicked man saw that, he greeted them, and the woman's husband answered the greeting, inviting him to approach. So the wicked man came up and sat down.

Then they conversed together, the woman's husband having no inkling of the stranger's plan and of what he really wanted. Thus they conversed with each other—the woman's father, and the woman's husband, and that impious creature who wanted to disturb the peace of the young man's house. The three men stayed together in the hall.

As soon as the woman inside had placed the meat on the platter, she brought it out into the hall. As soon as her husband rose to be handed the meat, the woman said, "Eat now, you three fools!"

Thereupon her father began, saying, "Well now, wherefore am I a fool?"

His daughter answered him, saying, "Please, father, eat first. Afterwards I shall tell you all about your foolishness."

But the father said, "No, I shall not eat, but you shall first tell me about my foolishness. After that, I shall eat."

Thereupon the daughter rose and said, "My father, you have sold an expensive object for a cheap one."

Her father said to her, "What is it that I have sold too cheaply?"

She said, "It is I, my father, whom you have sold too cheaply."

He said, "Why so?"

She said, "Father, you have no daughter and no child except only me and you went and sold me for a hundred cattle, yet you, father, have six thousand cattle anyhow. You have regarded a hundred cattle as more valuable than me. That is why I have said, 'You have given up a valuable thing for a cheap one.'"

The father answered, "That is true, my child, I was a fool."

Then her husband rose and said, "Now, please, tell me the nature of my foolishness too."

The woman said to him, "You are even a greater fool."

He said, "Why that?"

She said, "You inherited a hundred cattle from your parents; not a single calf more did you inherit. And you took them all and wedded me in exchange for them, in exchange for all your hundred cattle; yet there were so many women in your own town whose bride-price amounted to only ten or twenty cattle. But you did not look at them. Instead, you came and married me in exchange for all your cattle. And now you have nothing, not even anything to eat for me and for yourself, and you have become a servant of others. You go and milk the cows of other people to get something to eat. Had you kept half of your herd of cattle and married a woman with the other half, you would have had something to eat. Therefore, this is your foolishness, my dear husband."

Then the worthless knave asked, "And wherein does my foolishness consist? Tell me!"

Thereupon the woman rose and said, "You are even a greater fool than both the others."

And he asked her, "Why is that?"

She answered him, saying, "You wanted to get with a single quarter of beef what had been bought for a hundred cattle. Are you not, therefore, a fool?"

He jumped up in a hurry and ran away as quickly as he could.

The woman's father stayed with them for two days. On the third day he made his preparation for taking leave and then went home. When he arrived at his house, he unhobbled the cattle which he had received from his son-in-law and sent them back to him. With them he sent another two hundred. Thus his daughter could live in comfort with her husband for many days.

[SWAHILI]

Epilogue

SHE WAS AN OLD WOMAN of a family with a long genealogy. Leza Shikakunamo—"The Besetting One"—had stretched out his hand against her family. He slew her mother and her father while she was yet a child; and in the course of the years all connected with her perished. She said to herself, "Surely, I shall keep those who sit on my thighs"—but no, even they, the children of her children, were taken from her. She became withered with age, and it seemed to her that she herself was at last to be taken. But no, a change came over her: she grew younger. Then came into her heart a desperate resolution to find God and ask the meaning of it all. Somewhere up there in the sky must be His dwelling: if only she could reach it!

She began to cut down trees, immense, tall trees, joining them together, and so planning a structure that would reach to heaven. It grew and grew, but as it was getting to be as she wanted it, the lowest timbers rotted and it fell. She fell with it, but without being killed or breaking a bone. She set to work again and rebuilt the structure, but once again the foundations rotted and it fell. She gave it up in despair, but not her intention of finding Leza. Somewhere on earth there must be another way to heaven!

So she began to travel, going through country after country, nation after nation, always with the thought in her mind: "I shall come to where the earth ends, and there, where the earth and sky touch, I shall find a road to God, and I shall ask him, 'What have I done to Thee that Thou afflictest me in this manner?'"

The old woman never found where the earth ends, but, though disappointed, she did not give up her search. As she passed through the different countries the people asked her, "What have you come for, old woman?"

And her answer would be, "I am seeking Leza."

"Seeking Leza! For what?"

"My brothers, you ask me! Here in the nations is there one who suffers as I have suffered?"

And they would ask again, "How have you suffered?"

305

"In this way. I am alone. As you see me, a solitary old woman: that is how I am!"

And they answered again, "Yes, we see. That is how you are! Bereaved of friends and kindred? In what do you differ from others? Leza Shikakunamo sits on the back of every one of us, and we cannot shake him off!"

She never obtained her desire: she died of a broken heart.

[BAILA]

Sources of the Folktales

Glossary

Sources of the Folktales

BELOW are listed the works from which the tales are drawn. The table of sources, following, refers to this list. Where required, other information about the treatment of the material is given. Page numbers in the source are given only where the original title has been very much altered.

BEECH, M. W. H. *The Suk: Their Language and Folklore.* Oxford, 1911.

BLEEK, W. H. I. *Reynard the Fox in South Africa.* London, 1864.

—— and LLOYD, L. C. *The Mantis and His Friends: Bushman Folklore.* Edited by Dorothea F. Bleek. Capetown, 1923.

——. *Specimens of Bushman Folklore.* London, 1911.

BRUTZER, ERNST. *Der Geisterglaube bei den Kamba.* Leipzig, 1905.

BÜTTNER, C. G. *Anthologie aus der Suaheli-Litteratur.* Berlin, 1894.

——. "Märchen der Ova-Herero," *Zeitschrift für afrikanische Sprachen* (Berlin), 1888, 189–216.

CALLAWAY, HENRY. *Nursery Tales, Traditions, and Histories of the Zulus.* London, 1868.

CARDINALL, A. W. *Tales Told in Togoland.* London, 1931.

CHATELAIN, HELI. *Folk-tales of Angola.* (American Folk-Lore Society Memoirs, I.) Boston, 1894.

DAYRELL, ELPHINSTONE. *Folk Stories from Southern Nigeria.* London, 1910.

DENNETT, R. E. *Notes on the Folklore of Fjort.* (Folk Lore Society Publications, XLI.) London, 1898.

DRIBERG, J. H. *The Lango, a Nilotic Tribe of Uganda.* London, 1923.

HOLLIS, SIR CLAUD. *The Masai, Their Language and Folklore.* Oxford, 1905.

HUFFMAN, RAY. *Nuer Customs and Folk-Lore.* London, 1931.

JUNOD, HENRI A. *Les Ba-Ronga.* Neuchatel, 1898.

——. *The Life of a South African Tribe.* London, 1913. 2 vols.

LINDBLOM, GERHARD. "Tales of Supernatural Beings and Adventures" in his *Kamba Folklore.* (Archives d'Études Orientales, XX, 2.) Lund, 1935.

MEINHOF, CARL. *Afrikanische Märchen.* Jena, 1921.

Posselt, F. W. T. *Fables of the Veld*. London, 1929.

Rattray, R. S. *Akan-Ashanti Folk-tales*. Oxford, 1930.

Raum, J. *Versuch einer Grammatik der Dschaggasprache*. Berlin, 1909.

Roscoe, John. *The Baganda: An Account of Their Native Customs and Beliefs*. London, 1911.

Routledge, W. S. and K. *With a Prehistoric People: The Akikuyu of British East Africa*. London, 1910.

Smith, Edwin W., and Dale, A. M. *The Ila-speaking Peoples of Northern Rhodesia*. London, 1920. 2 vols.

Stayt, Hugh A. *The Bavenda*. London, 1931.

Talbot, P. Amaury. *In the Shadow of the Bush*. London, 1912.

Theal, G. McCall. *Kaffir Folk-lore*. London, 1882.

Torrend, J. *Specimens of Bantu Folk-lore from Northern Rhodesia*. London and New York, 1921.

Tremearne, A. J. N. *Hausa Superstitions and Customs*. London, 1913.

Wandres, Carl. "Texte" [i.e., contribution of Nama and German texts, pp. 149–77] in: Meinhof, Carl. *Lehrbuch der Nama-sprache*. (Lehrbücher des Seminars für orientalische Sprachen, XXIII.) Berlin, 1909.

TABLE OF SOURCES

Prologue: Talbot.
1. Rattray. English revised.
2. Cardinall. A number of passages have been combined.
3. Cardinall.
4. Rattray. English revised.
5. Dayrell.
6. Bleek and Lloyd, *Specimens*. English completely revised.
7. Lindblom.
8. Bleek and Lloyd, *Specimens*. English completely revised.
9. Talbot.
10. Talbot.
11. Cardinall.
12. Brutzer, as reprinted in Meinhof, pp. 65–66. Translated from German.
13. Bleek, *Reynard*.
14. Rattray. English revised.
15. Smith and Dale, Vol. II.
16. Roscoe.
17. Chatelain. Completely rewritten.
18. Smith and Dale, Vol. II.
19. Bleek and Lloyd, *Mantis*.
20. Roscoe.
21. Rattray. English revised.
22. Bleek and Lloyd, *Mantis*.
23. Büttner, *Märchen*, as reprinted in Meinhof, pp. 139–44. Translated from German.
24. Bleek, *Reynard*.
25. Callaway.
26. Hollis.
27. Dennett.
28. Dayrell.
29. Hollis.
30. Junod, *Life*, Vol. II.
31. Torrend.
32. Rattray. English revised.
33. Rattray. English revised.
34. Smith and Dale, Vol. II.
35. Beech.
36. Smith and Dale, Vol. II.
37. Theal.
38. Huffman.
39. Wandres. Translated from German.
40. Rattray. English revised.
41. Bleek and Lloyd, *Specimens*.
42. Dayrell.
43. Bleek, *Reynard*.
44. Posselt.
45. Hollis.

46. Routledge.
47. Hollis.
48. Torrend, pp. 85–89.
49. Torrend, pp. 14–17.
50. Torrend, pp. 66–72.
51. Dayrell.
52. Dennett.
53. Hollis.
54. Rattray. English revised.
55. Rattray. English revised.
56. Rattray. English revised.
57. Rattray. English revised.
58. Rattray. English revised.
59. Rattray. English revised.
60. Rattray. English revised.
61. Callaway.
62. Junod, *Ba-Ronga*. Translated from French.
63. Driberg.
64. Raum. Translated from German.

65. Lindblom.
66. Tremearne.
67. Tremearne.
68. Routledge.
69. Smith and Dale, Vol. II.
70. Dayrell.
71. Driberg.
72. Dennett.
73. Stayt.
74. Routledge.
75. Tremearne.
76. Callaway.
77. Torrend, pp. 50–53.
78. Dennett.
79. Theal.
80. Routledge.
81. Büttner, *Anthologie*, as reprinted in Meinhof, pp. 54–61. Translated from German.

Epilogue: Smith and Dale, Vol. II.

Glossary

T HIS LIST contains African words (including some of the proper names, when translations of their sense were to be found) and some other unfamiliar words. In general, words clearly onomatopoeic are not included. Occasionally, an explanation is quoted directly from the original translator or editor; the references pertain to the list of works on pp. 309–10. There is no attempt to give pronunciation. African words are usually pronounced phonetically, though the Zulu words, with their clicks, are a thing apart (see **udonqa**).

A

abedee—*antelope of an unidentifiable kind.* (*Ashanti word.*)

Abosom—*minor gods, tutelary spirits, of the Ashanti.*

adduwa—*according to the translator, a thorny tree from which gum is obtained; also described as the desert date-tree.*

adwo—*apparently a greeting.*

adwobere—*cool and gentle.*

ah-loo-rookok—*nonsense syllables as song refrain, approx. "fa-la-la."*

amasi—*a specially prepared whey or buttermilk, similar to yoghurt. (The "milk" of tale 37, "The Bird That Made Milk," is actually this.)*

assegai—*a slender hardwood spear, usually tipped with iron; also, a tree of the dogwood family from whose wood such spears were made. (Not a native African word, but one derived by the Boers from the Portuguese, who had it from the Arabs, the ultimate source apparently being Berber. Through Arabic, it is related to the Chaucerian "launcegay.")*

asuanu—*gold dust to the weight of approx. four pounds sterling.*

asuanu-and-suru—*gold dust to the weight of approx. five pounds sterling.*

asuasa—*gold dust to the weight of approx. six pounds sterling.*

awa—*a bag of skin carried on the back, for burdens, including children.*

B

bakoo—*an exclamation, approx. "Good heavens!" or stronger.*

bana—*an exclamation, approx. "Dear me!"*

baobab—*an African tree, whose trunk sometimes attains a diameter of thirty feet. Its fruit, called monkey-bread, are edible; its leaves yield medicines and condiments; its bark, besides being medicinal, is made into rope, cloth, and paper. The trunk of the living tree is sometimes hollowed out as a dwelling. The Hausa consider the tree the home of spirits.*

biridi—*swish.*

birrim—*boom, as of a drum.*

brim—*plop!*

C

Calabar—*southeastern seacoast of Nigeria.*

choo awaba—*onomatopoeic for a type of snore.*

cowrie—*a small yellow-and-white shell, particularly of the Indian Ocean, once used as money in many parts of Africa, and used widely for ornamentation. (Cf. plate 23.)*

D

Dasse—*wife of the Mantis, in Bushman folklore.*

dinn—*chirp of the cicada; also, the Ashanti word for silence.*

duiker—*a small antelope, given to diving* (duiker = Dutch "diver") *suddenly into the bush.*

E

eddo *or* koko-yam—*an edible starchy tuber* (Colocasia esculenta), *the taro of the Pacific, the dasheen of the southern United States, the elephant's ear of the garden.*

Egbo—"*The Egbo Society has many branches, extending from Calabar up to Cross River and as far as the . . . Cameroons. Formerly the Society used to levy blackmail to a certain extent and collect debts for people. The head Ju-Ju, or fetish man, of each society is disguised, and frequently wears a hideous mask* [cf. plates 15–17]. *There is a bell tied round his waist, hanging behind and concealed by feathers; this bell makes a noise as he runs. When the Egbo* [i.e., the fetish man] *is out, no women are allowed outside their houses. . . . The Egbo very often carries a whip in his hand, and hits out blindly at anyone he comes across. He runs round the town followed by the young men of his society beating drums and firing off guns. There is generally much drinking going on when the Egbo is playing. There is an Egbo House in most towns, the end part of which is screened off for the Egbo to change in. Inside the house are hung human skulls and the skulls of buffalo . . . ; also heads of the various antelopes, crocodiles, apes, and the other animals which have been killed by the members. The skulls of cows and goats killed by the Society are also hung up. A fire is always kept in the Egbo House; and in the morning and late afternoon, the members of the Society frequently meet there to drink gin and palm wine.*"—Dayrell (*1910*), *p. 4.*

ekpa ntan—*house without walls.*

eland—*largest of the African antelopes; the bull may be six feet at the shoulder and weigh over 1,200 pounds.*

erriten-kuan-kuan, gau-gaubu-ti—*Bushman phrases said by the translator to be untranslatable. They apparently constitute the magic name of the wind's son.*

eto—*yams, first boiled and then pounded.*

F

fatting house—*a room where a girl is kept for some weeks previous to her marriage. "She is given plenty of food, and made as fat as possible, as fatness is looked upon as a great beauty by the Efik people." Dayrell (1910), p. 3.*

fufu *or* fufuo—*yams or plantains boiled and mashed up. The resulting doughy lump is often then put into the soup.*

fura—*"Travellers take dry flour in bags and mix it with water en route, and evidently enjoy the paste thus formed, though it looks very uninviting to a European. A little sour milk makes the . . . [fura] a very dainty beverage."— Tremearne (1913), pp. 475–76.*

G

gemsbok—*the largest and handsomest species of the oryx, an antelope with long, nearly straight, ribbed horns.*

goat's gall bladder—*a term of flattery; for, inflated and dried, the bladder is stuck in the hair as a sign of honour.*

gungqu—*onomatopoeic for the noise produced by the Ugungqu-kubantwana, "said to resemble that made by a heavily laden wagon passing over a bad road. . . . She was so-called [also] because she swallowed everything that came in her way, so that when she moved the contents of her stomach rattled."—Callaway (1868), p. 176 n.*

gyedua—*umbrella tree (though perhaps a different sort from the American umbrella tree or magnolia). (Ashanti word.)*

H

hae—*an exclamation of joy, approx. "hurrah."*

halala—*to shout for joy.*

hartebeest—*a fairly large antelope, formerly common in south Africa, now nearly exterminated. The horns form a U.*

hemp—*the herb* Cannabis sativa, *from which bhang, hashish, and marihuana are derived.*

Hill Damara—*a little-known people of South West Africa, thought to be of Bantu origin, though some authorities consider them akin to the Hottentots, whose language they speak. They were enslaved, persecuted, and driven into the hills by both their kin the Herero (or Cattle Damara) and the Hottentots. They are held in small esteem: one of their names means "dung people."*

honey-guide—*a small African bird (genus* Indicator) *that actually leads men and animals to bees' nests.*

I

I—*exclamation of astonishment.*

ichneumon—*the mongoose, a small carnivorous mammal which, in its Indonesian form, was celebrated by W. Somerset Maugham for killing snakes. In Bushman folklore, the ichneumon is one of Kwammang-a's sons.*

imvuma—*goat slaughtered by the bridegroom's family to show that they acknowledge the betrothal.*

ingogo—*see* izingogo.

intontela—*a military kraal of the Zulu king; presumably this force was sent to do battle with the monster.*

Isikqukqumadevu—*a bloated, squatting, bearded monster. When spelled with an initial U, the name is personalized and flatters the monster, as if to say "Madame Monster."*

izingogo (*singular:* ingogo)—*"fabulous animals, degenerated men, who by living continually apart from the habitations of men have become a kind of baboon. They go on all fours, and have tails, but talk as men; they eat human flesh, even that of their own dead."—Callaway (1868), p. 177. (Cf. also note at the end of tale 76.)*

J

juju—*"all the uncomprehended, mysterious forces of Nature. These vary in importance from elementals, so powerful as to hold almost the position of demigods, to the* mana . . . *of herb, stone, or metal. In another sense the word also includes the means by which such forces may be controlled or influenced [such as amulets, charms, figures, masks, etc.].—Talbot (1912), p. 49. It may also mean the fetish-man himself; see* Egbo.

K

kafir corn—*a cereal, variously identified as a kind of millet and a kind of sorghum.*

Kamba—*adjectival form of the tribal name Akamba.*

kaross—*a square cloak of skins, basic garment of the Bushman.*

kerrie—*short club with a knobbed end, used originally as a missile weapon. (From a Hottentot word.)*

khhwe—*as pronounced by a Zulu, an exact imitation of the croak of a frog.*

kirijakija—*the cry of the guinea-fowl.*

koko-yam—*see* eddo.

kraal—*originally, a Hottentot village or cattle enclosure, now used in this sense throughout native Africa. (Of Portuguese origin; cf. Spanish* corral.)

kudu—*a large antelope. (From a Hottentot word.)*

kuisse—*an unidentifiable edible root. (Bushman word.)*

Kurtiale—*sense unknown, but apparently a mythical country. It may be noted that the Masai word for caterpillar is ol-kurto, so that this may be the archetypal homeland of caterpillars.*

kutlu—*adverb indicating satisfaction.*

Kwammang-a—*"a mythical person not identified with any animal, but seen in the rainbow."*—Bleek and Lloyd, Mantis (*1923*), Introduction, p. v. *He is married to Porcupine and has a son, "brave and quiet like his father," also named Kwammang-a.*

kyere-he-ne—*unknown, but apparently "jump down."*

L

Leza Shikakunamo—*Leza is the supreme being of the Baila; Shikakunamo is an attributive name, "besetting one."*

M

macuta—*a Portuguese colonial copper coin, now worth 5 centavos or about one sixth of a U. S. cent. (From an Ambundu word.)*

mametu—*a typical Zulu oath, literally "my mother," which is elliptical for "What I say is true; if not, I could be guilty of incest with my mother."* Mamo *appears to be a similar usage.*

mamo—*see* mametu.

Mangi Kihuti—*unknown, though the second word is thought to mean "tree."*

mason-wasp—*"the Prometheus of the Baila, with its indigo-blue wings, yellow abdomen, and black and orange legs, . . . builds its cell of mud not only on fireplaces, as the tale narrates, but also (and in this it is a great nuisance) on walls, books, and pictures in one's dwelling. In the cell it lays its eggs, together with a caterpillar or grub [the* Ngongwa *of the tale], and seals them up. . . . As the young grubs hatch out they eat the insects, which have been benumbed but not killed by the sting of the parent. . . . The [natives] suppose Ngongwa to metamorphose into a mason-wasp."*—Smith and Dale (*1920*), II, pp. 346–47.

mateva—*unknown, other than that it is a palm.*

mat-house—*a hive-shaped temporary shelter used on trek, consisting of rush mats stretched over poles stuck into the ground in a circle.*

mfulimuninga—*berries, exact kind unknown.*

mpintini—*a kind of wood tambourine.*

mpunia—*highway robber and murderer.*

Msura Kwivire-vire *etc.*—*untranslatable magic nonsense syllables.*

munsanje—*"the totemic name for 'rabbit,' more or less what the family name is for us."*—Torrend (*1921*), p. 170.

N

Ngongwa—*see* mason-wasp.

ngururu—*"shrill sounds produced, generally by women, by moving the tongue rapidly right and left. They mean triumph or welcome."*—Torrend (*1921*), p. 86 n.

N'jenge—*"a [mythical] animal which lived in old times; it was about the size of a sheep, had four legs, and was covered with hair. It fed on shamba [garden] produce, and it also ate meat."*—Routledge (*1910*), p. 315.

nkoroondo—*berries, exact kind unknown.*

nongwe—*the edible bulb of a plant identified by the translator merely as belonging to the genus* Hypoxis.

nsenkene—*unknown, according to the translator.*

nte—*a game of marbles, details unknown.*

ntenda—*basket.*

ntikuma—*a species of spider.*

Nzambi—*Mother Earth.*

O

odawuro—*a kind of gong to be struck with a stick by the public crier in making a proclamation; also used at public meetings, at certain plays, in the dances of fetish-men, and for such ceremonial purposes.*

odum—*a timber tree valued for its finely mottled wood.*

o-gaul'-iminga—*feller of lofty thorn-trees.*

okra—*the mucilaginous vegetable. (From an Ashanti word,* nkurum.) *Also, the Ashanti word for "cat."*

okraman—*dog. (Ashanti word.)*

olo—*an exclamation, approx. "halloo!"*

o-nsiba-zimakqembe—*one whose feathers are long and broad.*

oribi—*a small antelope having short straight ringed horns.*

osua—*gold dust to the weight of approx. two pounds sterling.*

P

paint-house—*"A girl arriving at the age [of puberty] is closely watched. The moment of her first menstruation is marked by the firing off of a gun, and this is followed by a dance. And now, while she little suspects it, she is caught and forced into . . . the paint-house. Here she is painted red, and carefully fed and treated, until . . . she is washed and led to her husband."—Dennett (1898), p. 20.*

pui-pui—*a cry of lamentation.*

pusu—*shake.*

Q

qaa—*exclamation indicating exasperation.*

quagga—*a pretty wild ass, related to the zebra. It could be trained to draw a little carriage; however, it was hunted for its handsome skin, and exterminated at the height of the Victorian period. The last quagga died in the gardens of the Zoological Society, in Regent's Park, London, in 1872, the year Stanley published* The Finding of Livingstone. *(Hottentot word.)*

R

rock-rabbit—*actually, the hyrax, a rabbit-sized rhinoceros.*

roodebok—*a reddish duiker (q.v.).*

rows—*"Lady Rows" is a literal translation of the character's African name.*

sango, sanguri—*apparently magic words connected with the eagle.*

sanguri—*see* sango.

sepirewa—*a musical bow; one assumes, a primitive violin.*

shimbec—*hut.*

silk-cotton tree—*one of the family* Bombacaceae, *which yields kapok, the stuffing of life-jackets.*

sommo—*an iron which, heated red hot, is used to burn the hole through a pipe stem.*

spit—*"Purposely mistranslated. The correct rendering will be sent with pleasure to anyone who requires it for scientific purposes," wrote Major Tremearne, in 1912.*

springbok—*a south African gazelle noted for its habit of springing lightly, gracefully, and suddenly into the air. It is brown with a white dorsal stripe and rump.*

sui sui—*onomatopoeic for a kind of snore, or perhaps snoreless breathing.*

suru—*see* asuanu.

T

tie-tie—*a prickly kind of palm; also said to be a rope of creepers tied together.*

Tororut—*the supreme being of the Suk; also, the sky.*

U

ubenthle—*a fibrous plant, from which garments can be woven.*

udonqa—*"a small bush which bears white berries; when ripe they are gathered and bruised and formed into a paste; the body is first anointed with fat, and then rubbed over with the paste of the* udonqa. *This is one mode of cleansing, which is supposed more effectual than water."—Callaway (1868), p. 243 n. (The italicized* q *indicates a click in the Zulu speech.)*

Ugungqu-kubantwana—*a mythical animal; see* gungqu; *also note at end of tale 76.*

umdhlubu—*garden of ground-nuts, i.e., peanut garden.*

unkosi-yasenthla—*king of the highlands.*

unkosi-yasenzansi—*king of the lowlands.*

unomabunge—*mother of beetles.*

unthlatu—*boa-constrictor man. (The character so called had bright and slippery skin, like a snake's.)*

untombinde—*tall maiden.*

uselese—*frog-man.*

Usikqukqumadevu—*see* Isikqukqumadevu.

uvati—*fire-making apparatus of the Zulu, consisting of two sticks, a pointed one about a foot long, called the male, and a larger one, notched, called the female. The one is rotated or "churned" in the other.*

V

varan—*a monitor lizard.* (*Word of Arabic origin.*)

vlei—"*a depression in the ground, sometimes dry, sometimes covered with coarse grass and rushes, and sometimes filled with water.*"—*Bleek and Lloyd,* Specimens (*1911*), *p. 105 n.*

W

wakra—*Have you awakened?*

wari—*a game similar to draughts, played in many ways all over west Africa.*

water chevrotain—*a small, hornless, deerlike ruminant, standing about a foot high, and sometimes called the mouse deer.*

wau—*answer to a call.*

wawa-wawa—*an unidentified tree, purportedly large.* (*Ashanti word.*)

we—*the innermost partitioned portion of the hut, where the wife sleeps, and the husband when feasible.*

wheatear—*a small European bird, also called the stonechat. The translator may have substituted the name for an African one. The name has nothing to do with wheat or ears but was originally "whitearse."*

Y

y'aku—*a greeting.*

yepu—*the sound one makes when one is out of breath.*

yiridi—*hurry.*

Z

zwart-storm—*a large tree, according to the Bushman narrator, with yellow flowers and no thorns.*

AFRICAN NEGRO SCULPTURE

Introduction[1]

THERE ARE two ways of looking at African Negro sculpture that, for fifty years, have impeded a true understanding of that art. One is the notion that an African carving or casting is "pure art" and that its quality can be fully assessed by European aesthetic standards, without reference to the culture in and for which it was made. The other and opposite view sees in an example of Negro sculpture not a work of art but merely a primitive utilitarian object made by a tradition-fettered artisan for a barbarous community devoid of aesthetic feeling of any kind.

It is true that African sculpture was first recognized in Europe as an art by a group of sophisticated painters living in Paris, who found it interesting because it expressed and satisfied some of their own aesthetic ideals. Vlaminck, Matisse, and Derain, among others, began about 1905 to collect African carvings. Before that, such work had been studied merely as ethnographic document (as in some quarters it continued to be until much later).

These were the French painters who, a few years later, were to be described as *les fauves*, "the wild beasts," because they intentionally distorted their drawing and intensified their colours to express strong emotions or to achieve forceful decorative contrasts. They thought they found similar characteristics in African art.

Up to this time practically nothing had been written upon African sculpture as art. This fact in itself appealed to the younger artists of the day, who were tired of art so overlaid with literature that its basic core of form was difficult to uncover. Anthropologists and ethnologists in their writings had completely overlooked the aesthetic qualities in the artifacts of primitive peoples or had only mentioned them perfunctorily. Leo Frobenius was the first European anthropologist to call attention to the productions of Africans as art.[2]

1. Some of the following material was originally published in an essay which the author contributed to *African Negro Art* (New York, 1935), the catalogue of an exhibition held at the Museum of Modern Art under the author's direction. It is used here, in revised form, with the kind permission of the Museum of Modern Art. Political names are as of 1952.

2. But his articles, "Die Kunst der Naturvölker," *Westermanns Monatshefte*, LXXIX (1895–96), 329–40 and 593–606, and "Die bildende Kunst der Afrikaner," *Mittheilungen der Anthropologischen Gesellschaft in Wien*, XXVI (1897), 1–17, still treated the subject primarily from non-aesthetic points of view.

The first book devoted entirely to what its author believed to be African sculpture—that is, plastic art—was Carl Einstein's *Negerplastik*. It was not published until 1915. Einstein felt that African art illustrated attitudes and qualities neglected or missing in modern European art. In his opinion African sculpture was "true sculpture," was in fact the only sculpture that, by direct methods, solved basic problems of expressing mass. For him European sculpture was infected by a pictorial treatment which, in the hands of modern sculptors, was "dissolving" three-dimensional form.

But those first painter-amateurs and their follower Einstein had only a subjective interest in African art. They treated it as if it were an adopted child of European art and not a self-consistent creation. They looked at it solely against a backdrop of European aesthetic theory, not against the spiritual setting from which it had sprung. European painters, sculptors, and critics in the first two decades of this century were constantly on the lookout for examples of primitive art that did not conform to the naturalistic convention which had dominated the art of their continent for most of two thousand years. African art gave them an ideal example of another tradition. More than that, it offered to their jaded taste the tonic of the unfamiliar, the appeal of the exotic, the intuitive and, from their point of view, the naïve. These were the qualities that attracted the first generation of European amateurs—and more especially such painters as Vlaminck and the others. And since their time European artists in each generation have been able to find in one or another aspect of Negro art something that seemed to justify their own theories; the expressionists found an emotional use of colour and distortion of shape, the cubists found "structure," the surrealists found fantasy, mystery—even a pathological inspiration.

Today such arbitrary and limited attitudes to African art are no longer tenable. Perhaps an undue emphasis on form in a work of art has lost its vogue. Perhaps in our own European art we are taking a more humanistic interest than did the painters and sculptors of forty years ago. Perhaps such field researches as those of Marcel Griaule, Michel Leiris, and their colleagues among the Dogon of French Sudan, or of Bernard and William Fagg in Nigeria, or of Frans Olbrechts among the Bushongo, have given new directions to our interest—and greater richness, too, by combining ethnographic and aesthetic viewpoints in expectation of the day when our meagre documentation will be expanded into a significant background.

In any case, we now realize that an over-simplified approach, long popular among amateurs of African art, has impoverished rather than enhanced our understanding. It seems as dangerous as it is absurd to separate an object from the thought that produced it and to look for emotions and seductions in material forms created by unknown hands, particularly when all the serious field research that has been done among Africans shows that their art's "aims, media, and products are primarily religious" and that "there is a sort of wilful misunderstanding in speaking of an art which should be separated from the intentions of its users, in order to comply with our definitions." [3] To do so is practically to put ourselves in a position similar to that of an African native never out of his parklands or forests to whom we might present for critical appraisal a late Turner. Or more fundamentally, it is as if we were to try to study mediaeval sculpture or Renaissance painting without any knowledge of Christianity.

This is the generally accepted outlook today—a much sounder attitude than that upon which the appreciation of African sculpture was based, in Europe, in the two opening decades of the twentieth century. If we are serious in our effort to enjoy African art with any degree of discernment, our view of it must combine ethnographic and aesthetic considerations, not rely on one or the other in isolation.

During the past fifteen years such ethnographers as Griaule, Fagg, and Olbrechts have been steadily contributing to our fund of information regarding the beliefs and sentiments underlying those African productions, which by themselves (owing to the unfamiliarity of their representational conventions) would convey to us little, if anything, of their native inspirations. Griaule, for example, gives a vivid description of the origin of certain masks and figures of the Dogon people of the French Sudan in the light of their legends and religious beliefs.[4] William Fagg, in his observations of the contemporary Yoruba of southern Nigeria, has shown what a strong aesthetic interest exists among both the present-day sculptors and the native patrons of their work. "The tribal artist," as Fagg has recounted, "is, in reality, a distinguishable and original personality, just as much as Cellini or Turner or Matisse, even though in most cases we know him only through his works. . . . I was constantly surprised at the individuality of the work of different traditional carvers. . . . It is quite true that tradition usually prescribes the general nature of the work . . . , but these traditional influences are in effect the framework within which the artist must work and create; . . . if he is a poor artist he will be completely dominated by them, but I should doubt whether they are any more restrictive of genius than were the conventions of religious art in Renaissance Italy." [5]

Fagg reports that in a district of Nigeria where traditional carving still flourishes, though on a limited scale, in northeastern Yorubaland around the towns of Illa, Omu, and Otun, "one may readily refute the common idea that there is little or no conscious articulate aesthetic appreciation, as such, among the Africans." Certain sculptors whom he met "competed for patronage over a wide area; one minor chief at Illa commissioned [the sculptor] Bamgboye, twenty miles away, to carve two large masks, and [another sculptor] Areogun of Osi, thirty miles away, to make some small figures carved in memory of

3. Marcel Griaule, *Folk Art of Black Africa*, trans. by M. Heron (Paris and New York, 1950), p. 24. (Orig. published as *Arts de l'Afrique noire*, Paris, 1947.)

4. *Ibid.*, pp. 60 ff.
5. William Fagg, "The Dilemma Which Faces African Art," *The Listener*, XLVI:1176 (Sept. 13, 1951), 414.

dead twins. Again, some owners of early works by Bamgboye apologized to me for their quality, as they were done 'before he became perfect.' " [6]

What Griaule and his colleagues have brought to light in the Sudan gives us a hint of the rich legendary and religious setting to which all the fine sculptures of Negro Africa belong, but from which, in most cases, they have been torn with little hope of any possible restoration. Fagg's observations among the Yoruba can be taken as indicative of the probable existence of a similar aesthetic consciousness among their ancestors, the people of Benin and Ife, as well as among less closely related peoples in other quarters of the sculpture-producing Guinea coast and Congo. Furthermore, Fagg's observations show us standards of judgment guiding both the creation and the evaluation of native arts in Africa that are quite foreign to ours.

For all this, however, we must still face the fact that our knowledge of the background of African art is elementary. And while we keep in mind the vital importance of enriching, wherever possible, the communication of a piece of Negro sculpture through the marriage of ethnographic and aesthetic considerations, we should not quixotically deny ourselves the aesthetic gratification which this art is able to provide each new generation of observers, foreign as that gratification may be to the essential character and message of Negro art. Too many scruples about our lack of background data, too much conscience about looking at an art from a foreign standpoint, would deprive us of some of our richest aesthetic pleasures.

For we look at all art, more or less, through a stranger's eyes. This holds for contemporary art that may be a decade in advance of the observer's experience and his ability to respond to it, as well as for paintings of the Ming period— and perhaps even more than we readily admit for European Renaissance and Baroque art. We may not appreciate the poetry of Homer, Dante, or Langland as their authors conceived it to be appreciated. When we enjoy reading it aloud, we may not even hear the same sounds their authors intended to give it. Still, it would be nonsensical to refuse on these grounds the pleasure our minds and ears are accustomed to receive from it. The same holds for much of the finest Negro sculpture, which has been torn from a framework that can never be completely replaced no matter how much we learn of other African works of art through the researches of Griaule, Fagg, Olbrechts, and their followers.

And we have to remember that it was artists, in spite of their limited information, not scholars, who revealed African Negro art to European taste. In fact they did so with little more knowledge of provenance or former history than in what curio shop they had been lucky enough to find the object and whether the dealer had a dependable source of supply.

Many examples of African art at the time had already been gathered into ethnographical museums, where they were usually lost in a clutter of other

6. *Ibid.*

exhibits, since their aesthetic character was of no interest to their discoverers or owners. One has only to look through the catalogues of W. D. Webster, an auctioneer of ethnological specimens, located in Bicester, Oxfordshire, at the prices paid for his sales from 1897 to 1904, to realize how little the finest African work was esteemed in those days. (It was from Webster that such fine continental collections as that of Berlin Museum für Völkerkunde drew some of their richest treasures.) Travellers, traders, and soldiers brought objects back to Europe as curiosities. The pieces of ivory or gold had an evident worth. Too often the gold objects would be melted down. Or the gold would be stripped off carved wood statuettes from the Gold Coast, where it was customary to cover them with precious metal. But objects made of material of no intrinsic value soon found their way into the hands of such dealers in ethnographical specimens as Webster, or, more often, into the hands of dealers in odds-and-ends. It was in such curiosity shops that the first French and Belgian amateurs made their acquaintance with Negro art.

The vogue at first was paid little commercial heed. But gradually it began to spread, and the supply, always extremely limited, dwindled. Dealers began to take steps to assure themselves of importations—practically always, without the slightest regard for any serious ethnographic documentation of their wares. An early and ready source of supply had been the liquidation of the estates of soldiers who had taken part in punitive expeditions against the natives. Then traders began to ship to Europe whatever they could persuade the Africans to part with. Even in Africa, however, the supply was small: fine pieces were no longer being produced in any quantity, owing to the decadence of the natives, which duly followed on their exploitation by the whites. Soon the traders were reduced to employing natives to manufacture copies for the growing market. When this in its turn failed to satisfy the demand, European forgeries, which soon surpassed the native copies in "character," began to appear in unfortunately generous quantities in Brussels, Paris, and other centres.

Today, Africa rarely yields art of the quality that we find in the great collections of Europe, formed half a century ago. From time to time, some unexploited region is opened up. But usually, as in the case of the Ife and Esie discoveries [7] of the last decade or so, it is work of a dead past, not the flowering of an active art. So, while African art may be considered "modern" on the ground that very few of the examples we know can have survived more than a century and a half (excepting, of course, certain ivories, the

7. ". . . in 1934 no fewer than seven hundred and sixty-five [stone] figures and heads were discovered in a clearing among oil palms, one and a half miles from Esie, in Ilorin province, Nigeria. . . . In the majority of these carvings the features are sufficiently individualized for them to be considered as portraits; their naturalism, however, is naïve and typically African."—Leonhard Adam, *Primitive Art* (revised edn., Melbourne [Penguin Books], 1949), pp. 120–21. Also see J. D. Clarke, "The Stone Figures of Esie," *Nigeria* (Lagos), No. 14 (June, 1938), 106–8, for a fairly detailed account.

Benin bronzes, and the Ife bronzes and terracottas), at the same time we must accept the fact that the art of Africa is already an art of the past.

But for all the physical youth of the examples of African art we know, particularly those carved from wood, there is no doubt of the antiquity of the tradition underlying their production. The collection of Armbraser and Weickmann in the Museum of Ulm, Germany, contained ivories and weapons brought back to Europe before 1600. And since the Middle Ages we have heard tales from travellers and explorers of kingdoms along the Gulf of Guinea and to the south of the Sahara, tales of fabulous wealth and culture. Undoubtedly there was a certain exaggeration in the reports. Still, we find sufficient evidence of a basic element of truth. And while the sculptures that we actually know are for the most part modern, there is no doubt that the traditional forms which they reflect in a broad way as a guide or framework have been handed down within the tribes for generations.

Long before the Portuguese, encouraged by Prince Henry the Navigator, had actually reached Great Benin in the last quarter of the fifteenth century, we have reports of other great Negro kingdoms to the north and west. In the early fourteenth century some Genoese seamen had already worked their way round the west coast of Africa considerably beyond the Canaries; and, in 1364 a party of Dieppe sailors are said to have gone probably as far as what is the Gold Coast of today. But it was usually from travellers in the interior and from traders that the more striking reports came; for example, descriptions of the vast Negro kingdom of Ghana (Guinea), which in the tenth and eleventh centuries extended from the Senegal River east to the bend of the Niger; of Melle, successor to Ghana in the thirteenth and fourteenth centuries; and of the Songhai empire of Gao, in the Niger bend, which rose from Melle's ruins, reaching its great power in the sixteenth century, when it extended from Lake Chad west to the Atlantic. To the north lay the Hausa states that grew out of the seven towns of Biram, Gobir, Kano, Rano, Zaria, Katsina, and Daura and were originally peopled by a Negro nation apparently related to the early Songhai. These original inhabitants were conquered in the tenth century by another people of obscure affinities, from the east. And these conquerors in their turn founded an empire which survived (with intervals such as the conquest by the Songhai, in 1512, and that by the Moors, in 1595) until they were subjected by the Fula, in 1807. Further south, along the coast, lay the kingdom of the Yoruba. At its height it comprised the whole region between the Niger and the Gulf of Guinea, extending westward from the mouth of the Niger as far as Ashantiland. And among the native civilizations of Africa it is of an outgrowth of Yoruba, the kingdom of Great Benin, that we possess the fullest documentation.

While this documentation is not really extensive, or even historically exact, the fact that we have some concrete information regarding Benin has inclined us to lay a very likely undue importance upon it and its culture, in contrast to the other great Negro kingdoms and empires that have left us no records beyond such evidence of artistic genius as surviving sculptures may provide. Nevertheless, our few facts about Benin have played an important role in the consideration of African art. For they have helped to dissipate the notion that Negro art is a chance production of a people entirely lacking in culture or social organization.

The first Europeans to reach Benin were, as we have said, a group of Portuguese; this was in 1472. The company actually reached Great Benin, or Oedo, as the capital was then called; and from its members we have report of other important contemporary Negro kingdoms to the north and west. The chronicler João de Barros tells us that Alfonso d'Aveiro brought back with him from Benin a native ambassador to the court of Portugal.

The first descriptive details of the capital, however, became known in Europe about 1600. The publishers De Bry printed a description given them by a certain mysterious traveller, "D.R." The city, according to this account, lay about seventy-five miles inland from the mouth of the Benin or Formosa River. Its main street was seven or eight times wider than the great street of Amsterdam and stretched out of sight into the distance.

Somewhat later, in 1668, a Dutch traveller, Dr. Olfert Dapper, added some further details about the wealth and importance of the city. It was fortified by a solid rampart ten feet high. A similar wall protected the royal palace, which "was as large as the whole city of Haarlem." The magnificent structures that composed it were linked together by impressive long colonnades of wooden pillars, covered from top to bottom with bronze plaques depicting battle scenes. Thirty broad streets ran the length of the city, each lined with carefully constructed houses. The dwellings were low but large, with long interior galleries and numerous rooms, the walls of which were made of smooth red clay polished till it gave the appearance of marble.

In 1704, another traveller, named Nyendael, found the city practically in ruins, scarcely inhabited. The corridors of the palace were now supported by wooden pillars so rudely carved that the chronicler was scarcely able to discern what was represented. There was no longer any evidence of the bronze plaques that had formerly attracted so much attention. And since no traveller after Nyendael makes any mention, it may be supposed that, during the civil war which ravaged Benin in the last years of the seventeenth century, they had been hastily pulled down and hidden in the storehouses where the British were to find them two hundred years later.

In the course of the eighteenth century, the city rose again from its ruins. It never returned, however, to its ancient splendour. And in 1820, the palace was again destroyed during an insurrection.

It was not until 1897 that the first bronzes from Benin reached Europe. The British had established themselves in 1851 at Lagos, on the coast. The oba, or king, of Benin had for centuries maintained by force of arms a hegemony over a wide area of southern Nigeria west of the Niger. In 1896, the British consul, J. R. Phillips, attempted to enter the capital city during a religious festival, to come to an understanding with the reigning oba, Overami, who was notorious for the savagery and scale of his human sacrifices. Overami had prohibited the consul's visit during the festival. Phillips and his party were ambushed and killed. "A punitive expedition reached Benin in January 1897, deposed the Oba, established British rule there, and removed, as an indemnity, the accumulated riches found, largely in a state of dire neglect, in the Oba's palace, and in the houses of some of the chiefs. . . ."[8]

The bronzes and ivories were shipped to London either as curiosities or as scrap. Felix von Luschan, in his catalogue *Die Altertümer von Benin*,[9] was later able to list twenty-four hundred objects. So at a stroke almost the entire artistic remains of a great but decayed culture left Nigeria for Europe. Pieces soon began to reach the market through such channels as Webster, the Oxfordshire auctioneer, or second-hand shops in England or on the continent to which the returning officers of the British expedition or their families had sold them.

Out of these spoils three great collections (as well as many smaller ones) came into being, two of which are still in England—in the British Museum and in the Pitt-Rivers Museum, at Farnham, Dorset—while the largest of all, which went to Berlin in 1898, was, as William Fagg has written, "evacuated to Silesia during the late war and has vanished, apparently eastwards."[10]

These Benin pieces both from a technical and an artistic point of view completely mystified Europeans who realized what their quality implied. At the turn of the century Africa was still regarded as the "dark continent" as much for its unenlightenment as for its vast unexplored areas. The natives were "savages," and their productions hitherto had held no interest for Europe save as evidence of their barbarism or at best as souvenirs of a sojourn rarely looked back upon with relish. When the bronzes from Benin appeared, of which von Luschan wrote, "Cellini himself could not have made better casts, nor anyone else before or since to the present day," an explanation had to be found. It could not be supposed that unenlightened savages had produced such remarkable examples of bronze-casting without aid. Finally the representation of certain figures in Portuguese garb on some of the plaques suggested that the method of bronze-working had been imported by the Portuguese on their first visit to the capital, in the fifteenth century. To bear out the theory, one English researcher managed to discover a tradition, allegedly local, to the effect that one Ahammangiwa, a member of the first party of white men to set foot in Benin, in the reign of the Oba Esigie, introduced bronze-casting.[11]

8. William Fagg, "Ancient Benin," foreword to the catalogue of an exhibition, "Art of Primitive Peoples," Berkeley Galleries, London, Dec. 1, 1947, to Jan. 31, 1948.   9. Berlin, 1919; 3 vols.

10. Fagg, "Ancient Benin."
11. C. H. Read and O. M. Dalton, *Antiquities from the City of Benin and Other Parts of West Africa in the British Museum* (London, 1899), pp. 6–7.

This theory, however, has now been generally abandoned. There is no evidence that the Portuguese had any such skill to communicate. And in the light of a better knowledge of African history, an analysis of the stylistic features of Benin art shows it to be fundamentally negroid. Finally, the discoveries made in 1910 by Leo Frobenius at Ife, only a hundred and ten miles away, as well as subsequent disclosures there, confirm the tradition of the Bini, the natives of Benin, that they had learned the art of casting bronze from the Yoruba of Ife, who in their turn had possibly come under the influence of the cultures of the upper Nile. While the actual origins of this art are still a matter of deep uncertainty, Fagg offers the following as a working hypothesis: "In the course of the first centuries of the Christian era, the Yoruba, having come from the east (perhaps the banks of the upper Nile), had already before this migration a knowledge of the techniques of bronze-casting by the *cire-perdue* process [12] well known to the Egypt of the Pharaohs and to the last Graeco-Nubian civilization of Meroë (although their casts were of a much more reduced scale than those of Ife and of other bronze manufacturers); and a germ, if one may so express it, of decadent realism appropriate to Greek art subsisted, slight as it was, from the odyssey of the Yoruba and found its rebirth and a considerable development after their establishment on the Gulf of Guinea." [13]

Despite the great weight of historical data we possess in regard to the kingdom of Benin, the chronology of its artistic productions is still almost as uncertain as that of other regions of Africa. Tradition among the Bini has it that bronze-casting by the *cire-perdue* method was introduced into Benin from Ife under Oba Oguola about 1280. [14]

This date is not impossible in view of the attributed resemblances between the Benin and Ife work and the superior quality of the latter. The age of the Ife heads that we know is still uncertain. But it is generally accepted that they date from the fifteenth century, at the latest before the arrival of the Portuguese. In any case, we can feel safe in dating the period of production of the finest Benin bronzes earlier than the decadence which set in after the civil war in the latter part of the seventeenth century.

The German ethnologists von Luschan and Bernhard Struck have attempted to date the Benin bronzes by a system of reference to the royal

12. In the *cire-perdue* ("lost wax") process of metal-casting the sculptor builds up a wax model around an earthen core. The wax of the model is then covered with several coats of fine potter's clay in a completely liquid state. Each coat is allowed to dry separately. When the coats are of a satisfactory thickness, the model is enveloped in earth, which solidifies in drying. When sufficiently dry, the whole is heated, and the wax melts and escapes through vents arranged for the purpose. Molten metal is then poured through these holes and takes the place left empty by the melted wax. After the metal within has cooled, the mold is broken off, leaving a precise reproduction in metal of what the artist had originally modelled in wax. The oldest method of metal-casting known, it is still practised throughout the world.

13. William Fagg, "De l'art des Yoruba," in *L'Art Nègre* (Présence Africaine 10–11; Paris, 1951), p. 116. (Author's translation.)

14. Adam, *op. cit.*, p. 114.

chronology of Benin. Such a classification is clearly unsatisfactory. Perhaps a greater precision may be possible when scientific excavations on the site of Benin itself have been carried out.

We can see that the history of African art still remains its least rewarding facet. Such a summary review, however, of what we know of Benin, the most powerful kingdom of the Guinea coast over a long period—how it was influenced by Yoruba and in turn exerted its artistic influence over such neighbours as Abomey and Zagnanado, in Dahomey—gives us a notion of what may have been the culture and power of those great empires of Melle and Ghana in the north and of Lunda in the region now Belgian Congo, of which we know even less than we know of Benin. Also it helps us to envisage, at least in part, the standard of culture that doubtless obtained there and its results: seemingly a general prosperity; large, populous cities; extensive areas of land under cultivation; and orderly, peace-loving inhabitants keenly sensitive to beauty in their environment, habiliments, and art. Finally, we may agree with Frobenius, who observed that the legend of the barbarous Negro current in Europe during the latter half of the nineteenth century is primarily the creation of European exploiters who needed some excuse for their depredations.

Those regions, however, of whose past we possess any information (even through oral tradition) make a very small part of the vast area of central and west Africa which has produced art which may be said to offer predominantly negroid characteristics. At the same time, when we consider the vast areas drawn upon, the production of Negro sculpture as we know it seems incredibly small. For the area from which this art comes embraces the greater part of that region in which the "true" Negro [15] peoples predominate, as well as the immense "heart of Africa" peopled by the western branch of the Bantu-speaking peoples. The relative integrity of this sculpture-producing area, its more or less stable racial pattern over the last several centuries, is actually the result of ethnic movements. Tribal expansion was the prime stimulus to migration. But we also find another reason for it among the Negroes: a craving for salt and a concomitant desire to control the sources of supply. As a result, in west Africa there was a continuous movement towards the sea, which had its effect in disseminating tribal traditions. And the difficulty in allocating stylistic traits of Negro art with certainty to definite regions or tribes may in great part be attributed to it.

Cultures were also bound to vary with different types of country, different conditions of environment. For example, the large states and federations such as Ghana, Melle, the Hausa, the Yoruba, and Lunda were all outgrowths of parkland and forest edge, where communication was not difficult. In the denser forest, central control of a wide area was impossible—each village remained small and independent, and architecture never received the attention accorded it in the capital cities of the more open areas.

15. For an explanation of the term "true Negro," see the preface of this book.

The type of religion of the Negro, also determined in great part by environment, we find particularly reflected in his art. Ancestor worship is most common among peoples who through seeing men wielding great power in this world come to feel that the souls of the great should still be powerful after death. This is the cult that in many regions of Africa has been productive of the finest sculpture, not only through symbolizing the dead as in the stylized burial fetishes of the Ogowe River district, in Gabon (Plates 142–44), but also through actual portraits. Without doubt many of the ancestor figures of Sudan, Benin, and Congo fall into this category—for example, the famous royal statues of the Bakuba kings (Plates 81, 82), which the English ethnologists E. Torday and T. A. Joyce found in the Belgian Congo and felt could be dated with confidence on the basis of their portrait character. They were clearly individualized in feature—evidently intended as realistic portraits though somewhat altered in keeping with the sculptural conventions of the region—and recognized by the natives as representing certain rulers still known and reverenced by name.

Still more realistic "portraits" survive in the bronze heads, the terracotta heads, and the half-length figures found at Ife and nearby. In the bronze heads, particularly such as those in Plates 132–38, African sculpture in the naturalistic convention achieves a level of subtlety rarely matched, much less surpassed, in the Mediterranean region during classic times or the Renaissance.

Ancestor worship, however, is practically confined to the parklands and the forest edge. In the denser jungle, where the tribes are disseminated, we find little evidence of it. There animistic beliefs predominate. Trees, streams, rocks, even animals, take the character of minor supernatural forces, and each has its cult celebrated by rituals in which sculptured masks and fetishes play an important part.

Religion with the Negro, as with all races, has been the main stimulus to artistic expression. Even in minor manifestations we find it as productive in Africa as in Europe. For example, some of the finest expressions take the form of fertility idols such as those in Plate 46 from the Sudan, Plate 60 from northeast Yoruba, or Plate 84 from the Belgian Congo; fetishes for conjuration, such as Plates 96–97, and the well-known "Konde" nail-studded figures (Plate 79) used for driving away illnesses by one's hammering a nail into the figure at the moment of conjuration; representations of the spirit of the dead (Plate 142); and figures to insure successful childbirth as well as protect the child till the age of puberty.

Certainly the broadest variety of expression, if not the highest, in Negro art is in the ritual mask. Masks range in form from the most realistic, employing monkey hair (Plates 34–35), or even human hair, to heighten the representation, to the most purely architectonic (Plate 6) or non-realistic (Plate 29); in size, from the immense casques of the Baluba fetish-men (Plate 22) or the huge and awesome "Kakunga" masks of the Bayaka (Plate 28), to the small dance masks worn by women and children. Some masks that are intended to be

handed down from one fetish-man to another within the tribe are meticu-
lously carved; others, to be worn at a single ceremony then to be thrown
away, may be crudely contrived out of soft wood and painted with gaudy
colours in some traditional pattern. The purposes of the masks are as numerous
as their varieties: sanctuary masks, fetish-men's war masks, hunting masks,
circumcision-ritual masks, masks worn at funeral and memorial ceremonies—
different variations of type in every tribe for every purpose—in wood,
wicker, cloth, straw, parchment, ivory, and endless combinations of materials.

Still, African Negro art is by no means restricted to ritual objects. In practically every accessory of life, even the commonest utensil, the Negro's sensi-
tivity and craftmanship are illustrated; spoons (Plates 54–55), bobbins (Plates
56–58), headrests (Plates 93–95), musical instruments (Plates 53, 63, 76, 78,
80). In the Belgian Congo, particularly among the Bushongo along the
Kasai River, we find textiles woven of coco-palm fibre in elaborate patterns
which have their relation to the surface patterns of the sculpture of the region.

Even tattooing among the Negroes is art itself, to such an extent that the
patterns which we find on the bodies of the natives are often the basis of those
with which they decorate their sculptures (Plates 85, 86–87) and permit us in
many cases to assign them to styles of specific tribes. On the northern shore of
the Gulf of Guinea, especially in the Gold Coast and Ivory Coast, we find a
curious expression of lyric fantasy in small bronzes produced by the *cire-
perdue* method and used by the natives for weighing gold dust. These are
frequently as remarkable in their technical mastery as they are individual in
their imaginative conceptions (Plates 106–8).

Although the materials employed are usually dictated by circumstances of
environment and expediency, immediate availability is not always a con-
trolling factor. This we see illustrated by one of the main arguments in favour
of the theory of Egyptian rather than Portuguese influence in the Benin
bronzes. For while tin is ready to hand in southern Nigeria, it has been found
that the copper employed by the Bini in their earliest work was brought
down from Egypt. In most cases, however, we find carving done in wood
because of its ease of handling. When stone is used, it is almost universally
steatite (soapstone). Gold work is practically limited to those regions where
the mineral is found in surface soil or streams. The finest matting and tufted
textiles are produced from the fibre of the coco-palm in the Congo region.
Ivory, however, is widely employed, from the Ivory Coast as far east as
Tanganyika.

Because of the migrations and intermingling of tribes, it is difficult to at-
tribute stylistic traits in African art with any confidence. And our knowledge
of Africa is still so slight that names are frequently as misleading as they are
helpful. In an attempt to simplify the classifications of types, names have been
applied with very little scientific basis. And the political boundaries dictated
by Europeans mean little to influences which have been spreading among the
natives for generations. As an example, the characteristics which we might be

tempted to associate with Gabon are frequently to be found in Rio Muni (Plate 74) and the Cameroons (Plate 68).

Certain features, however, are notable. For example, the definite character of surface decoration in Bakuba cups and boxes (Plate 91) offers a ready contrast to the simpler, more architectonic though somewhat more naturalistic sculpture of the Baluba tribe (Plates 83–84), also of the Belgian Congo. In carvings from Gabon, masks and figures alike, we find a suavity of harmonious relationships in the rounded surfaces and a swelling, bulbous character in the volumes (Plates 72, 77) that offer a distinct contrast with the severe staccato counterpoint of angular forms in Sudan statuettes (Plates 39–43) or masks (Plates 1, 2). And the surface decoration of an ornate Ivory Coast mask is readily distinguished by the emphasis it lays on relationships among its unit masses (Plate 9) from the strictly linear patterns of the Belgian Congo (Plates 90, 91).

In the end, however, it is not the tribal characteristics of Negro art nor its strangeness that are interesting. It is the sculptural quality—its vitality of forms, its simplification without impoverishment, its consistent three-dimensional organization of structural planes in architectonic sequences, and above all its uncompromising truth to material.

This is the basic language through which African Negro art must always speak to outsiders and possibly through which the great African art of yesterday must speak even to African Negroes of today. But a view of African art in this light should not exclude the importance of as full a knowledge as possible of the framework in which and for which it was made.

We speak of the African sculptor's "respect for his materials." This was one of the qualities which first recommended African Negro sculpture to European artists. In it they recognized an apparent willingness on the part of the Negro sculptor to allow the material in many cases to dictate form or variations of form—to allow it to collaborate, as it were, in the final product. Griaule stresses the fact that as a result of the Negro's animistic religious outlook the raw materials he employs are never inert. "The trees they cut down are the elaborate dwellings of supernatural powers; the Mbanga, the Na, and the Kulfa of [the river] Salamat kill them with assegai blows as if they were alive." [16] The European's sensibility to natural materials and their quality has gradually dulled, but the African Negro, through his religous respect for the spirit immanent, continued to enjoy his; and the vitality of the result appealed even to those Europeans who were unaware of what lay behind it.

Form and the organization of forms are the language through which sculpture of all ages and peoples must first speak to us—our own, as well as the Sumerian, the Mayan, or the Egyptian. Without some knowledge of the human setting in which and for which it was made it remains only the bare bones of expression, much as the music of the *Paradiso* would remain to one with no knowledge of thirteenth-century philosophy, history, or religion.

16. Griaule, *op. cit.*, p. 47.

The non-African can only hope to respond directly through his visual experience—his personal non-African eye. But the more he can bring to the basic sculptural expression the richer will be his response and enjoyment. That will be the gift of the ethnographer; the widening of horizons, the broadening of our embrace, the opening of new fields of aesthetic experience to explore into which, alone, we might never find our way.

1952   *JAMES JOHNSON SWEENEY*

Postscript (1963)

And that is what has happened in the past dozen years. Not only have fresh sources of African art been opened up and numerous hitherto unfamiliar expressions of it been disclosed, but by study and research we have acquired a deeper understanding of its meaning within the philosophico-religious system that tribal art embodies—a meaning largely foreign to Western thought and action and the West's more materialistic basis. The result is that African art has today an aesthetic interest per se which it did not have for its first European amateurs five decades ago.

In 1905 the newly found art of African tribes interested its discoverers primarily for the remedies it offered to European art. For that earlier generation it was a dramatic example of what might strengthen certain weaknesses, supply lacks, or correct abuses which they recognized in the Western painting and sculpture of their day. They saw in African art, on the one hand, a frank stress on basic three-dimensional form and its aesthetic order and, on the other, an encouragement of emotional expression, reinforced by the exaggeration and distortion of conventional representational forms. The consequence of this approach was that African art was seen more often than not in this subsidiary relationship to European art rather than as an artistic expression in its own right.

But within the past thirty-five years African art has assumed its place as an art entirely independent of European associations and has shown itself to possess its own logic—"far from the Cartesian," as William Fagg has said, but equally as rigorous. This changed perspective is due principally both to the wealth of objects that have come out of Africa—or have been discovered in Africa and remained there—and to the broader and deeper interest in the psychological, sociological, environmental, and philosophical background of African tribal art which these new disclosures have stimulated.

The variety of fresh work of quality is in itself astonishing. Each month for the past ten years and still today there are unfamiliar arrivals from Africa or the report of new discoveries there: new types of ritual items—masks and fetishes—and new types of utilitarian objects carved as symbolic figures. These finds have been in many widely separated places—Ijara, Ife, Guinea, Mali, Upper Volta, Chad, Esie, Nok—and often they are vastly different in character from those objects which first won the interest and admiration of Europeans in the early years of this century.

An example is the "porpianong" (Plate 175), a type of stylized representation of the hornbill, made by the Senufo, of Ivory Coast. Though sometimes more than seven feet tall, these birdform fertility symbols are worn on the heads of members of the tribe's Lo Society during rituals. They have become known outside Africa only in recent years. Another unfamiliar cult object is the "kakilambe" (Plate 177). These great serpent figures of polychrome wood are made by the Landuma, in Guinea, and are nine or more feet in height. They are stylizations of the Gabon viper and symbolize at once both fertility and survival after death. Butterfly masks of painted wood and braided rope (Plate 173) are worn by the Bobo, of Upper Volta, in dances celebrating the approach of spring, heralded in that region by swarms of butterflies. When the butterflies appear, the tilling of the fields begins afresh, and ritual dances invoke the "do" spirits to imbue the soil with their divine powers. From this area also come the same tribe's owl-like bird masks (Plate 166), worn principally in hunting rites, and the antelope head-dresses (Plates 167 and 168) of the Kurumba, worn in the mourning ceremonies to drive the souls of the deceased out of the village. And an object strictly utilitarian, but dignified by symbolic carving, is a housepost over six feet high made by the Dogon, of Mali (Plate 178). In the past dozen years there have also been major new examples of familiar styles to come out of Africa, such as the famous "Queen" (Plate 181), from the Bambara (Mali), so closely akin to other masterpieces of dramatic carving previously known to us.

But perhaps more important than the discovery of such types of cult expression, stimulating as they may be, are the links in the chain of tradition which have appeared during the past decade and the breadth of development they illustrate, as well as the antiquity of the sculptural arts in Africa to which they testify. For example, in November 1957 a workman leveling a low mound at Ita Yemoo, on the outskirts of the town of Ife, came upon a group of evidently ancient works of art, "the first fruits," as Fagg has described them, "of what may well prove to be the richest site yet discovered in all West Africa." And this small group, according to Fagg, "has thrown much new light on the Ife culture already, and, what is perhaps more valuable, it has raised a number of new problems." [1] One of the most unusual items of the Ita Yemoo find is the pair of royal figures with linked arms (frontispiece). The face of one figure was damaged by a workman's pick; but, as Fagg points out, entirely aside from any aesthetic considerations, this piece and the figure of an Oni of Ife found with it establish a major point in our view of African bronze sculpture. Frequently in the past it was suggested that the idealized naturalism of the Ife bronzes in contrast to African wood carving—even those of the Yoruba, in the same region of Nigeria—was a consequence of the importation of foreign metalworkers. Until this recent discovery no full-length Ife figures had come to light. Now with this royal pair and the Oni statue found with it we have the fact established, as Fagg writes, "once and for all that the sculptures were made by Africans." Their proportions evidence this: the heads, despite the idealized naturalism of the faces, are on a markedly larger scale than the bodies; they are twice as large as the natural proportion— just as in modern Yoruba wood carvings. "Modern Ife," Fagg writes, "is built on twenty-five feet of potsherds and other remains. . . . If it is not, as its traditions hold, the place where the world and man were created, it was without doubt a fountainhead of artistic impulses whose diverse effects on neighbouring peoples have still, for the most part, to be brought to light."

Compared with the Nok terracottas, the Esie stone figures, and the recent discoveries at Ijara—all in Nigeria—and with the 15,000 pieces of bronze and terracotta found in 1948 at the sanctuary of Tago in the Republic of Chad, these Ife works are, for all their mystery, relatively young. But young or old, it is just such discoveries as these which have given the scholar during the past few years a wider and more profound view of the religious, philosophic, and even historical environment of African art. And from this wider view and the greater familiarity with the fundamentals of African expression which it provides has come that desire to look at African art for itself rather than for its associations with the art of Europe: a desire that has developed so notably in the recent past and continues to grow in the present.

JAMES JOHNSON SWEENEY

1. William Fagg, "Ife, the Original City," foreword to the catalogue of an exhibition, "The Latest Ife Finds," The Museum of Primitive Art, New York, October 29–December 2, 1958.

PLATES

The Catalogue of Plates follows the plates.

1. MASK. Wood, h. 14½ in. *Dogon, Mali*

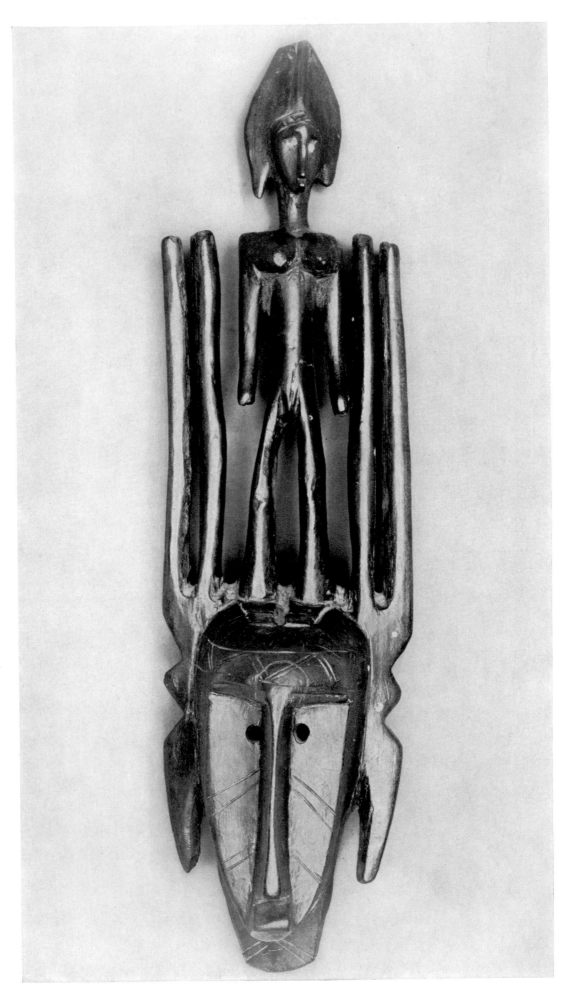

2. MASK. Wood, h. 25 in. *Bambara, Mali*

3. MASK. Wood, h. 22½ in. *Toma, Liberia*

4. MASK. Polychrome wood, h. 9 in. *Dan, Liberia, border of Ivory Coast*

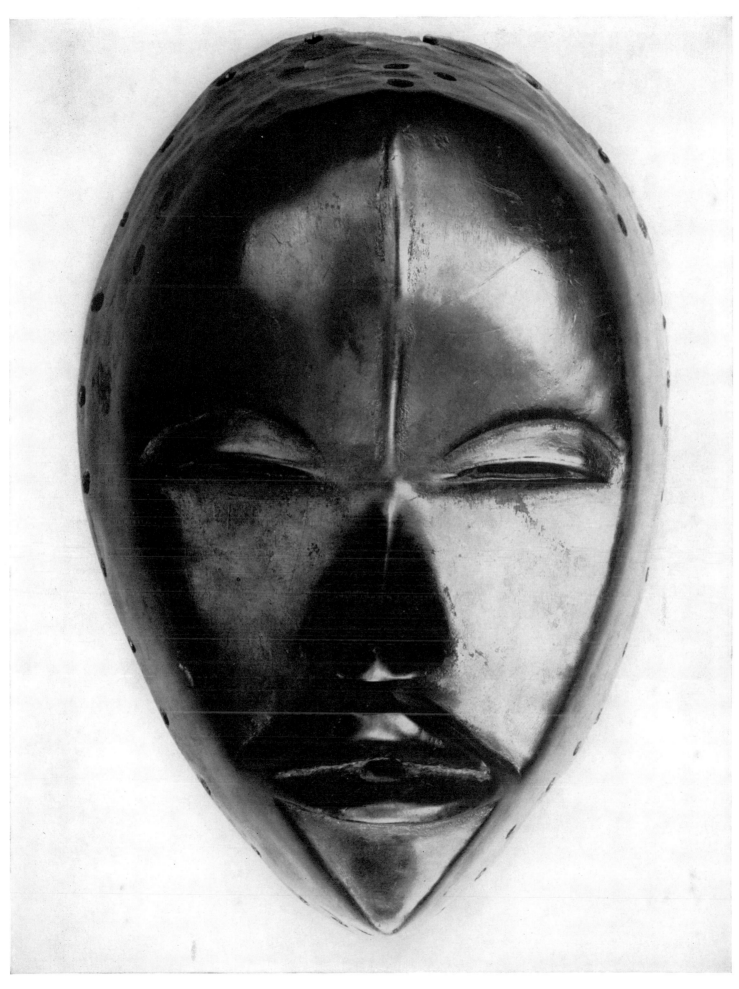

5. MASK. Wood, h. 9⅛ in. *Dan, Ivory Coast*

6. Mask. Wood, h. 9½ in. *Dan, Ivory Coast*

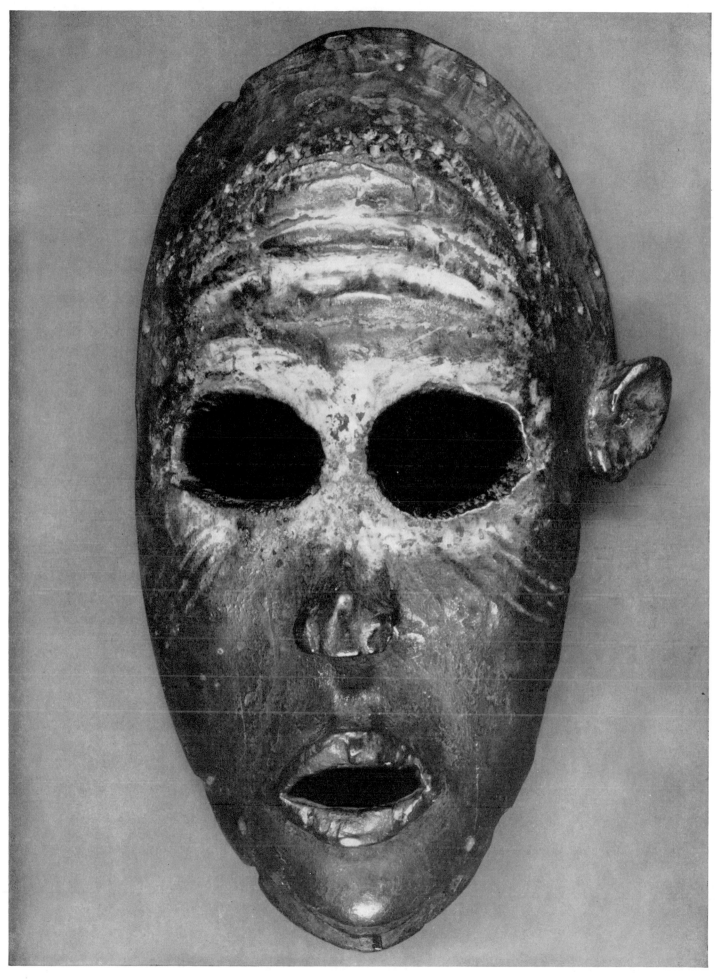

7. MASK. Wood, h. 10⅝ in. *Dan, Ivory Coast*

8. MASK. Wood, h. 18½ in. *Bambara, Mali*

9. MASK. Wood with metal plates, h. 15¾ in. *Baule, Ivory Coast*

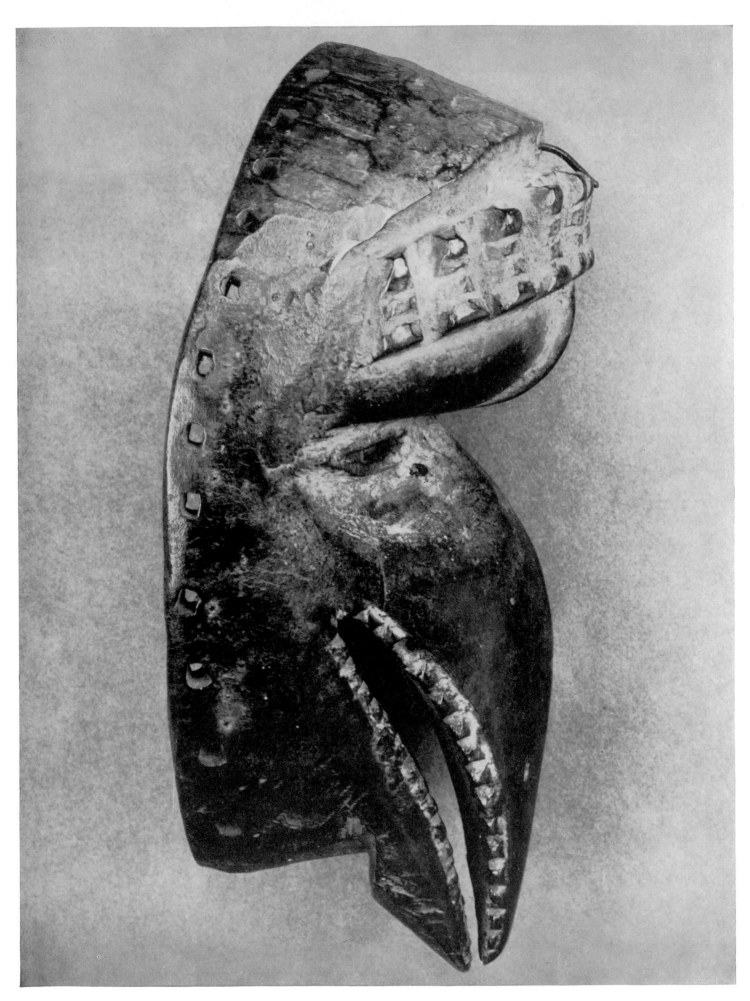

10. MASK. Wood, h. 8 in. *Dan, Liberia*

11. MASK. Polychrome wood, h. 15 in. *Baule, Ivory Coast*

12. MASK. Wood, h. 17 in.
Ekoi, Nigeria

13. MASK (HEAD-DRESS). Wood, h. 14½ in. *Mama, Nigeria*

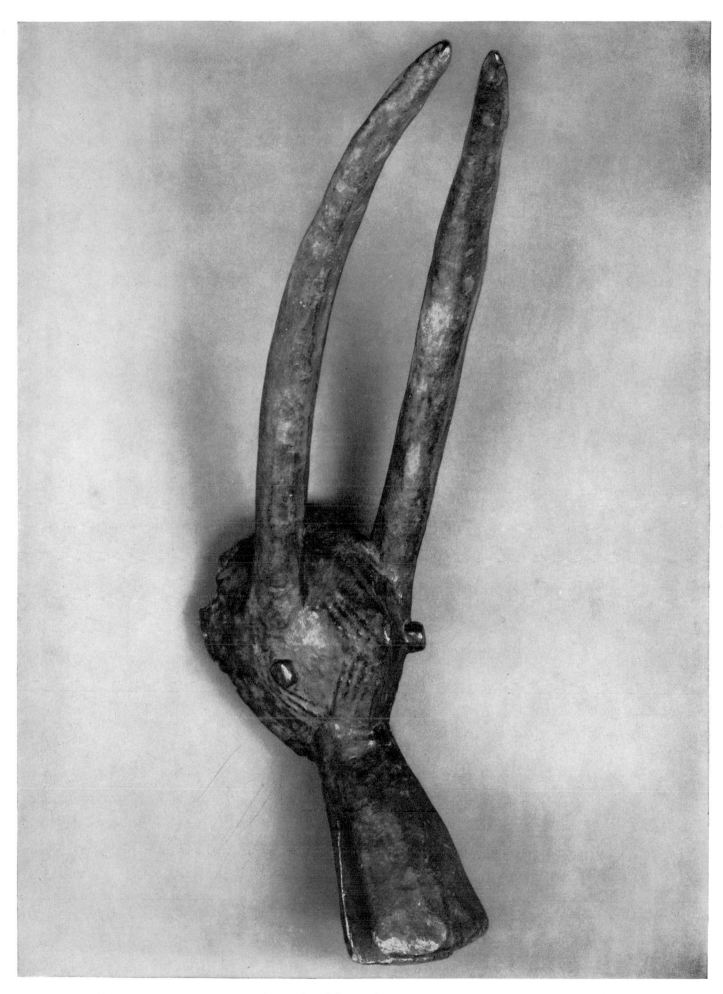

14. HEAD-DRESS. Wood, h. 26 in. *Mama, Nigeria*

15. MASK. Wood, h. 26⅜ in. *Bamenda, Cameroon*

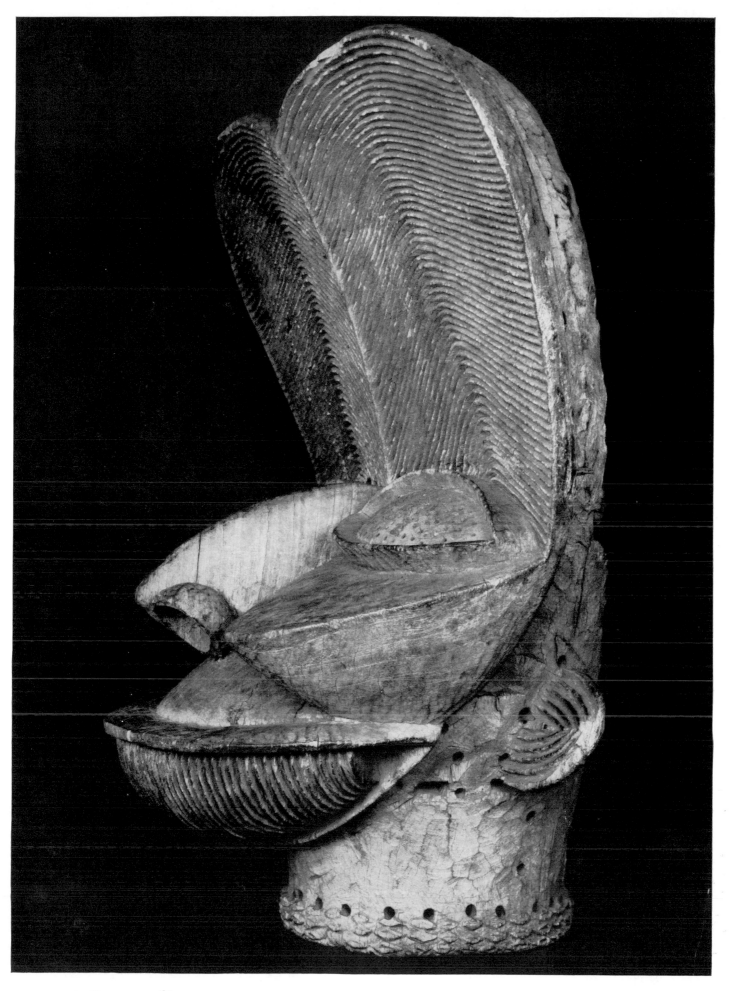

16. Same, profile

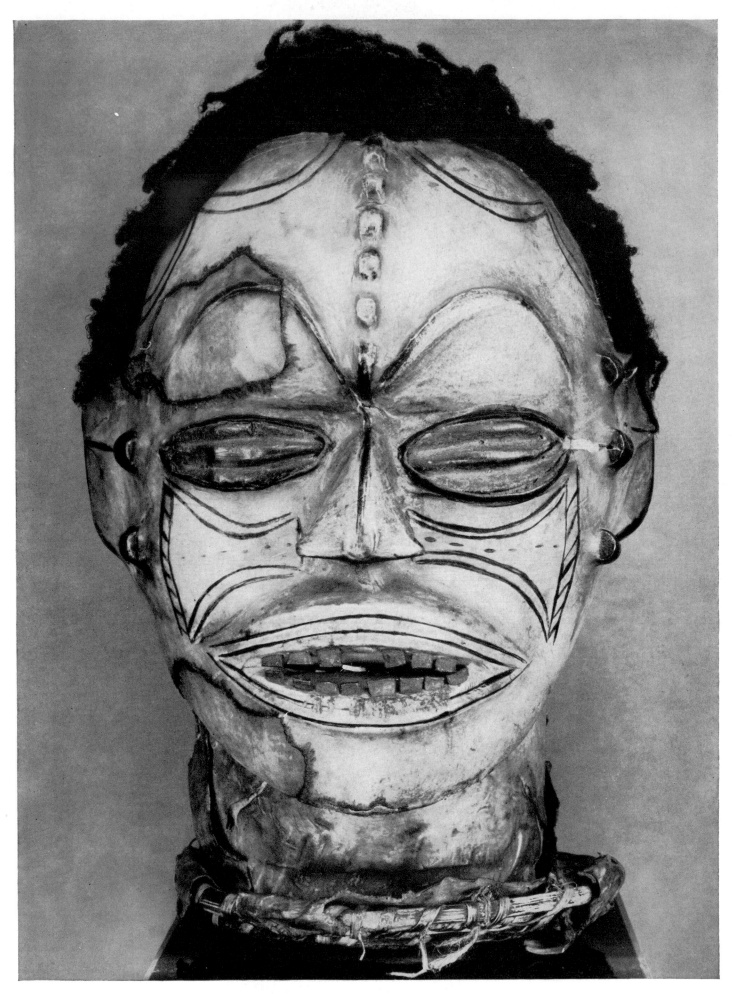

17. JANUS HEAD (view of one face). Parchment over wood, h. 9⅞ in. *Ekoi, Nigeria*

18. MASK. Wood, h. 17¼ in. *Bamenda, Cameroon*

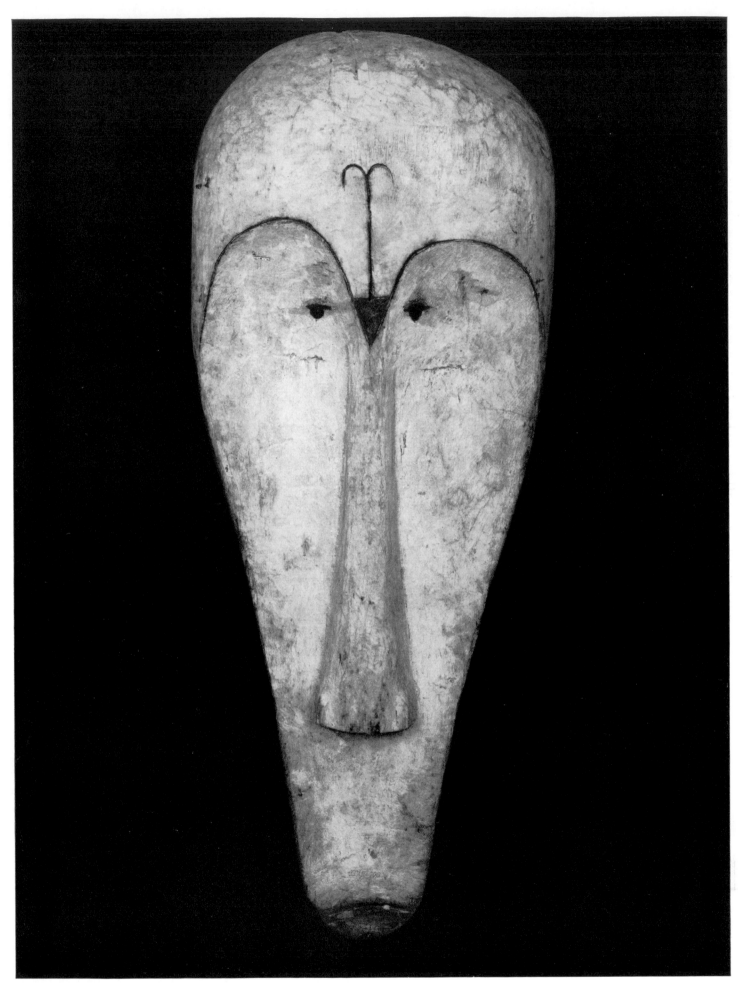

19. MASK. Whitened wood, h. 29½ in. *Fang, Gabon*

20. FOUR-FACED MASK, IN CASQUE FORM. Whitened wood, h. 13⅜ in. *Mpongwe, Gabon*

21. MASK. Polychrome wood, h. 9½ in. *Bakwele, Cameroon*

22. MASK, IN CASQUE FORM. Wood, h. 24½ in.
Baluba, Congo (Leopoldville)

23. MASK. Polychrome wood, metal, cloth, and shells, h. 12¾ in. *Baluba, Congo (Leopoldville)*

24. MASK. Polychrome wood, h. 20 in. *Baluba, Congo (Leopoldville)*

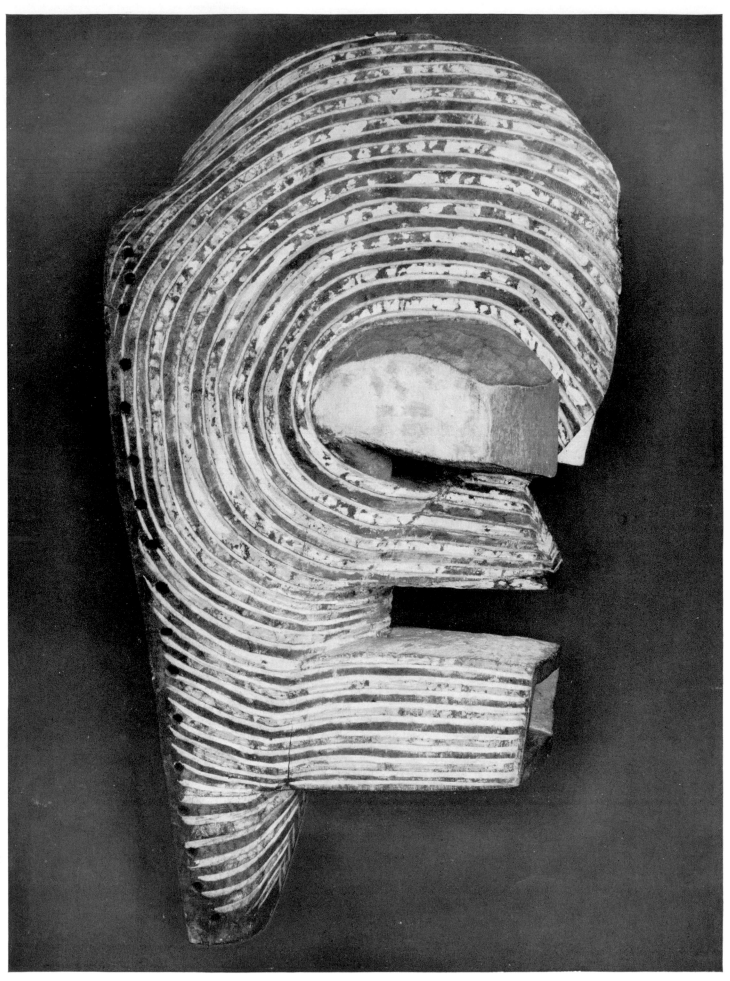

25. MASK. Polychrome wood, h. 24¾ in. *Basonge, Congo (Leopoldville)*

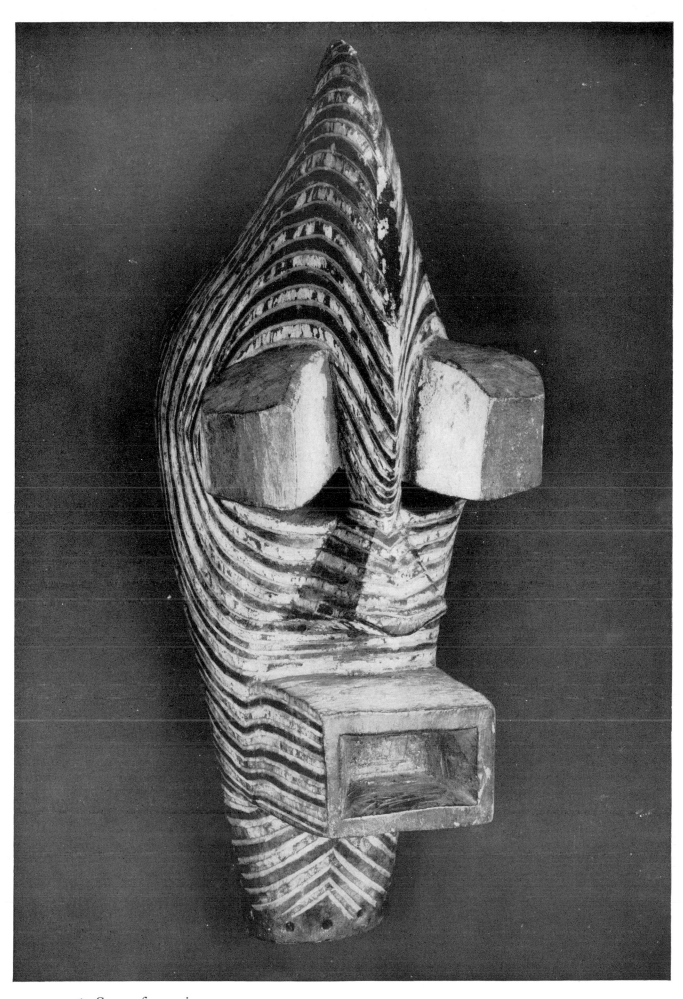

26. Same, front view

27. MASK. Polychrome wood and raffia, h. 12 in. *Bayaka, Congo (Leopoldville)*

28. KAKUNGA MASK. Wood and raffia, h. 36 in. *Bayaka, Congo (Leopoldville)*

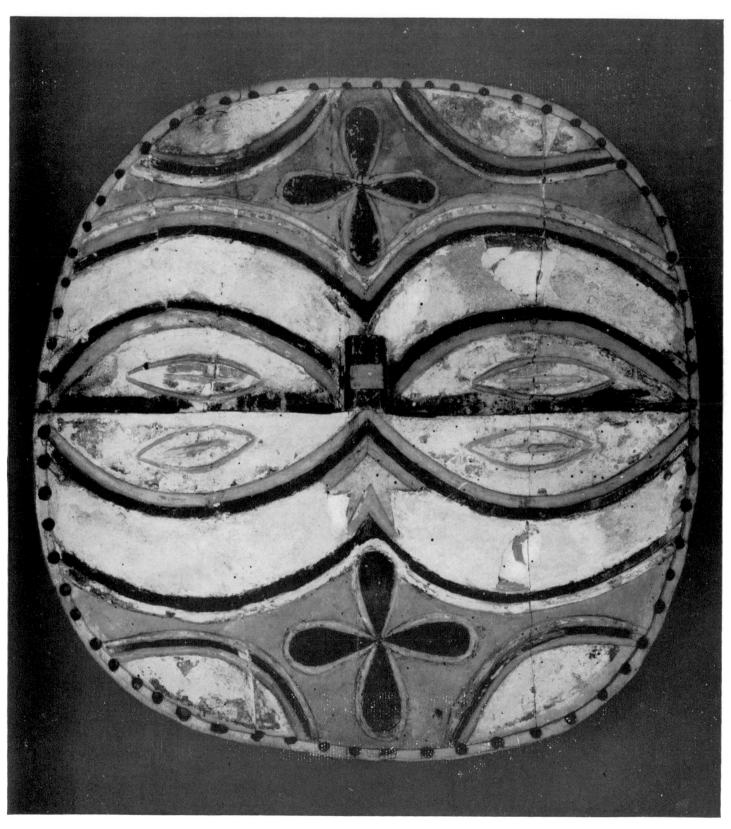

29. MASK. Polychrome wood, h. 11½ in. *Bateke, Congo (Leopoldville)*

30. MASK. Polychrome wood, h. 12 in. *Baboa, Congo (Leopoldville)*

31. MASK. Polychrome wood, h. 11¾ in. *Kanioka, Congo (Leopoldville)*

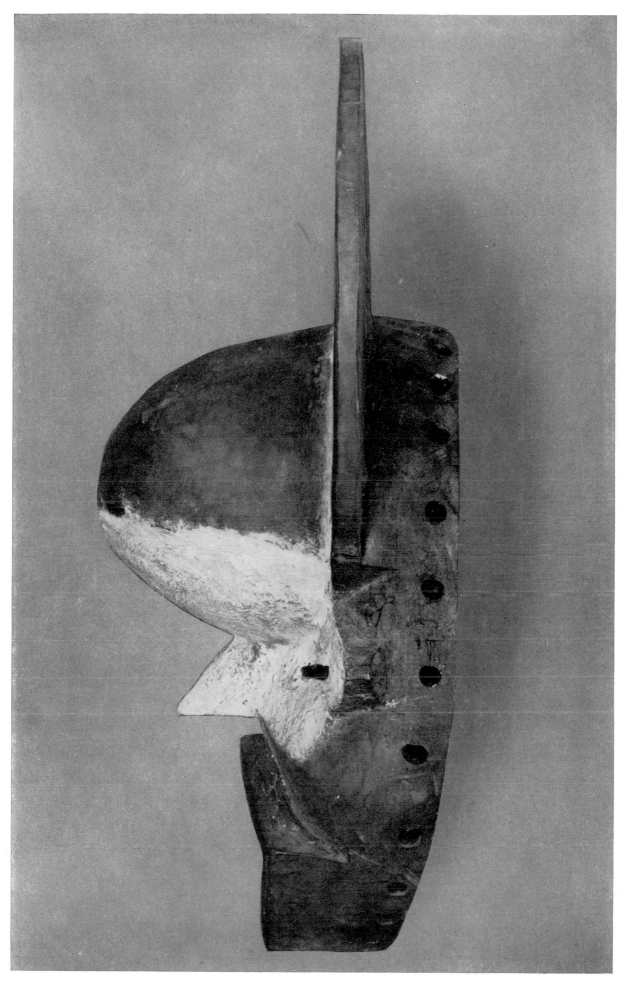

32. Same, profile

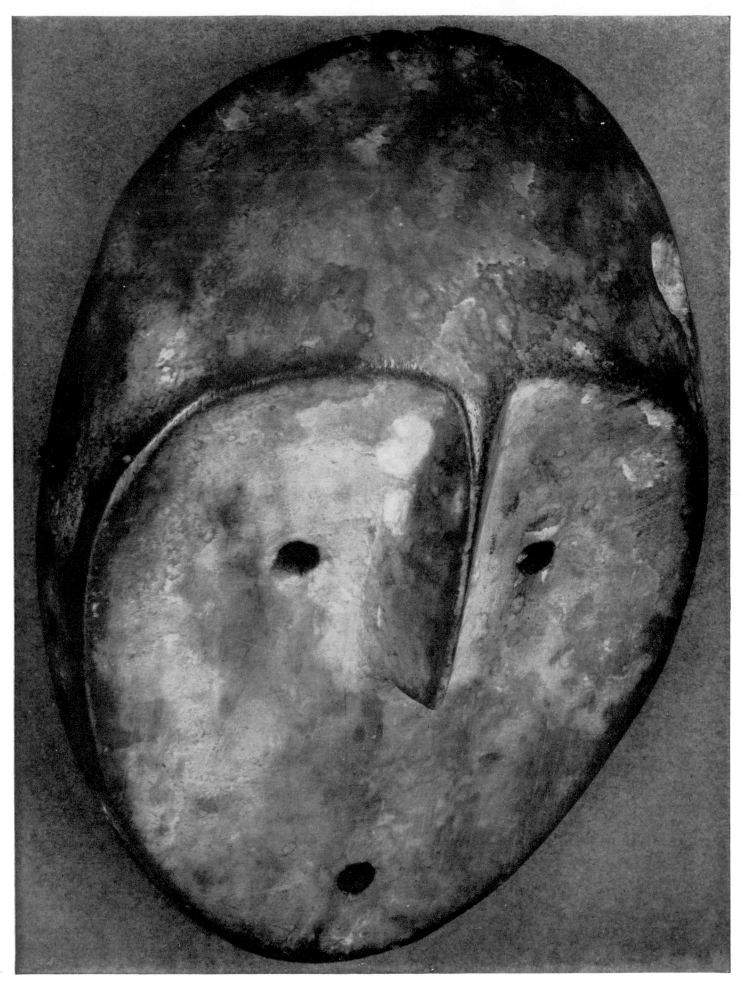

33. Mask. Wood, h. 8⅝ in. *Warega, Congo (Leopoldville)*

34. MASK. Wood, h. 23¼ in. *Makonde, Tanganyika*

35. MASK. Wood, h. 10 in. *Makonde, Tanganyika*

36. Hobbyhorse Head. Wood, h. 14½ in. *Bambara, Mali*

37. HEAD-DRESS. Wood, h. $31\frac{7}{8}$ in.
Bambara, Mali

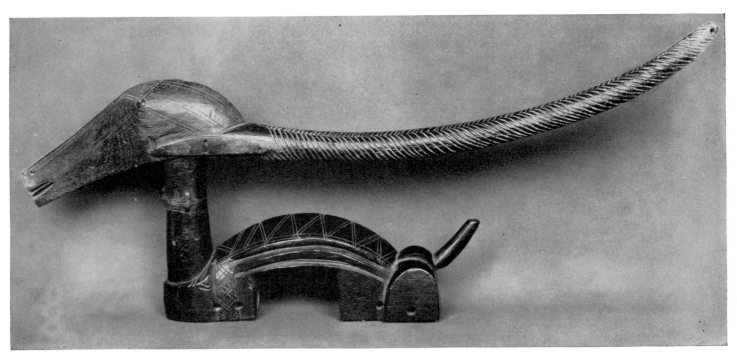

38. HEAD-DRESS. Wood, h. 26 in. *Mandingo (Suguni), Mali*

39. HERMAPHRODITIC FIGURE. Wood, h. 27½ in. *Dogon, Mali*

40. MALE AND FEMALE FIGURES. Wood, h. 15 in. *Dogon, Mali*

41. Same, rear view

42. STATUETTE. Wood, h. 17½ in. *Dogon, Mali*

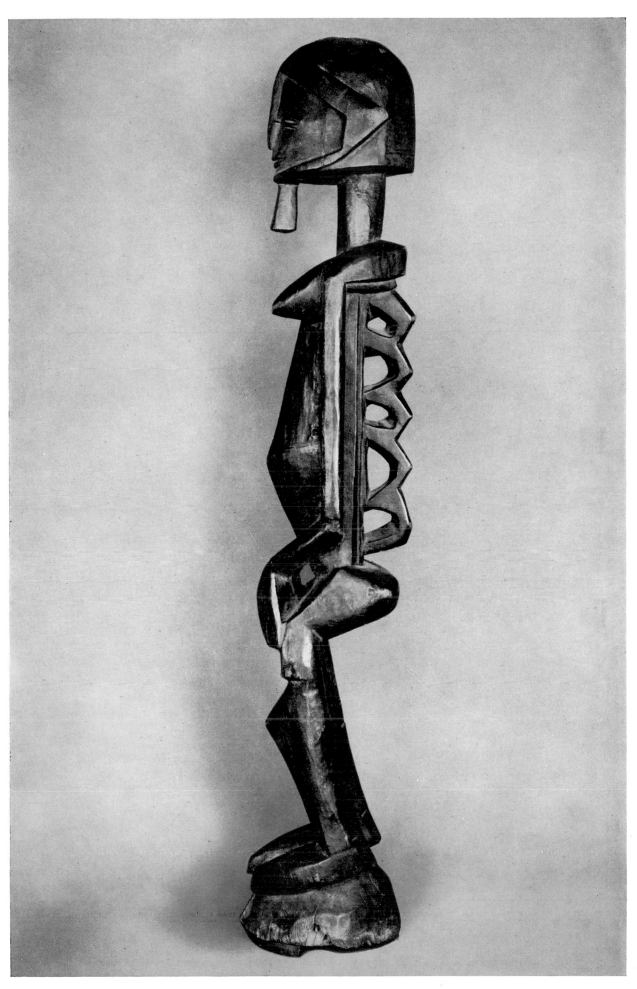

43. FIGURE. Wood, h. 30 in. *Dogon, Mali*

44. DOOR. Wood, h. 18⅞ in. *Dogon, Mali*

45. URN. Wood, h. 29½ in. *Dogon, Mali*

46. Female Figure. Wood, h. 21½ in. *Dogon, Mali*

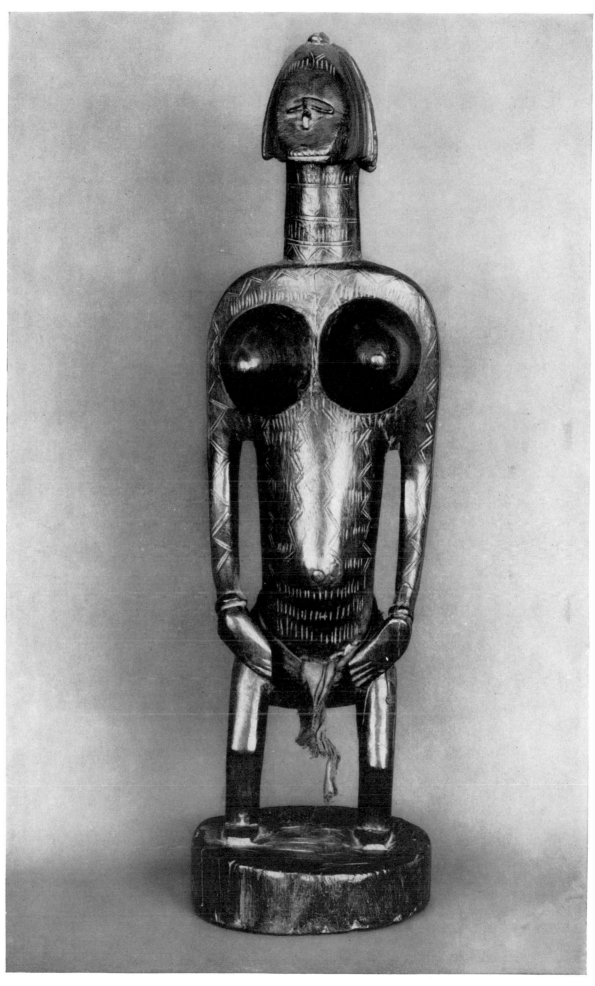

47. FEMALE FIGURE. Wood, h. 19⅝ in. *Bambara (?), Mali*

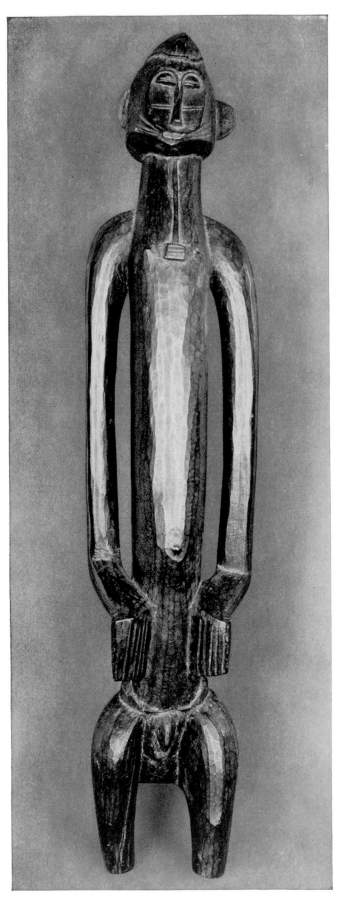

48. FIGURE. Wood, h. 35 in.
Senufo, Mali and Ivory Coast

49. Same, profile

50. LATCH IN FEMALE FORM. Wood, h. 21½ in. *Mali*

51. HEAD-DRESS. Wood, partly overlaid with metal, h. 40½ in.
Baga, Guinea

52. Same, detail of front

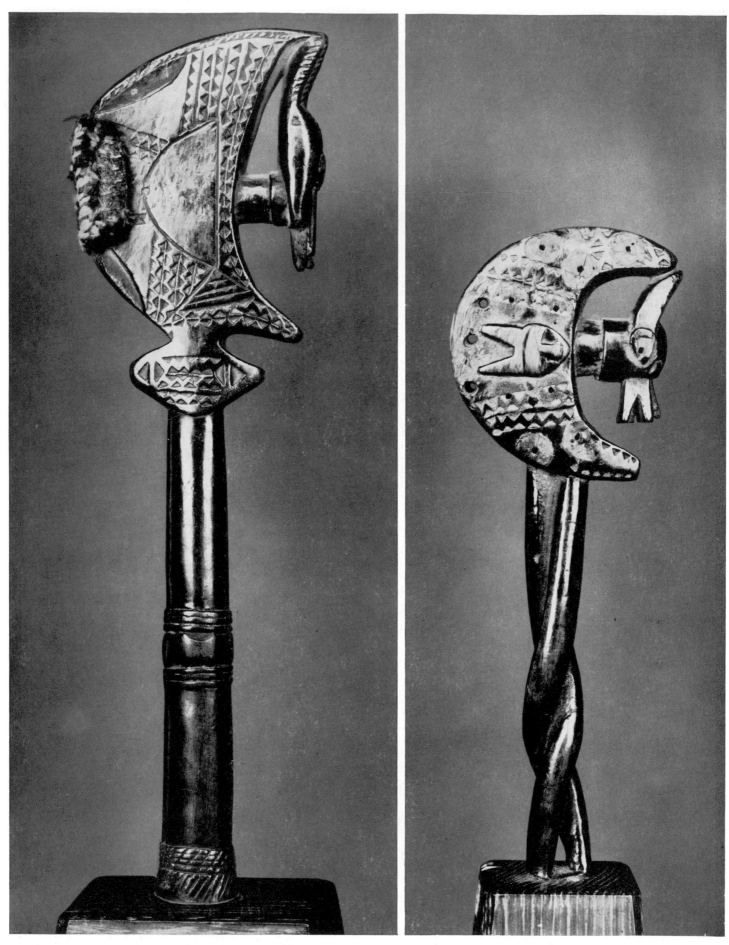

53. Two Gong Hammers. Wood, h. 9 and 6⅞ in. *Baule, Ivory Coast*

54–55. Two Spoons. Wood, h. 8⅝ and 8¼ in. *Baule, Ivory Coast*

56. Bobbin. Wood, h. 5⅞ in.
Senufo, Ivory Coast

57–58.
Two Bobbins. Wood, h. 7½ and 6⅛ in.
Guro, Ivory Coast

59. EQUESTRIAN FIGURE. Polychrome wood, h. 15¾ in. *Yoruba, Dahomey*

60. MOTHER AND CHILD. Wood, h. 20 in. *Yoruba (?), Nigeria*

61. RAM'S HEAD. Wood, h. 15 in. *Yoruba, Nigeria*

62. ANCESTOR FIGURE. Wood, h. 42 in. *Ibibio, Nigeria*

63. DRUM. Wood, h. 44⅛ in. *Bamenda, Cameroon*

64. CHIEF'S STOOL WITH FIGURE. Wood, h. 71 in.
Bekom, Cameroon

65. MORTUARY FIGURE. Wood, h. 32 in.
Bangwa, Cameroon

66. MENDICANT FIGURE WITH BOWL.
Wood, h. 33⅛ in. *Bangwa, Cameroon*

67. Same, front view

68. ANCESTOR FIGURE. Wood, h. 23 in. *Fang, Gabon*

69. SEAT WITH FIGURES. Wood, h. 22 in. *Yoko, Cameroon*

70. FIGURE. Wood, h. 17¼ in. *Bamum, Cameroon*

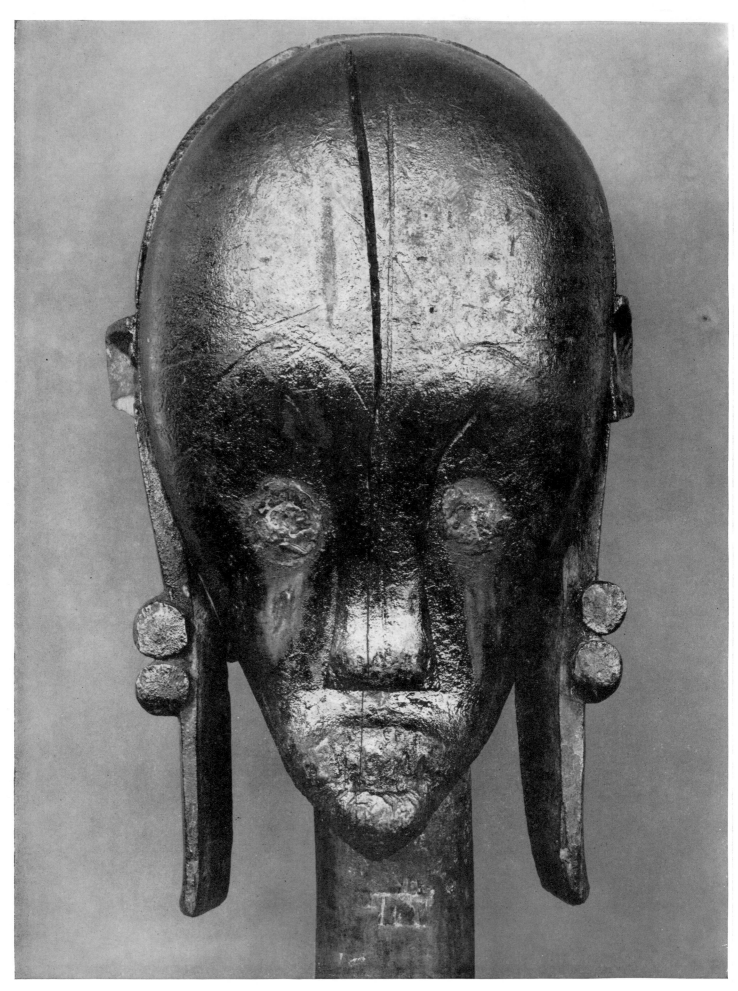

71. ANCESTOR FIGURE, HEAD. Wood, h. 17¾ in. *Fang, Gabon*

72. ANCESTOR FIGURE.
Wood, h. 11¾ in. *Fang, Gabon*

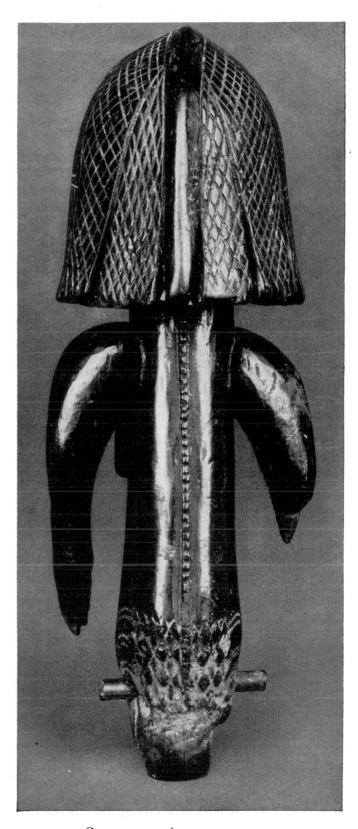

73. Same, rear view

74. MALE FIGURE. Wood, h. 27 in. *Fang, Gabon*

75. Same, detail of head, profile

76. TWO MUSICAL INSTRUMENTS. Wood, h. 6½ in. *Loango* (?), *Congo (Brazzaville)*

77. ANCESTOR FIGURE. Wood, h. 24⅞ in. *Fang, Gabon*

78. DRUM. Wood, h. $39\frac{1}{3}$ in., l. $79\frac{1}{2}$ in. *Yangere, Congo (Leopoldville)*

79. NAIL FETISH. Wood, h. 3½ ft. *Bakongo, Congo (Leopoldville)*

80. DRUM. Wood, h. 72 in. *Bashilele (?), Congo (Leopoldville)*

81. PORTRAIT FIGURE. Wood, h. 24 in. *Bakuba, Congo (Leopoldville)*

82. PORTRAIT FIGURE. Wood, h. 24 in. *Bakuba, Congo (Leopoldville)*

83. FEMALE FIGURE. Wood, h. 18, in. *Baluba, Congo (Leopoldville)*

84. FEMALE FIGURE. Wood, h. 18 in. *Baluba, Congo (Leopoldville)*

85. FEMALE FIGURE: DETAIL. Wood, h. 5 in. *Bena Lulua, Congo (Leopoldville)*

86. CARVED BATON. Wood, h. 14 in.
Bena Lulua, Congo (Leopoldville)

87. Same, profile

88. FIGURE. Wood, h. 17⅜ in.
Bena Lulua, Congo (Leopoldville)

89. Same, profile

90. Cup. Wood.
Basonge, Congo (Leopoldville)

91. Box, with Cover. Wood. *Bakuba, Congo (Leopoldville)*

92. FIGURE WITH DRUM. Wood, h. 15¼ in. *Kanioka, Congo (Leopoldville)*

93. HEADREST. Wood, h. 6¾ in.
Central Baluba, Congo (Leopoldville)

94. Same, rear view

95. Same as plate 93, three-quarter view

96. FIGURE. Wood, surmounting a calabash, with shells, h. 14⅛ in.
Central Baluba, Congo (Leopoldville)

97. Same, in full, rear view

98. FIGURE. Wood, h. 9¼ in. *Warega, Congo (Leopoldville)*

99. STOOL. Wood, h. 18½ in. *Northeastern Baluba, Congo (Leopoldville)*

100. Same, front view

101. SCEPTRE. Wood, h. 15¾ in. *Bachokwe, Angola*

102. Same, in full, front view

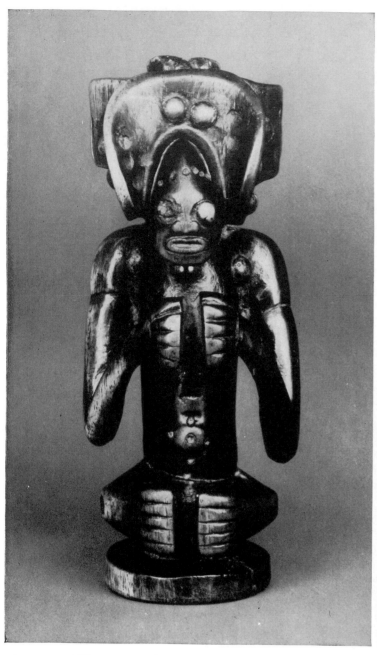

103. FIGURE. Wood, h. 5¾ in.
Bachokwe, Angola

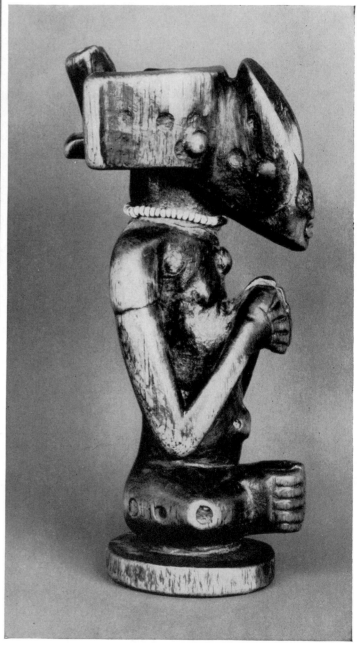

104. Same, profile

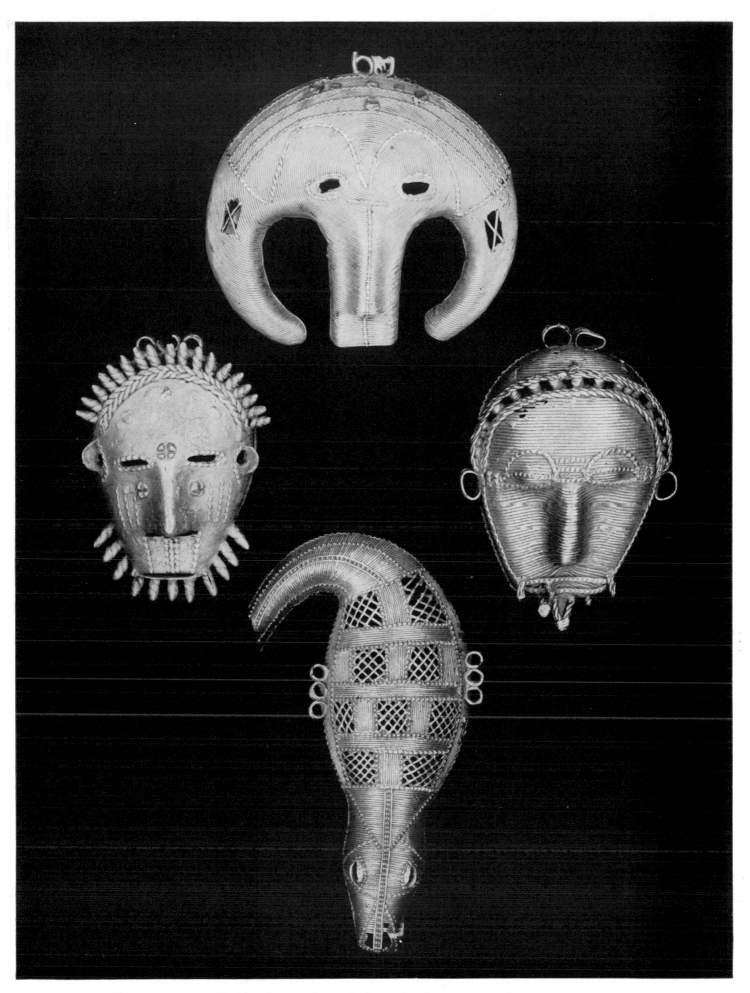

105. ORNAMENTS. Gold, cire-perdu technique, h. about 3 to 4 in.
(top and bottom) *Baule, Ivory Coast* (center), *Lobi, Ghana*

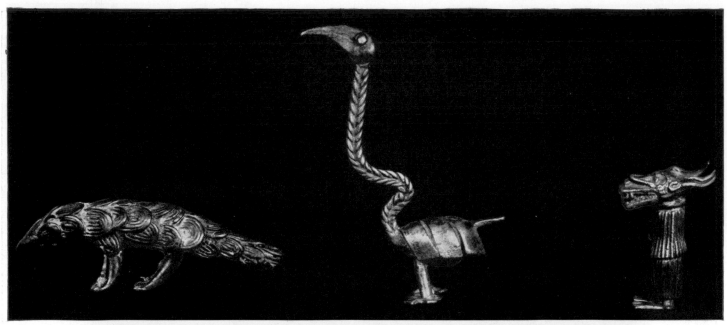

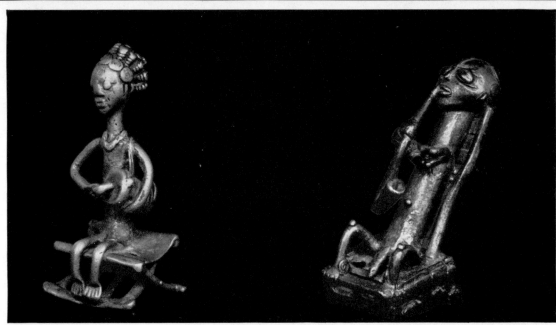

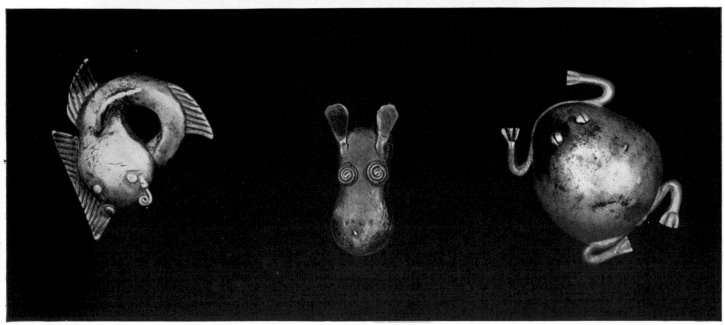

106–108. GOLD-DUST WEIGHTS. Bronze, cire-perdu technique, actual size.
Baule, Ivory Coast or *Ashanti, Ghana*

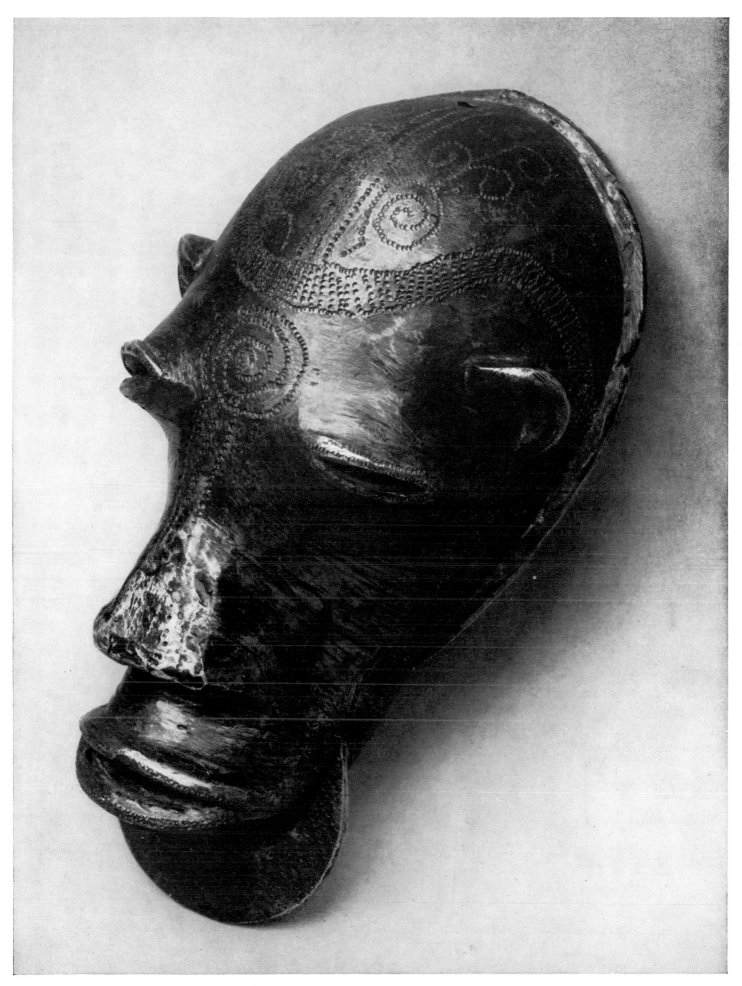

109. MAN'S HEAD. Bronze, cire-perdu technique, h. 6 in. *Bron, Ghana*

110. FEMALE FIGURE. Bronze, h. 30 in. *Yoruba, Nigeria*

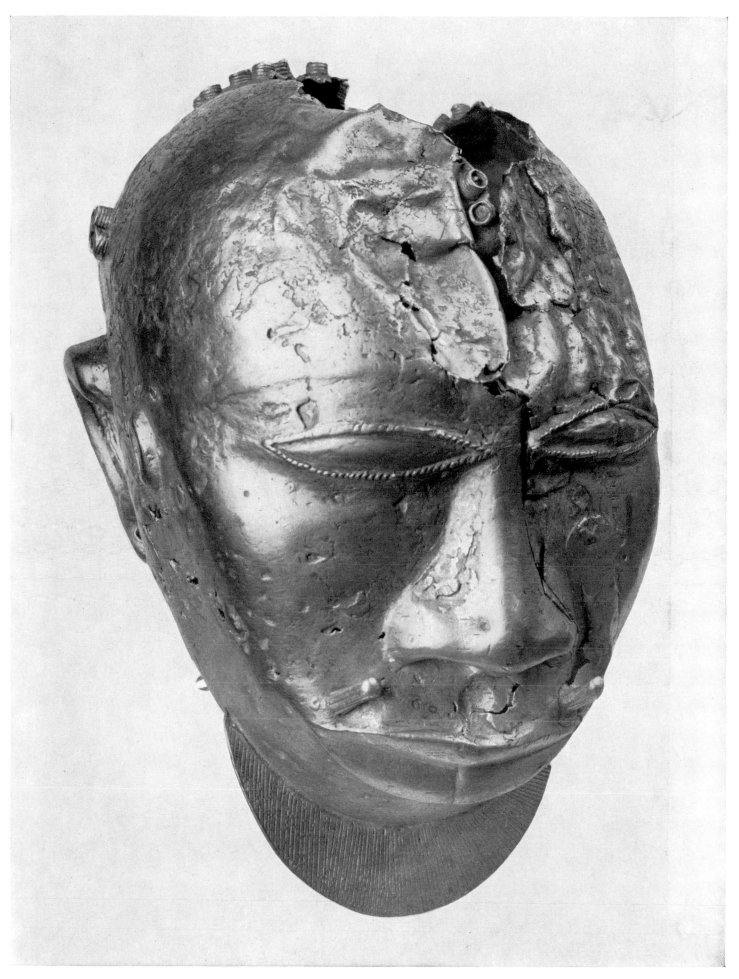

111. MASK. Gold, hollow cast, h. 6⅞ in. *Ashanti, Ghana*

112. FIGURE. Hammered brass, h. 41½ in. *Fon, Dahomey*

113. Same, detail

114. Same as plate 115, detail of head, side view

115. FIGURE. Iron, h. 65 in. *Fon, Dahomey*

116. Plaque: Hunter. Bronze, 18½ x 12⅝ in. *Benin, Nigeria*

117. PLAQUE: FRUIT-GATHERERS. Bronze, h. 21⅞ in. *Benin, Nigeria*

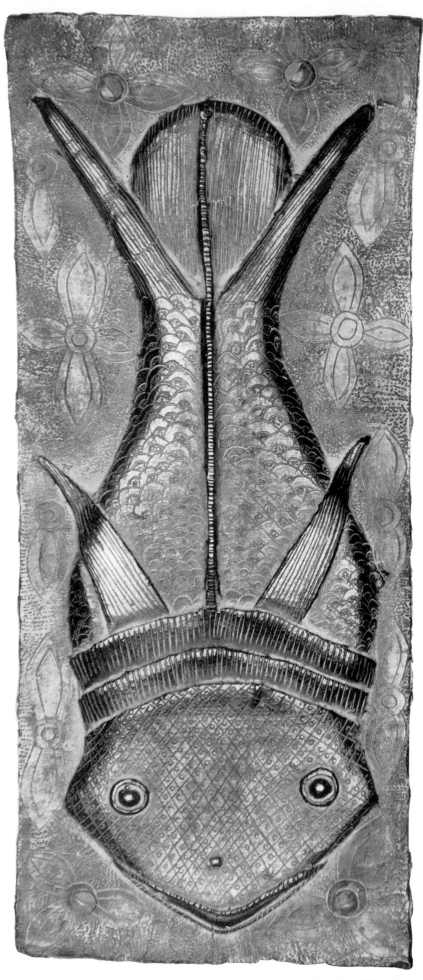

118. PLAQUE: FISH. Bronze, 17 x 7⅛ in. *Benin, Nigeria*

119. LEOPARD. Bronze, l. 28 in. *Benin, Nigeria*

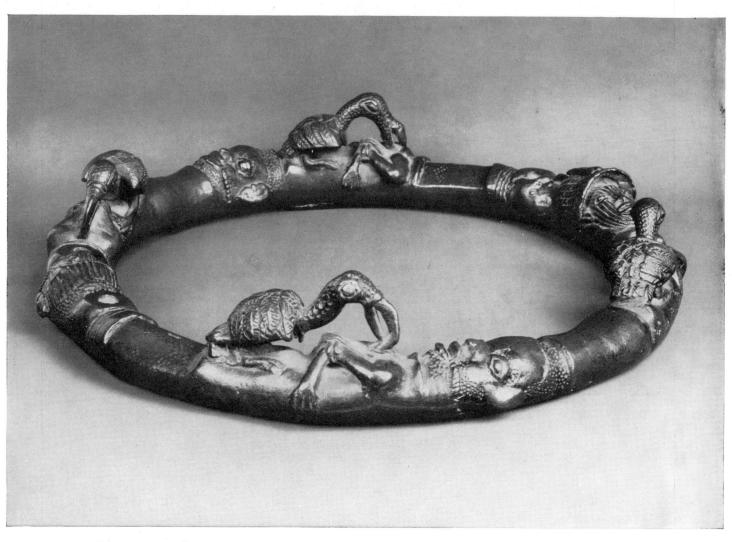

120. Necklet. Bronze, diameter 10 in. *Benin, Nigeria*

121. REPTILE HEAD. Bronze, l. 20⅛ in. *Benin, Nigeria*

122. FIGURE. Bronze, h. $13\frac{3}{8}$ in. *Benin, Nigeria*

123. Same, rear view

124. Head. Bronze, h. 6⅜ in. *Benin, Nigeria*

127. FIGURE. Bronze, h. 24⅝ in. *Benin, Nigeria*

128. Same as plate 127, full view, front

129. Same, rear view

130. HEAD. Bronze, h. 7¾ in. *Benin, Nigeria*

131. GIRL'S HEAD. Bronze, life size. *Benin, Nigeria*

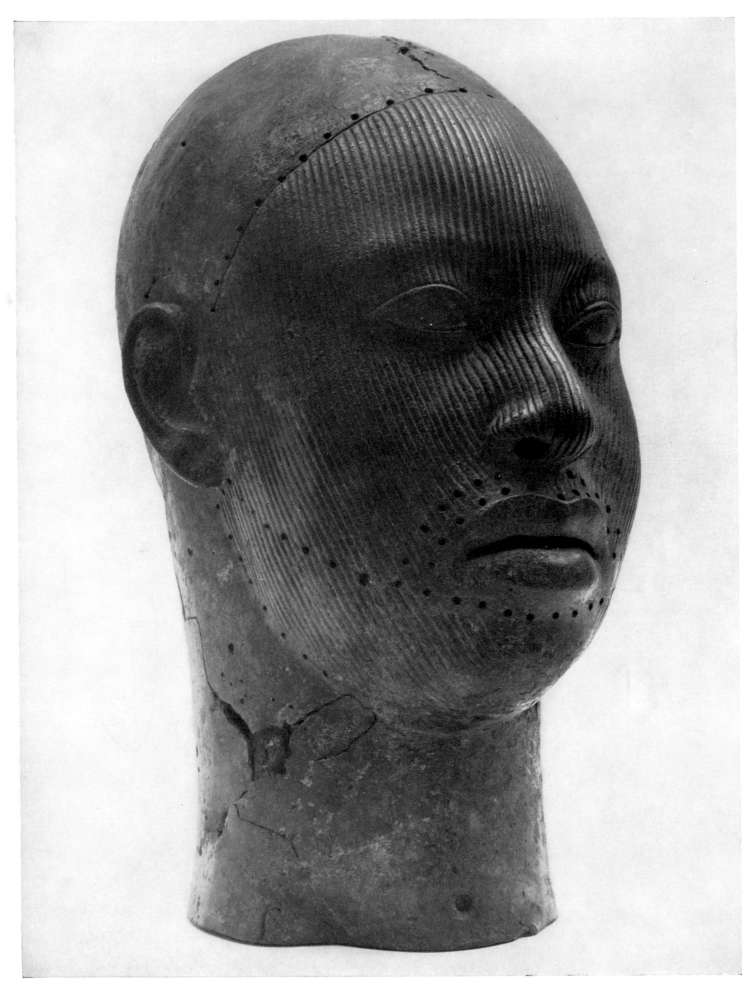

132. HEAD. Bronze, h. 13½ in. *Ife, Nigeria*

133. Head. Bronze, h. 11½ in. *Ife, Nigeria*

134. GIRL'S HEAD. Bronze, h. 12½ in. *Ife, Nigeria*

135. HALF-FIGURE. Bronze, h. 14½ in. *Ife, Nigeria*

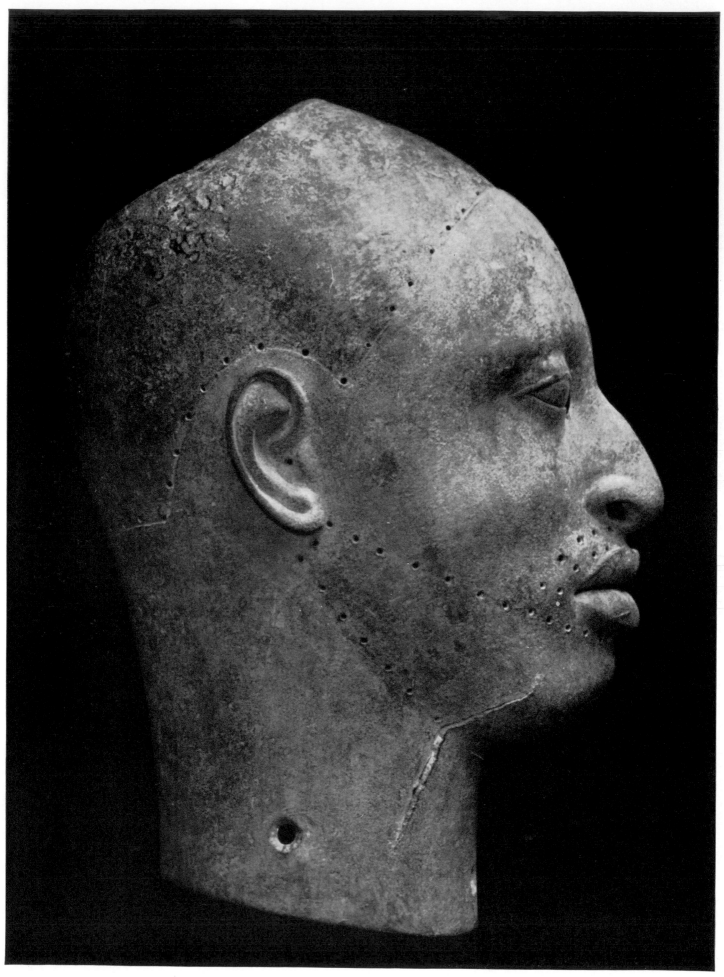

136. HEAD. Bronze, h. 13½ in. *Ife, Nigeria*

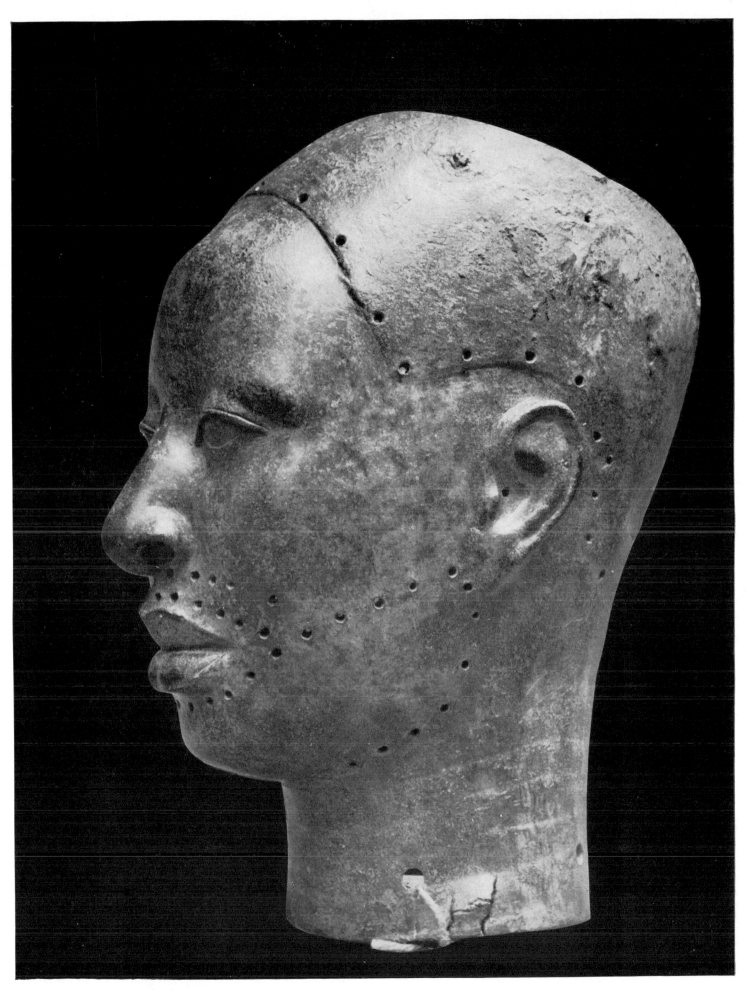

137. HEAD. Bronze, h. 13½ in. *Ife, Nigeria*

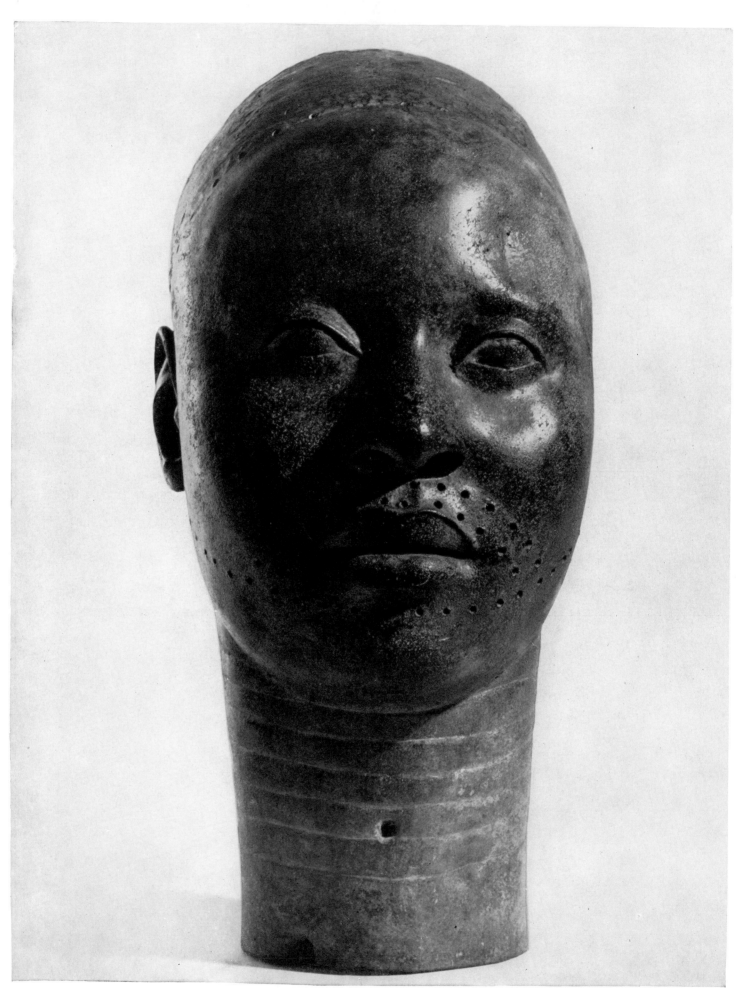

138. HEAD. Bronze, h. 12½ in. *Ife, Nigeria*

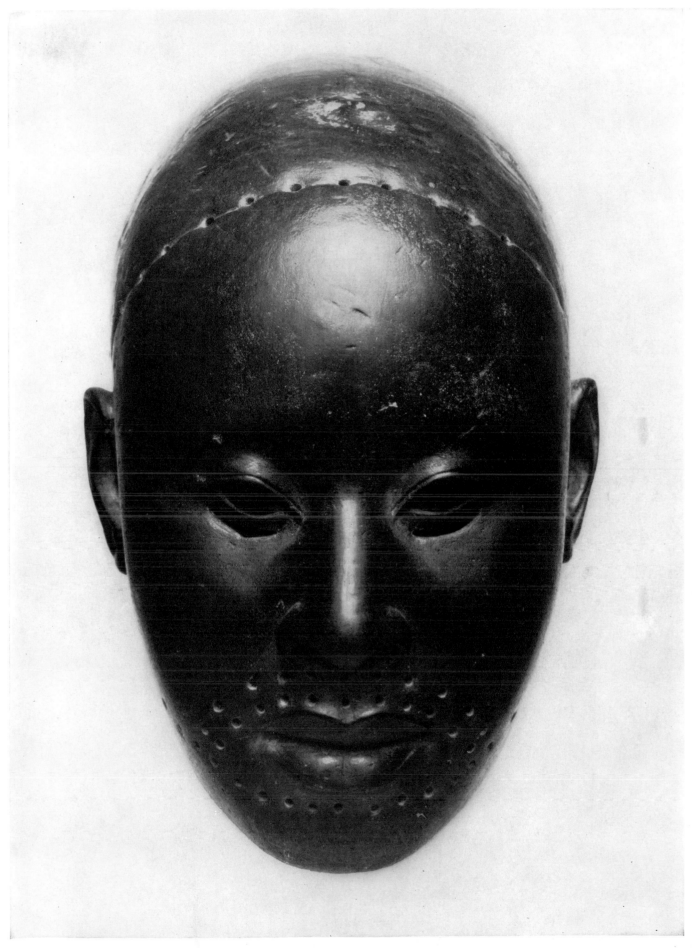

'139. MASK. Bronze, h. 13 in. *Ife, Nigeria*

140. DOUBLE BELL. Iron, h. 24⅜ in. *Bamum, Cameroon*

141. NECKLET. Bronze, diameter 10⅝ in. *Bamum, Cameroon*

142. Funerary Figure.
Wood covered with copper strips, h. 22½ in.
Bakota, Gabon

143. FUNERARY FIGURE. Wood covered with copper strips, h. 22 in. *Bakota, Gabon*

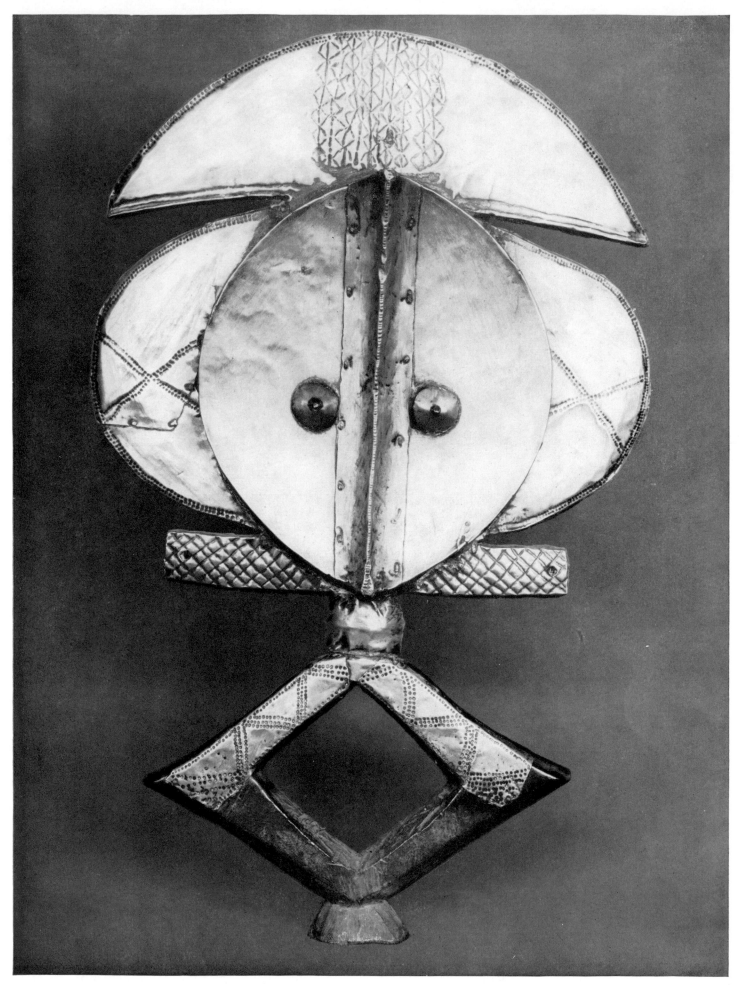

144. FUNERARY FIGURE. Wood covered with copper strips, h. 22½ in. *Bakota, Gabon*

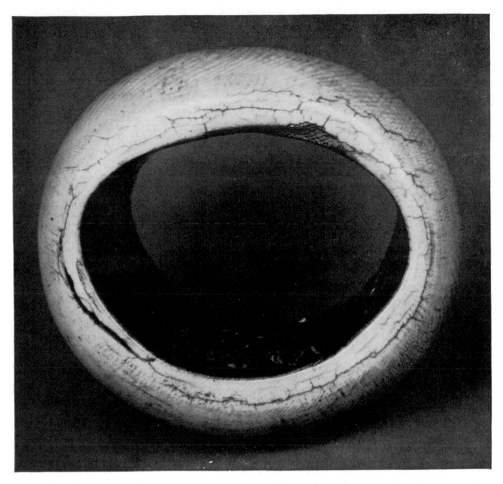

145. BRACELET. Ivory, diameter 4½ in. *Guro, Ivory Coast*

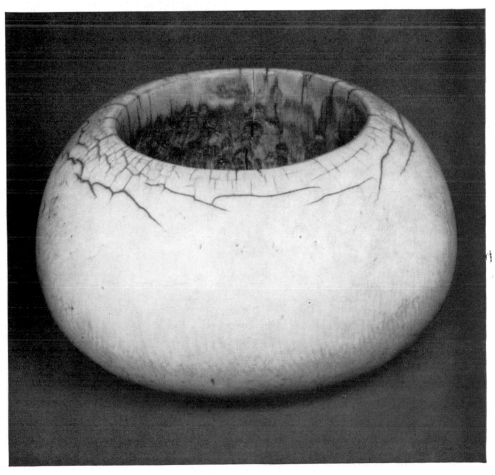

146. BRACELET. Ivory, diameter 4½ in. *Guro, Ivory Coast*

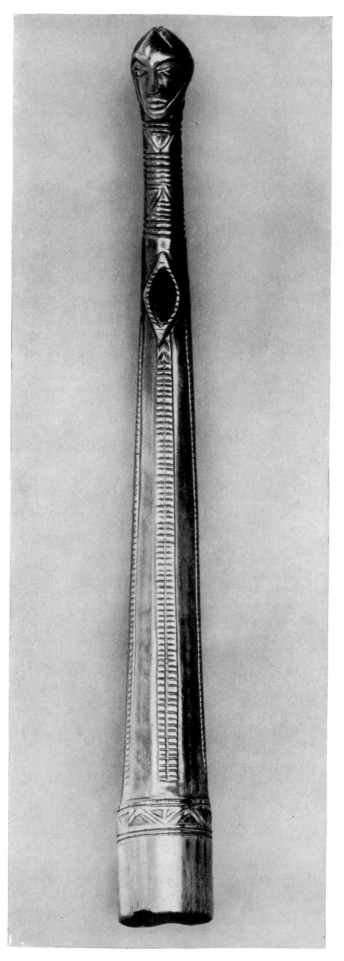

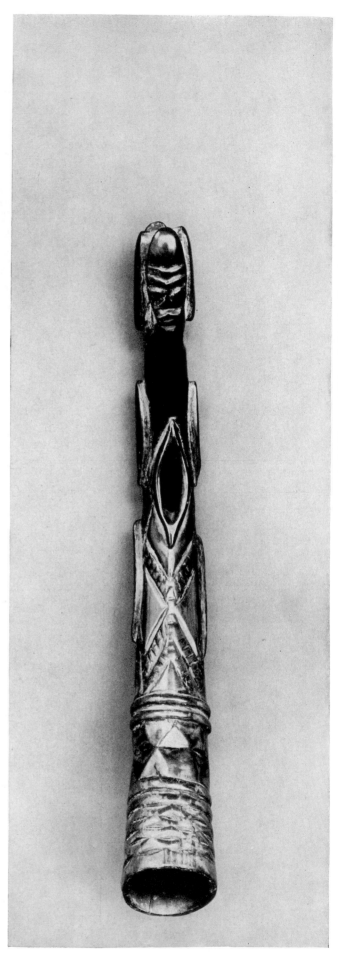

147. Trumpet. Ivory, l. 21¼ in.
Upper Ogowe River, Gabon

148. Trumpet. Ivory, l. 18⅛ in.
Upper Ogowe River, Gabon

149. PENDANT. Ivory, h. 2⅜ in. *Bapende, Congo (Leopoldville)*

150. HEADREST. Ivory, h. 6½ in.
Baluba, Congo (Leopoldville)

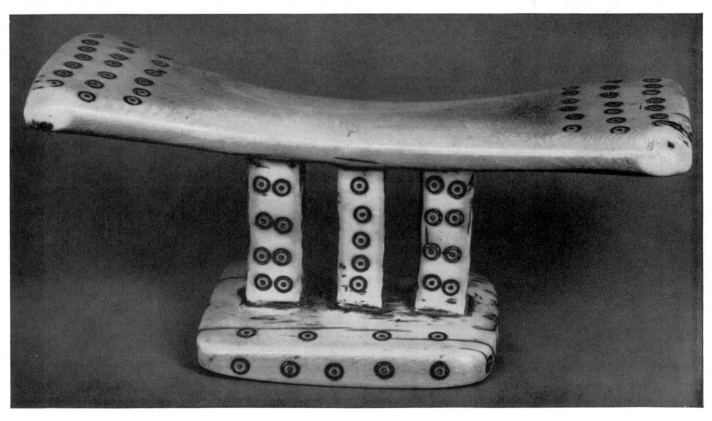

151. HEADREST. Ivory, h. 4 in., l. 10⅞ in. *Warega, Congo (Leopoldville)*

152. FIGURE. Ivory, h. 10¼ in. *Warega, Congo (Leopoldville)*

153. MASK. Ivory, h. 8¼ in. *Warega, Congo (Leopoldville)*

154. MASK. IVORY, h. 7⅝ in. *Warega, Congo (Leopoldville)*

155. HEAD. Ivory, h. 6¼ in. *Warega, Congo (Leopoldville)*

156. BATON. Ivory, h. 5⅞ in. *Congo (Leopoldville)*

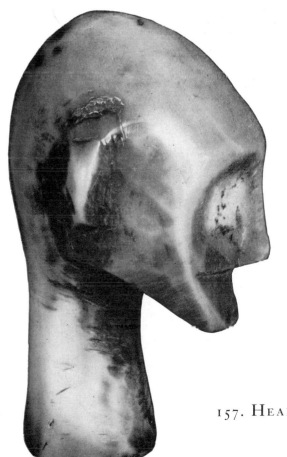

157. HEAD. Ivory, h. 4¾ in. *Warega, Congo (Leopoldville)*

158. FIGURE. Soapstone, h. 9¾ in.
Sierra Leone

159. FEMALE FIGURE. Soapstone, h. 14 in.
Mende, Sierra Leone

160. HEAD. Soapstone, h. 9¾ in. *Mende, Sierra Leone*

161. FUNERARY FIGURE. Terracotta, h. 15 in. *Agni, Ivory Coast*

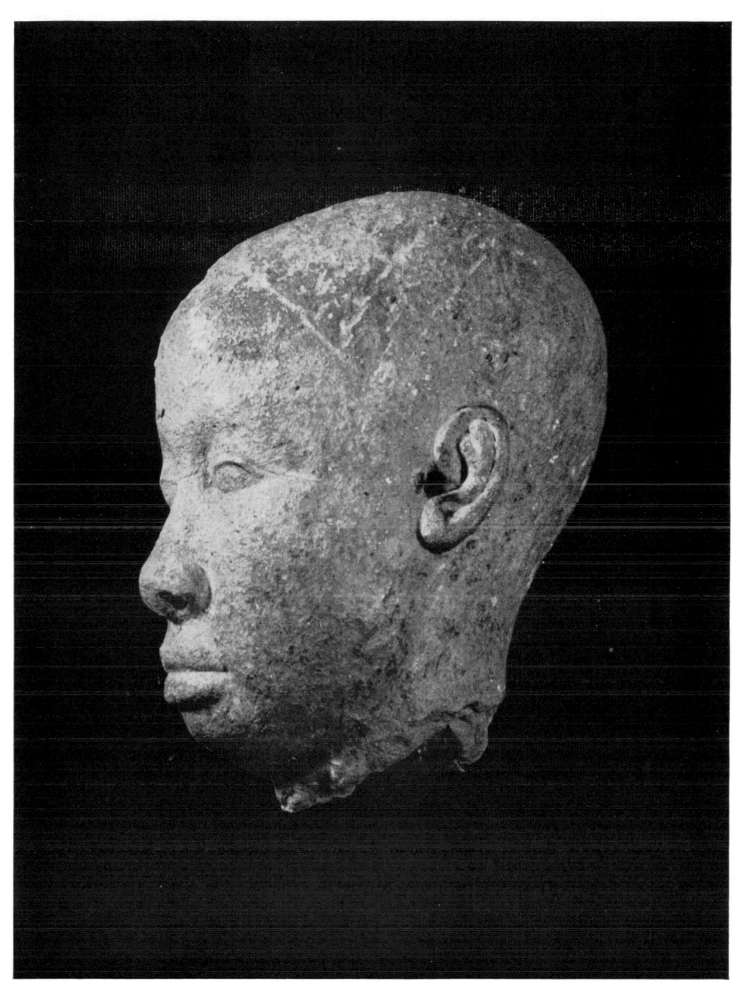

162. HEAD. Terracotta, h. 6½ in. *Ife, Nigeria*

163. HEAD. Terracotta, h. 6¾ in. *Ife, Nigeria*

164. HEAD. Terracotta, h. 11½ in. *Ife, Nigeria*

165. HEAD. Terracotta, h. 8¾ in. *Nok, Nigeria*

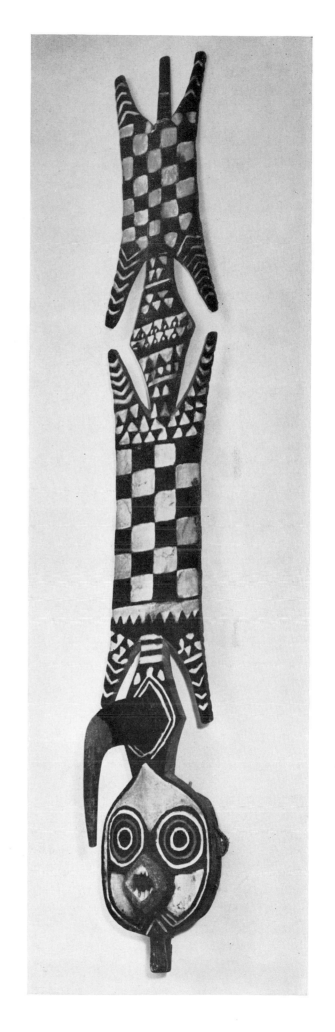

166. BIRD MASK. Painted wood, h. 72 in.
Bobo, Upper Volta

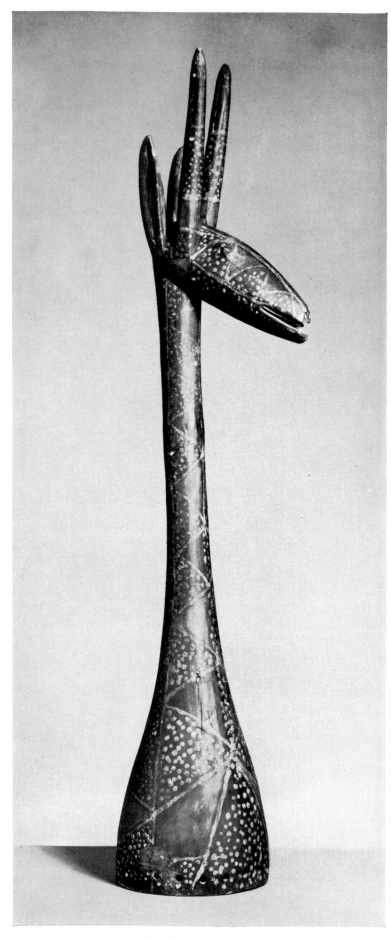

167. FEMALE ANTELOPE HEAD-DRESS.
Painted wood, h. 43¾ in. *Kurumba, Upper Volta*

168. MALE ANTELOPE HEAD-DRESS. Painted wood, h. 36 in.
Kurumba, Upper Volta

169. MASK. Wood, h. 62 in.
Bambara, Mali

170. Same, side view

171. MASK. Wood and raffia, (mask alone) h. 24⅜ in. *Fang, Gabon*

172. CULT OBJECT. Wood, 78 x 21 x 17½ in. *Dogon, Mali*

173. BUTTERFLY MASK. Painted wood and braided rope, w. 51¼ in. *Bobo, Upper Volta*

174. FETISH. Wood covered with mud, w. 20½ in. *Bambara, Mali*

175. BIRD. Painted wood, h. 59⅝ in. *Senufo, Ivory Coast*

176. Ritual Object. Wood and metal,
h. 19 in., l. 36½ in. *Baga, Guinea*

177. SERPENT. Painted wood, h. 102 in. *Landuma, Guinea*

178. HOUSEPOST. Wood, h. 74¼ in. *Dogon, Mali*

179. Female Figure. Wood, h. 10½ in. *Dogon, Mali*

180. Horse with Rider. Wood, h. 27⅛ in. *Dogon, Mali*

181. ANCESTRAL FIGURE. Wood, h. 40¼ in.
Bambara, Mali

182. Bust. Wood, h. 18 in. *Bapende, Congo (Leopoldville)*

183. PREHISTORIC HEAD. Steatite, h. 10¼ in. *Kissi, Guinea*

184. VESSEL. Terracotta, h. 14½ in. *Provenience unknown*

185. STONE SCULPTURE. Steatite, h. 9¾ in. *Provenience unknown*

186. PEDESTAL BOWL. Bronze, h. 4¾ in. *Ife, Nigeria*

187. FEMALE HEAD. Terracotta, h. 10⅝ in. *Ife, Nigeria*

Catalogue of Plates

Catalogue of Plates

In general, the whereabouts of the objects noted here are those which obtained when the photographs were made, and there is a likelihood that many of the pieces have subsequently changed hands. (Exception: the frontispiece and plates 166–187, which have been added to the second edition.) The objects photographed by Walker Evans were, in nearly every case, exhibited at the Museum of Modern Art, New York, in 1935, and those by Eliot Elisofon were made in 1951. Political names have been revised (1964).

Frontispiece: Pair of Royal Figures. Bronze, 12 in. high. Ife, Nigeria. *Coll. the Oni of Ife (photo: British Museum).*

12th–15th century; discovered in a mound at Ita Yemoo, near Ife, in 1957. These personages were perhaps a nobleman and his wife.

1. Mask. Wood, about 14½ in. high. Dogon, Mali. *Musée de l'Homme, Paris (photo: Elisofon).*

Represents a monkey. From the Mopti clan, Iréli village.

2. Mask. Wood, 25 in. high. Bambara, Mali. *Coll. Earl Horter, Philadelphia (photo: Evans).*

Used in the rites of a young boys' secret society; represents the N'tomo, a spirit effective against evil.

3. Mask. Wood, 22½ in. high. Toma, Liberia. *Coll. Jacques Lipchitz, Paris (photo: Evans).*

4. Mask. Polychrome wood, 9 in. high. Dan, Liberia, border of Ivory Coast. *Coll. Pierre Loeb, Paris (photo: Evans).*

5. Mask. Wood, 9⅛ in. high. Dan, Ivory Coast. *Coll. Miss Laura Harden, New York (photo: Evans).*

6. Mask. Wood, 9½ in. high. Dan, Ivory Coast. *Coll. Dr. Paul Chadourne, Paris (photo: Evans).*

7. Mask. Wood, 10⅝ in. high. Dan, Ivory Coast. *Coll. Paul Guillaume, Paris (photo: Evans).*

8. Mask. Wood, 18½ in. high. Bambara, Mali. *Coll. Louis Carré, Paris (photo: Evans).*

9. Mask. Wood, with metal plates, 15¾ in. high. Baule, Ivory Coast. *Coll. Paul Guillaume, Paris (photo: Evans).*

Surmounted by a bird.

10. Mask. Wood, 8 in. high. Dan, Liberia. *Coll. Princess Gourielli, New York (photo: Evans).*

In the form of a bird's head.

11. Mask. Wood, black and red, 15 in. high. Baule, Ivory Coast. *Coll. Felix Fénéon, Paris (photo: Evans).*

12. Mask. Wood, 17 in. high. Ekoi, Nigeria. *Coll. K. C. Murray, London (photo: Central Office of Information).*

13. MASK (HEAD-DRESS). Wood, 14½ in. high. Mama, Nigeria. *Coll. Charles Ratton (photo: Ratton)*.

Represents a buffalo, and is worn on the head, while a fibre garment covers the body.

14. HEAD-DRESS. Wood, painted red, 26 in. high. Mama, Nigeria. *Coll. Charles Ratton (photo: Evans)*.

Represents an antelope.

15. MASK. Wood, 26⅜ in. high. Bamenda, Cameroon. *Coll. Baron Eduard von der Heydt, Ascona, Switzerland (photo: Evans)*.

16. Same, profile.

17. JANUS HEAD (one face). Parchment over wood, 9⅞ in. Ekoi, Nigeria. *Coll. Antony Moris, Paris (photo: Evans)*.

Represents a deceased ancestor. These heads are carved in wood, and the skin, formerly human but more recently monkey or antelope, is stretched over. They are worn on top of the head and used in funerary rites.

18. MASK. Wood, 17¼ in. high. Bamenda, Cameroon. *Coll. Baron Eduard von der Heydt, Ascona, Switzerland (photo: Evans)*.

19. MASK. Whitened wood, 29½ in. high. Fang, Gabon. *Museum für Völkerkunde, Berlin (photo: Evans)*.

Kaolin is the usual whitening element, in such masks.

20. FOUR-FACED MASK, IN CASQUE FORM. Whitened wood, 13⅜ in. high. Mpongwe, Gabon. *Coll. Paul Guillaume, Paris (photo: Evans)*.

21. MASK. Polychrome wood, 9½ in. high. Bakwele, Cameroon. *Coll. Tristan Tzara, Paris (photo: Evans)*.

22. MASK, IN CASQUE FORM. Wood, about 24½ in. high. Baluba, Congo (Leopoldville). *Musée Royal du Congo, Tervueren, Belgium (photo: Musée)*.

Carved from a single block, including horns. The beard is probably raffia. Discovered 1899 by the Commandant Michaux.

23. MASK. Polychrome wood, metal, cloth, and cowrie shells, 12¾ in. high. Baluba, Congo (Leopoldville). *Schomburg Collection, New York Public Library (photo: Evans)*.

24. MASK. Polychrome wood, about 20 in. high. Baluba, Congo (Leopoldville). *Musée Royal du Congo, Tervueren, Belgium (photo: Musée)*.

25. MASK. Polychrome wood, 24¾ in. high. Basonge, Congo (Leopoldville). *Coll. Sydney Burney, London (photo: Evans)*.

26. Same, front view.

27. MASK. Polychrome wood and raffia, 12 in. high. Bayaka, Congo (Leopoldville). *Schomburg Collection, New York Public Library (photo: Evans)*.

28. KAKUNGA MASK. Wood and raffia, about 36 in. high. Bayaka, Congo (Leopoldville). *Musée Royal du Congo, Tervueren, Belgium (photo: Musée)*.

Such a mask, one of the largest to be found in the Congo, was worn by a dancer impersonating the Kakunga, or male spirit, in an initiation rite.

29. MASK. Polychrome wood, 11½ in. high. Bateke, Congo (Leopoldville). *Coll. André Derain, Paris (photo: Evans)*.

30. MASK. Polychrome wood, 12 in. high. Baboa, Congo (Leopoldville). *Musée Royal du Congo, Tervueren, Belgium (photo: Musée)*.

A war and dance mask. Characteristic of this type is the stylized representation of the ears by large kaolin-whitened rings.

31. MASK. Polychrome wood, 11¾ in. high. Kanioka, Congo (Leopoldville). *Museum für Völkerkunde, Hamburg (photo: Evans)*.

32. Same, profile.

33. MASK. Wood, 8⅝ in. high. Warega, Congo (Leopoldville). *Coll. Charles Ratton, Paris (photo: Evans)*.

34. MASK. Wood, 23¼ in. high. Makonde, Tanganyika. *Museum für Völkerkunde, Berlin (photo: Evans)*.

Representation of a rabbit, with monkey hair.

35. MASK. Wood, 10 in. high. Makonde, Tanganyika. *British Museum, London (photo: Museum)*.

With monkey hair.

36. HOBBYHORSE HEAD. Wood, 14½ in. high. Bambara, Mali. *Cleveland (Ohio) Museum of Art (photo: Evans)*.

May represent a mule; presumably serves the same purpose as the object in plate 37.

37. HEAD-DRESS. Wood, 31⅞ in. high. Bambara, Mali. *Coll. Antony Moris, Paris (photo: Evans)*.

> Represents an antelope. The carving is mounted on a small cap of basketwork and worn on top of the head by a dancer, who imitates the leaps of antelopes in sowing and harvest feasts. The head-dress or mask is called the Tji-Wara, which is variously said also to be the name of evil spirits being propitiated or of a goddess of fecundity and earth.

38. HEAD-DRESS. Wood, 26 in. high. Mandingo (Suguni), Mali. *Coll. Louis Carré, Paris (photo: Evans)*.

> See note on plate 37.

39. HERMAPHRODITIC FIGURE. Wood, 27½ in. high. Dogon, Mali. *Coll. Louis Carré, Paris (photo: Evans)*.

> See note on plate 40. From the region of Bandiagara.

40. MALE AND FEMALE FIGURES. Wood, about 15 in. high. Dogon, Mali. *Barnes Foundation, Merion, Pennsylvania (photo: Cahiers d'Art)*.

> Such figures are believed to embody the spirit of the family. They commonly pass from one generation to the next, and are placed in the rock caves with the dead for several days. The female statuette wears a beard-like chin ornament. From the region of Bandiagara.

41. Same, rear view.

42. STATUETTE. Wood, 17½ in. high. Dogon, Mali. *Musée de l'Homme, Paris (photo: Elisofon)*.

> From the "Great Sanctuary" of the village of Yougo, Mali. Discovered by the Dakar-Djibouti expedition, 1931–33.

43. FIGURE. Wood, 30 in. high. Dogon, Mali. *Coll. Miss Laura Harden, New York (photo: Evans)*.

> See note on plate 40. From the region of Bandiagara.

44. DOOR. Wood, 18⅞ in. high. Dogon, Mali. *Musée de l'Homme, Paris (photo: Evans)*.

> Probably the door or shutter of a granary.

45. URN. Wood, 29½ in. high. Dogon, Mali. *Coll. Mme. Bela Hein, Paris (photo: Evans)*.

> An equestrian figure surmounts the urn. Used for offerings at the spring festival of sowing.

46. FEMALE FIGURE. Wood, 21½ in. high. Dogon, Mali. *Coll. Princess Gourielli, Paris (photo: Evans)*.

47. FEMALE FIGURE. Wood, 19⅝ in. high. Bambara (?), Mali. *Coll. André Level, Paris (photo: Evans)*.

> An ancestral figure.

48. FIGURE. Wood, 35 in. high. Senufo, Mali–Ivory Coast. *Coll. André Derain, Paris (photo: Evans)*.

49. Same, profile.

50. LATCH, IN FEMALE FORM. Wood, 21½ in. high. Mali. *Coll. Raphael Stora, Paris (photo: Evans)*.

> Tribal source unknown.

51. HEAD-DRESS. Wood, partly overlaid with metal, 40½ in. high. Baga, Guinea. *Coll. Georges Salles, Paris (photo: Cahiers d'Art)*.

> A kind of head-dress, carried by a dancer, whose body and the supports of this object were covered with a raffia garment. It was used in dances of the Simo secret society. Possibly represents a maternity goddess.

52. Same, detail of front.

53. TWO GONG HAMMERS. Wood, 9 and 6⅞ in. high. Baule, Ivory Coast. *Coll. Paul Guillaume, Paris (photo: Evans)*.

54. SPOON. Wood, 8⅝ in. high. Baule, Ivory Coast. *Coll. Félix Fénéon, Paris (photo: Evans)*.

55. SPOON. Wood, 8¼ in. high. Baule, Ivory Coast. *Coll. Paul Guillaume, Paris (photo: Evans)*.

56. BOBBIN. Wood, 5⅞ in. high. Senufo, Ivory Coast. *Coll. Louis Carré, Paris (photo: Evans)*.

57. BOBBIN. Wood, 7½ in. high. Guro, Ivory Coast. *Coll. Frank Crowninshield, New York (photo: Evans)*.

58. BOBBIN. Wood, 6⅛ in. high. Guro, Ivory Coast. *Coll. Louis Carré, Paris (photo: Evans)*.

59. EQUESTRIAN FIGURE. Polychrome wood, 15¾ in. high. Yoruba, Dahomey. *Coll. Louis Carré, Paris (photo: Evans)*.

> Represents Shango, god of thunder.

60. MOTHER AND CHILD. Wood, 20 in. high. Yoruba (?), Nigeria. *Horniman Museum, London (photo: Victoria and Albert Museum)*.

> Probably from northeast Yorubaland, though it may come from a related culture further east.

61. RAM'S HEAD. Wood, 15 in. high. Yoruba, Nigeria. *Coll. Maurice Cockin, London* (*photo: British Museum*).

From Owo.

62. ANCESTOR FIGURE. Wood, 42 in. high. Ibibio, Nigeria. *Coll. K. C. Murray, London* (*photo: British Museum*).

Such figures, called Ekpu, were made by the Oron clan, of Calabar. Only men are represented.

63. DRUM. Wood, 44⅛ in. high. Bamenda, Cameroon. *Coll. Dr. Paul Chadourne, Paris* (*photo: Evans*).

64. CHIEF'S STOOL WITH FIGURE. Wood, 71 in. high. Bekom, Cameroon. *Museum für Völkerkunde, Berlin* (*photo: Evans*).

Also described as a grave figure—a mortuary representation of the royal stool. From Bamenda.

65. FIGURE. Wood, about 32 in. high. Bangwa, Cameroon. *Coll. Princess Gourielli, New York* (*photo: Man Ray*).

An ancestor figure, holding a calabash. From Djang.

66. MENDICANT FIGURE WITH BOWL. Wood, 33⅛ in. high. Bangwa, Cameroon. *Coll. Charles Ratton, Paris* (*photo: Evans*).

67. Same, front view.

68. ANCESTOR FIGURE. Wood, 23 in. high. Fang, Gabon. *Coll. Miss Laura Harden, New York* (*photo: Evans*).

69. SEAT WITH FIGURES. Wood with traces of copper, 22 in. high. Yoko, Cameroon. *Coll. Etienne Bignou, Paris* (*photo: Evans*).

Faces, hands, and feet of the figures were overlaid with copper, some of which remains. Used by nobles at council gatherings.

70. FIGURE. Wood, 17¼ in. high. Bamum, Cameroon. *Coll. Baron Eduard von der Heydt, Ascona, Switzerland* (*photo: Evans*).

71. ANCESTOR FIGURE, HEAD. Wood, 17¾ in. high. Fang, Gabon. *Coll. Paul Guillaume, Paris* (*photo: Evans*).

72. ANCESTOR FIGURE. Wood, 11¾ in. high. Fang, Gabon. *Coll. Dr. Paul Chadourne, Paris* (*photo: Evans*).

73. Same, rear view.

74. MALE FIGURE. Wood, with eyes of copper discs, about 27 in. high. Fang, Gabon, border of Rio Muni. *Coll. Jacob Epstein, London* (*photo: Cahiers d'Art*).

75. Same, detail of head, profile.

76. TWO MUSICAL INSTRUMENTS. Wood, about 6½ in. high. Loango (?), Congo (Brazzaville). *Coll. Princess Gourielli, New York* (*photo: Evans*).

Small drums, played with the fingers or with rubber-headed mallets.

77. ANCESTOR FIGURE. Wood, 24⅞ in. high. Fang, Gabon, frontier of Rio Muni. *Coll. Louis Carré, Paris* (*photo: Evans*).

78. DRUM. Wood, 39⅓ in. high, 79½ in. long. Yangere, Congo (Leopoldville). *Musée de l'Homme, Paris* (*photo: Emmanuel Sougez*).

79. NAIL FETISH. Wood, about 3½ ft. high. Bakongo, Congo (Leopoldville). *Musée Royal du Congo, Tervueren, Belgium* (*photo: Elisofon*).

Covered with nails and knife blades, each of which represents a petition.

80. DRUM. Wood, about 72 in. high. Bashilele (?), Congo (Leopoldville). *Coll. A. Blondiau, Brussels* (*photo: Raoul*).

81. PORTRAIT FIGURE. Wood, about 24 in. high. Bakuba, Congo (Leopoldville). *Musée Royal du Congo, Tervueren, Belgium* (*photo: Elisofon*).

Kata Mbula (fl. 1800–1810), 109th Bushongo nyimi. See note on plate 82.

82. PORTRAIT FIGURE. Wood, 24 in. high. Bakuba, Congo (Leopoldville). *British Museum, London* (*photo: Museum*).

Shamba Bolongongo (fl. 1600), ninety-third Bushongo nyimi, or king. Most illustrious of Bushongo sovereigns, he established the custom of commissioning a carved wooden image of the king, a tradition that endured into the nineteenth century. Some dozen of these idealized portrait figures have been identified, all of them similar in attitude and style: the nyimi seated cross-legged, wearing the characteristic flat Bushongo crown, his body individually decorated, and before him some object symbolic of his reign.

83. FEMALE FIGURE. Wood, about 18 in. high. Baluba, Congo (Leopoldville). *Musée Royal du Congo, Tervueren, Belgium* (*photo: Elisofon*).

Such begging figures are a frequent theme in Baluba sculpture. The kneeling woman represents the *kabila*, a spirit protective of maternity. During the period of childbirth, the figure is placed on the threshold, so that passersby may drop gifts into the bowl. Buli style, from the village so named.

84. FEMALE FIGURE. Wood, about 18 in. high. Baluba, Congo (Leopoldville). *British Museum, London (photo: Museum)*.
Wearing a skirt of raffia.

85. FEMALE FIGURE: DETAIL. Wood, approx. 5 in. high. Bena Lulua, Congo (Leopoldville). *Musée Royal du Congo, Tervueren, Belgium (photo: Elisofon)*.
The head of a figure such as that in plate 86.

86. CARVED BATON. Wood, about 14 in. high. Bena Lulua, Congo (Leopoldville). *Brooklyn Museum (photo: Museum)*.
Represents mother and child. In this and the two following objects, the intricate ornamentation, including tattooing, constitutes tribal markings.

87. Same, profile.

88. FIGURE. Wood, 17¾ in. high. Bena Lulua, Congo (Leopoldville). *Museum für Völkerkunde, Berlin (photo: Evans)*.

89. Same, profile.

90. CUP. Wood. Basonge, Congo (Leopoldville). *Museum für Völkerkunde, Munich (photo: Evans)*.

91. BOX, WITH COVER. Wood. Bakuba, Congo (Leopoldville). *Coll. Mrs. Edith J. R. Isaacs, New York (photo: Evans)*.

92. FIGURE WITH DRUM. Wood, 15¼ in. high. Kanioka, Congo (Leopoldville). *Coll. Baron Eduard von der Heydt, Ascona, Switzerland (photo: Evans)*.

93. HEADREST. Wood, 6¾ in. high. Central Baluba, Congo (Leopoldville). *Coll. Baron Eduard von der Heydt, Ascona, Switzerland (photo: Evans)*.

94. Same, rear view.

95. Same as plate 93, front view.

96. FIGURE. Wood (surmounting a calabash, with shells: see next plate), over-all 14⅛ in. high. Central Baluba,

Congo (Leopoldville). *Coll. Tristan Tzara, Paris (photo: Evans)*.

97. Same, in full, rear view.

98. FIGURE. Wood, 9¼ in. high. Warega, Congo (Leopoldville). *Coll. John P. Anderson, Red Wing, Minnesota; formerly coll. Charles Ratton, Paris (photo: Evans)*.

99. STOOL. Wood, 18½ in. high. Northeastern Baluba, Congo (Leopoldville). *Museum für Völkerkunde, Leipzig (photo: Evans)*.
Probably an ancestor figure.

100. Same, front view.

101. SCEPTRE. Wood, 15¾ in. high. Bachokwe, Angola. *Coll. Charles Ratton, Paris (photo: Evans)*.
Said to be a ceremonial staff, or a carrying stick. Such carvings are characteristically in a hard wood, highly polished, so that a metallic effect is attained.

102. Same, in full, front view.

103. FIGURE. Wood, 5¾ in. high. Bachokwe, Angola, *Coll. Frank Crowninshield, New York (photo: Evans)*.
See note on plate 101.

104. Same, profile.

105. ORNAMENTS. Gold, *cire-perdu* technique. (*Top*) 3½ in. long. Baule, Ivory Coast. (*Centre*) 2⅞ and 3½ in. high. Lobi, Ivory Coast–Upper Volta. (*Bottom*) 4½ in. long. Baule, Ivory Coast. *Colls. Tristan Tzara, Paris; Paul Guillaume and Georges Keller, Paris; and Tzara (photo: Evans)*.
Represent, top to bottom, a ram's head, a crocodile, and masks. All probably pendants.

106. WEIGHTS FOR MEASURING GOLD DUST. Bronze, *cire-perdu* technique, approx. actual size. Ashanti, Ghana, or Baule, Ivory Coast. *Colls. Miss Laura Harden, New York, and Charles Ratton, Paris (photo: Evans)*.

107. WEIGHTS FOR MEASURING GOLD DUST. Bronze, *cire-perdu* technique, approx. actual size. Ashanti, Ghana, or Baule, Ivory Coast. *Colls. Louis Carré and Charles Ratton, Paris (photo: Evans)*.

108. WEIGHTS FOR MEASURING GOLD DUST. Bronze, *cire-perdu* technique, approx. actual size. Ashanti,

Ghana, or Baule, Ivory Coast. *Colls. Miss Laura Harden, New York, and Mme. Bela Hein, Paris (photo: Evans).*

109. MAN'S HEAD. Bronze, *cire-perdu* technique, 6 in. high. Bron, Ghana. *Coll. Webster Plass, London (photo: collector).*

110. FEMALE FIGURE. Bronze, 30 in. high. Yoruba, Nigeria. *Coll. Nigerian Government (photo: Victoria and Albert Museum).*

From the Ogboni Society house, Apomu, Ibadan. Found in 1917, said to have been lost when Apomu was abandoned, about 1800. One of the largest bronzes known from the Yoruba.

111. MASK. Gold, hollow cast, about $\frac{1}{8}$ in. thick, $6\frac{7}{8}$ in. high, weight 3 lb. 6 oz. Ashanti, Ghana. *Wallace Collection, London (photo: Collection).*

"Part of the treasure of King Koffee-Kalkalli of Ashanti brought from Coomassie on the occasion of the late Field-Marshal Viscount Woolseley 1873–1874. Burial mask of virgin gold. It was the custom on the death of the Chief of a tribe to bury his likeness together with the body."—Label on the object.

112. FIGURE. Hammered brass, $41\frac{1}{2}$ in. high. Fon, Dahomey. *Coll. Charles Ratton, Paris (photo: Evans).*

Said to represent a god of war. From the treasure of Behanzin, last king of Dahomey, who reigned 1889–93.

113. Same, detail.

114. Same as plate 115, detail of head, side view.

115. FIGURE. Iron, 65 in. high. Fon, Dahomey. *Musée de l'Homme, Paris (photo: Evans).*

Said to represent a god of war, Egbo. Probably made from old ship's iron.

116. PLAQUE: HUNTER. Bronze, $18\frac{1}{2}$ by $12\frac{5}{8}$ in. Benin, Nigeria. *Museum für Völkerkunde, Berlin (photo: Evans).*

Such reliefs as this and the two following were put up to cover wooden columns of the Benin king's palace.

117. PLAQUE: FRUIT-GATHERERS. Bronze, $21\frac{7}{8}$ in. high. Benin, Nigeria. *Staatliche Museen, Dresden (photo: Evans).*

See note on plate 116.

118. PLAQUE: FISH. Bronze, 17 by $7\frac{1}{8}$ in. Benin, Nigeria. *Coll. Charles Ratton, Paris (photo: Evans).*

See note on plate 116.

119. LEOPARD. Bronze, 28 in. long. Benin, Nigeria. *Coll. Charles Ratton, Paris (photo: Evans).*

From the collection of G. W. Neville, who was a member of the Benin Punitive Expedition, 1897. Leopards such as this were placed at either side of the entrance to the king's palace.

120. NECKLET. Bronze, 10 in. diameter. Benin, Nigeria. *Coll. Charles Ratton, Paris (photo: Evans).*

Represents predatory birds devouring the vitals of manacled human figures.

121. REPTILE HEAD. Bronze, $20\frac{1}{8}$ in. long. Benin, Nigeria. *Museum für Völkerkunde, Berlin (photo: Evans).*

Probably part of an entire creature. Similar figures were reported in 1701, hanging from the walls of the king's palace.

122. FIGURE. Bronze, $13\frac{3}{8}$ in. high. Benin, Nigeria. *Museum für Völkerkunde, Berlin (photo: Evans).*

With a bell at the neck.

123. Same, back view.

124. HEAD. Bronze, $6\frac{3}{8}$ in. high. Benin, Nigeria. *Museum für Völkerkunde, Berlin (photo: Evans).*

125. Same, full view.

126. HEAD. Bronze, $8\frac{7}{8}$ in. high. Benin, Nigeria. *Coll. Louis Carré, Paris (photo: Evans).*

Said to be the portrait of a queen mother.

127. FIGURE. Bronze, $24\frac{5}{8}$ in. high. Benin, Nigeria. *Coll. Louis Carré, Paris (photo: Evans).*

Represents a flute-player.

128. Same, full view, front.

129. Same, rear view.

130. HEAD. Bronze, $7\frac{3}{4}$ in. high. Benin, Nigeria. *Coll. Capt. A. W. F. Fuller, London (photo: Elisofon).*

Tribal marks are on the forehead.

131. GIRL'S HEAD. Bronze, approx. life size. Benin, Nigeria. *British Museum, London (photo: Elisofon).*

Wearing a coral-bead head-dress.

132. HEAD. Bronze, $13\frac{1}{2}$ in. high. Ife, Nigeria. *Coll. the Oni of Ife (photo: Elisofon).*

This head, and the next five, were excavated in 1938–40 near the walls of the palace of the Oni of Ife. Those which are adorned with head-dresses were almost certainly portraits of early

Onis, and possibly the others were also. The striations on some of the heads may represent ritual scarification; however, they resemble present-day tribal marks of the Yoruba. The holes in the face may have been intended for human hair, as beard, but more probably for some ritual band or veil. These pieces have been tentatively dated thirteenth century.

133. HEAD. Bronze, 11½ in. high. Ife, Nigeria. *Coll. the Oni of Ife (photo: Elisofon).*

See note on plate 132.

134. GIRL'S HEAD. Bronze, 12½ in. high. Ife, Nigeria. *Coll. the Oni of Ife (photo: Elisofon).*

See note on plate 132.

135. HALF-FIGURE. Bronze, 14½ in. high. Ife, Nigeria. *Coll. the Oni of Ife (photo: Elisofon).*

Perhaps half of a seated figure. Probably thirteenth century. The dress is the same as that still worn by the Onis at coronation.

136. HEAD. Bronze, 13½ in. high. Ife, Nigeria. *Coll. the Oni of Ife (photo: Bernard Fagg).*

See note on plate 132.

137. HEAD. Bronze, 13½ in. high. Ife, Nigeria. *Coll. the Oni of Ife (photo: Bernard Fagg).*

See note on plate 132.

138. HEAD. Bronze, 12½ in. high. Ife, Nigeria. *Coll. the Oni of Ife (photo: Elisofon).*

See note on plate 132.

139. MASK. Bronze, 13 in. high. Ife, Nigeria. *Coll. the Oni of Ife (photo: A. C. Cooper).*

Said to represent the Oni Obalufon II.

140. DOUBLE BELL. Iron, 24⅜ in. high. Bamum, Cameroon. *Museum für Völkerkunde, Berlin (photo: Evans).*

141. NECKLET. Bronze, 10⅝ in. diameter. Bamum, Cameroon. *Coll. Charles Ratton, Paris (photo: Evans).*

The elements represent buffalo heads.

142. FUNERARY FIGURE. Wood covered with copper strips, 22½ in. high. Bakota, Gabon. *Musée de l'Homme, Paris (photo: Elisofon).*

These stereotyped ancestor images, which are found among various tribes of the Gabon area, are placed upon baskets or boxes containing the skulls of ancestors. Their purpose is to keep strangers away. They are also called *bieri*.

143. FUNERARY FIGURE. Wood covered with copper strips, about 22 in. high. Bakota, Gabon. *Musée de l'Homme, Paris (photo: Elisofon).*

See note on plate 142. The basket containing skulls may be seen below the *bieri*.

144. FUNERARY FIGURE. Wood covered with copper strips, 22½ in. high. Bakota, Gabon. *Coll. Princess Gourielli, New York (photo: Evans).*

145. BRACELET. Ivory, 4½ in. diameter. Guro, southeast Ivory Coast. *Coll. Charles Ratton, Paris (photo: Evans).*

146. BRACELET. Ivory, 4½ in. diameter. Guro, southeast Ivory Coast. *Coll. Charles Ratton, Paris (photo: Evans).*

147. TRUMPET. Ivory, 21¼ in. long. Upper Ogowe River, Gabon. *Coll. Paul Guillaume, Paris (photo: Evans).*

Curved, following the shape of the ivory tusk.

148. TRUMPET. Ivory, 18⅛ in. long. Upper Ogowe River, Gabon. *Coll. Charles Ratton, Paris (photo: Evans).*

See note on plate 147.

149. PENDANT. Ivory, 2⅜ in. high. Bapende, Congo (Leopoldville). *Coll. C. G. Seligman, Oxford (photo: Evans).*

In mask form; an amulet, worn suspended around the neck on a string.

150. HEADREST. Ivory, 6½ in. high. Baluba, Congo (Leopoldville). *Coll. Charles Ratton, Paris (photo: Evans).*

151. HEADREST. Ivory, 4 in. high, 10⅞ in. long. Warega, Congo (Leopoldville). *Coll. Louis Carré, Paris (photo: Evans).*

152. FIGURE. Ivory, 10¼ in. high. Warega, Congo (Leopoldville). *Coll. Alphonse Stoclet, Brussels (photo: Evans).*

The ivory has become much darkened.

153. MASK. Ivory, 8¼ in. high. Warega, Congo (Leopoldville). *Coll. Alphonse Stoclet, Brussels (photo: Evans).*

This and the following mask were used in the rites of the Mwami secret society.

154. MASK. Ivory, 7⅝ in. high. Warega, Congo (Leopoldville). *Coll. Louis Carré, Paris (photo: Evans).*

See note on plate 153.

155. HEAD. Ivory, 6¼ in. high. Warega, Congo (Leopoldville). *Coll. Mme. Bela Hein, Paris (photo: Evans).*

With a cowrie shell for one eye, and originally for both.

156. BATON. Ivory, 5⅞ in. high. Congo (Leopoldville). *Coll. Tristan Tzara, Paris (photo: Evans).*

With three heads. Tribe unknown, though in style this object resembles Warega or Bapende work.

157. HEAD. Ivory, 4¾ in. high. Warega, Congo (Leopoldville). *Coll. Mme. Bela Hein, Paris (photo: Evans).*

158. FIGURE. Soapstone, 9¾ in. high. Sierra Leone. *Fuller Collection, London (photo: British Museum).*

See note on plate 160.

159. FEMALE FIGURE. Soapstone, 14 in. high. Mende, Sierra Leone. *British Museum, London (photo: Museum).*

See note on plate 160.

160. HEAD. Soapstone, 9¾ in. high. Mende, Sierra Leone. *Fuller Collection, London (photo: Central Office of Information).*

This unusually large soapstone head is typical of these *nomori*, as they are called, of the Mende country. They are found buried in the ground; the modern Mende do not know their origin, and their style is completely different from modern wood carving. Still, their stylistic similarity to certain old wooden figures carved in the *nomori* style indicates that they cannot be of great antiquity. Such heads and the soapstone figures of the region (plate 159) are used in the cult of the rice spirit.

161. FUNERARY FIGURE. Terracotta, 15 in. high. Agni, Ivory Coast. *Coll. Tristan Tzara, Paris (photo: Evans).*

162. HEAD. Terracotta, 6½ in. high. Ife, Nigeria. *Coll. the Oni of Ife (photo: Bernard Fagg).*

Excavated at Abiri in 1949, accidentally, by a Yoruba farmer who was preparing foundations for a building. A number of other objects of terracotta were later found, in archaeological investigation, including the next object.

163. HEAD. Terracotta, 6¾ in. high. Ife, Nigeria. *Coll. the Oni of Ife (photo: Bernard Fagg).*

Perhaps the portrait of an early Oni. See note on plate 162.

164. HEAD. Terracotta, about 11½ in. high. Ife, Nigeria. *Coll. the Oni of Ife (photo: Bernard Fagg).*

Said to be a representation of Lajuwa, an early usurper of the throne of Ife.

165. HEAD. Terracotta, 8¾ in. high. Nok, Nigeria. *Coll. Nigerian Government (photo: British Museum).*

Found at Jemaa, northern Nigeria, about 25 miles northeast of Nok, whose ancient culture has provisionally been dated, on geological evidence, to the latter half of the first millennium B.C. It has come to light only within the past eight or nine years, through excavations in tin-bearing gravel about 25 feet deep.

166. BIRD MASK. Painted wood, 72 in. high. Bobo, Upper Volta. *The Museum of Primitive Art, New York (photo: Charles Uht).*

The round face of the mask suggests an owl and is surmounted by a high board painted in a checkerboard pattern. It is used mostly in hunting rites.

167. FEMALE ANTELOPE HEAD-DRESS. Painted wood, 43¾ in. high. Kurumba, Aribinda region, Upper Volta. *Dominique and John de Menil Collection, Houston (photo: Taylor and Dull).*

Used in mourning ceremonies to drive the souls of the deceased out of the village.

168. MALE ANTELOPE HEAD-DRESS. Painted wood, 36 in. high. Kurumba, Aribinda region, Upper Volta. *Private collection (photo: Taylor and Dull).*

See note on plate 167.

169. MASK. Wood, 62 in. high. Bambara, Mali. *Coll. Mr. and Mrs. Arnold Newman, New York (photo: Newman).*

An animal mask used by the Koré society of the Bambara.

170. Same, side view.

171. MASK. Wood and raffia, mask alone 24⅜ in. high. Fang, Gabon. *Coll. Mr. and Mrs. Gustave Schindler, New York (photo: Taylor and Dull).*

Said to be a mask for the Ngi secret society, which is based upon a cult of fire and symbolized by the gorilla. Initiates of the society kept order in the villages by detecting and punishing sorcerers and criminals.

172. CULT OBJECT. Wood, 78 in. long, 21 in. wide, 17½ in. high. Dogon,

Mali. *Museum of Fine Arts, Houston, gift of Dominique and John de Menil (photo: Taylor and Dull).*

> Ceremonial vessel for secret-society rituals. The form suggests a horse, whose trunk is a hollow box with relief sculpture on its sides.

173. BUTTERFLY MASK. Painted wood and braided rope, $51\frac{1}{4}$ in. wide. Bobo, Upper Volta. *The Museum of Primitive Art, New York (photo: Charles Uht).*

> This mask is used in a dance celebrating the approach of spring, when there are swarms of butterflies.

174. FETISH. Wood covered with mud, $20\frac{1}{2}$ in. wide. Bambara, Mali. *The Museum of Primitive Art, New York (photo: Charles Uht).*

> This type of fetish, known as a *boli*, serves as an altar in the rites of the Komo, a secret society important in the religious and social life of the Bambara people.

175. BIRD. Painted wood, $59\frac{5}{8}$ in. high. Senufo, Ivory Coast. *The Museum of Primitive Art, New York (photo: Charles Uht).*

> Such figures, *porpianong*, are worn as headdresses during certain rituals of the Senufo initiation society.

176. RITUAL OBJECT. Wood and metal, $36\frac{1}{2}$ in. long, 19 in. high. Baga, Guinea. *Georges de Menil Collection, Houston (photo: Taylor and Dull).*

> This object, called an *anok* or *matchiole*, and associated with the Simo secret society, is believed to house a protective spirit. The headpiece combines human and animal features.

177. SERPENT. Painted wood, 102 in. high. Landuma, Guinea. *Dominique and John de Menil Collection, Houston (photo: F. Wilbur Seiders).*

> A stylized representation of the Gabon viper, a type of snake common in Guinea. This serpent figure, *kakilambe*, symbolizes fertility.

178. HOUSEPOST. Wood, $74\frac{1}{4}$ in. high. Dogon, Plain of Séno, Mali. *The Museum of Primitive Art, New York (photo: Charles Uht).*

> Houseposts are frequently given more than utilitarian importance by being carved in the shape of symbolic figures.

179. FEMALE FIGURE. Wood, $10\frac{1}{2}$ in. high. Dogon, Bandiagara region, Mali.

Dominique and John de Menil Collection, Houston (photo: Taylor and Dull).

> Probably used as a ritual implement and dating from the 19th century.

180. HORSE WITH RIDER. Wood, $27\frac{1}{8}$ in. high. Dogon, Mali. *The Museum of Primitive Art, New York (photo: Taylor and Dull).*

181. ANCESTRAL FIGURE. Wood, $40\frac{1}{4}$ in. high. Bambara, Bougouni region, Mali. *The Museum of Primitive Art, New York (photo: Charles Uht).*

> This type of figure, also known as "Queen," functions as an ancestral as well as a fertility image.

182. BUST. Wood, 18 in. high. Bapende, Congo (Leopoldville). *Coll. Mr. and Mrs. Harold Rome, New York (photo: Arnold Newman).*

> Presumably from a housepost; found in a riverbed, possibly the Kasai.

183. PREHISTORIC HEAD. Steatite, $10\frac{1}{4}$ in. high. Kissi, Guinea. *The Museum of Primitive Art, New York (photo: Charles Uht).*

> Of unknown origin and date, such heads as this one are found in the area of the Kissi, who regard them as images of deceased ancestors and use them as implements of divination.

184. VESSEL. Terracotta, $14\frac{1}{2}$ in. high. Provenience unknown. *Dominique and John de Menil Collection, Houston (photo: Taylor and Dull).*

> Shows impressions of a basket mold around bottom; use unknown.

185. STONE SCULPTURE. Steatite, $9\frac{3}{4}$ in. high. Provenience unknown. *Private collection (photo: Taylor and Dull).*

> Eight human faces carved in the round; use unknown.

186. PEDESTAL BOWL. Bronze, $4\frac{3}{4}$ in. high. Ife, Nigeria. *Coll. the Oni of Ife (photo: British Museum).*

> 12th-15th century. The body of the bowl is encircled by a royal female figure holding a staff with a human head; a ritual vessel which was probably associated with human sacrifice.

187. FEMALE HEAD. Terracotta, $10\frac{5}{8}$ in. high. Ife, Nigeria. *Coll. the Oni of Ife (photo: British Museum).*

> 12th-15th century; discovered in a mound at Ita Yemoo, near Ife, in 1957.

Index

Index

Place names and tribal names are listed, the latter in small capital letters.

355

INDEX

356